Second Edition, 2005

With an Introduction by Harry Farrell,
Columnist, San Jose Mercury News (1981)

And Epilogue by Norman Y. Mineta,
Member of Congress (1981)

WATER

in the Santa Clara Valley: A History

California History Center & Foundation
Cupertino, California
Local History Studies Volume 40

Water in the Santa Clara Valley: A History

First Edition: Chapters 1-8. Edited by Seonaid McArthur, Director, California History Center. Assistance provided by Santa Clara Valley Water District personnel and their Director of Public Relations, James R. Melton. Published in 1981 through a grant from the Santa Clara Valley Water District.

Second Edition: Chapters 9-15 with Epilogue and expanded appendices. Edited by Cheryl Wessling. Assistance provided by Santa Clara Valley Water District personnel, the Board of Directors and the Association of Retired District Employees. Proofreading provided by James Williams, Mary Jo Ignoffo and Lisa Christiansen of the California History Center. Publishing assistance provided by Tom Izu, Director, California History Center. Published in 2005.

Graphic Design by Suzanne Bauer.

Second Edition
Library of Congress Cataloging-in-Publication Data

Water in the Santa Clara Valley : a history / edited by Seonaid McArthur and Cheryl Wessling.— 2nd ed.
    p. cm. — (Local history studies, ISSN 0276-4105 ; v. 40)
    First section of text is a reprint of the 1981 ed. and the second section is an update with its own preface and appendices.
    Includes index.
    1. Water resources development—California—Santa Clara Valley (Santa Clara County)—History. I. McArthur, Seonaid. II. Wessling, Cheryl. III. De Anza College. California History Center. IV. Santa Clara Valley Water District (Calif.) V. Title. VI. Series.

TC424.C2W295 2005
333.91'150979492—dc22

2005031242

Front cover: Aerial of Chesbro Reservoir in Santa Clara County, courtesy of 111th Aerial Photography Squadron.
Back cover: 1) Women playing in a creek, circa 1925, SCVWD archives. 2) A small tributary of Los Gatos Creek, 2004, courtesy Cait Hutnik.
Photo credits: All photographs used in this book are the property of the Santa Clara Valley Water District unless otherwise indicated.

Printed in the USA   Printed on elemental chlorine-free paper made from 10 percent postconsumer waste.

"In an area that gets the same meager rainfall as Los Angeles or parts of North Africa,
the visionaries who created our water system realized that unchecked groundwater pumping
could not long sustain the vast orchards of the Santa Clara Valley,
let alone the population boom that would soon come.
With Herculean effort, they built a network of reservoirs, tunnels and pipelines that today
helps protect one of California's largest metropolitan areas from nature's caprices of drought and floods.
This is their story."

~ Frank Sweeney, retired *San Jose Mercury News* environmental reporter

TABLE OF CONTENTS

Alamitos Percolation Pond in San José, 1998.

Preface

First Edition, Chapters 1-8

When Frederick Remington painted his famous "Fight for the Water Hole," he surely must have had the Santa Clara Valley on his mind. At least it's true that few people in California have had to work harder for their water supply. People from all walks of life have thrown their energies into it, and they have never given up their pursuit of the one truly necessary resource.

This history, compiled by students from the California History Center at De Anza College and staff of the Santa Clara Valley Water District, is a chronicle of events that led to our present-day water system; it is also a brief glimpse of just a few of the thousands of people who have brought the dream of good and plentiful water into reality.

These pages tell the story of how water development came to be of such great consequence, and how various events within that story came about.

We are proud to have worked with the California History Center to publish this history of water in Santa Clara Valley. It has been needed for years, and will serve as a key reference for years to come.■

Second Edition Note: *The first edition of this history book was published in 1981 as a small book providing chapters 1 through 8. The second edition preserves this text and continues the history with chapters 9 through 15.*

James J. Lenihan
Chairman of the Board, 1981
Director, District 5

Arthur T. Pfeiffer
Director, District 1

Patrick T. Ferraro
Director, District 2

Robert W. Gross
Director, District 3

Maurice E. Dullea
Director, District 4

Sig Sanchez
Director, At-Large

Linda Peralta
Director, At-Large

1

Introduction

by Harry Farrell, Columnist, *San Jose Mercury News*

In 1946, when I joined the *San Jose News* as a cub reporter newly mustered out of the Army, city editor Dick Barrett sent me out to cover a number of beats he deemed too inconsequential for the attentions of a journeyman newswriter. One of them, in an office suite of two or three rooms on North Second Street, across from Trinity Episcopal Church, was the Santa Clara Valley Water Conservation District. It owned and operated six dams, relatively small ones built in the 1930s, to catch runoff water from our eastern and western mountains—Stevens Creek, Guadalupe, Almaden, Calero, Coyote and Vasona.

G. Walter Hunt was the district engineer; Bob Roll was his assistant and (I think) his whole staff. The elder statesman of the operation was former state Senator Herbert C. Jones, whose office, reached by an antique "bird cage" elevator, was in the shabbily genteel Porter Building on the northeast corner of Second and Santa Clara streets.

With Santa Clara Valley's postwar boom on the horizon, the Water District was getting ready for a new era, with plans for two big new dams, Anderson and Lexington, that would multiply its conservation capacity almost four-fold. I covered the development of these dams from blueprints to dedication. Governor Earl Warren, later to become chief justice, addressed the Anderson dedication ceremony, held on the dam crest, and Governor Goodwin Knight dedicated Lexington a year or two later.

Lexington and Anderson were my introduction to a continuing story I have now been covering for 35 years, as reporter, political writer, political editor and columnist—the story of water for Santa Clara Valley. If this story were to be given a name, it would have to be taken symbolically from Frederic Remington's classic canvas, "The Fight for the Water Hole."

In that elemental struggle, I have learned, strife is eternal. It is only natural that man's deepest passions are stirred by any matter having to do with the possession, control and distribution of water—without which he would die. Nothing comes easy: Lexington Dam didn't; the South Bay Aqueduct didn't; the San Felipe Project, conceived in the 1940s and still not scheduled to deliver its first flow until at least 1987, hasn't. If today the "water hole" battles are fought with ballots instead of bullets, they are no less intense, no less emotional, no less personal.

Thus, the never-ending effort to quench the thirst of a growing Santa Clara Valley has often been slowed, tragically it has seemed, by bickering, politics, litigation and chicanery. At one stage the battle was "public vs. private," pitting governmental water agencies against the San Jose Water Works. At another stage, it was "state vs. federal," with local adherents to the Sacramento and Washington water bureaucracies in rival hostile camps. Of late, it has been "growth vs. no-growth," with no-growth forces challenging the fundamental premise that we will, in the long run, need every drop of water we can get. In another environmental aspect, the contest has been joined between those who would impound the waters of distant wild rivers and those who, in the alternative, would recycle our sewer effluent.

But if the ongoing struggle has been agonizingly slow, because of the need to reconcile diverse and strongly held views, it has also been grandly successful in the long view. The dreamers and planners of half a century ago, returning now, would see their grand design realized beyond their fondest hopes. And those who, over the intervening years, seemed "obstructionists," today deserve honor along with the dreamers. Their role, to test and challenge, enhanced the essential soundness of the water supply solutions we have arrived at in the face of dismaying difficulties.

Over the last three decades, growth has brought many troubles to Santa Clara Valley, along with many blessings. Our traffic chokes us; our air is foul; our bay often polluted; our sewers have overflowed. But thanks to the farsightedness and the occasional obstinance of those who have waged our "fight for the water hole," clean water is the one resource we have continued to enjoy, save for a few temporary lapses, in plentiful supply.

The struggle will continue on new fronts. Changing technology and economics will lead us into undertakings in methods which today are only experimental or theoretical. Recycling and desalination will be argued in the future as importation and percolation have been argued in our past. But those who wage these future battles, fiercely no doubt, will do so with ample and honorable precedent.

~ *San José, March 8, 1981*

Uvas Reservoir

. . . man's deepest passions are stirred by any matter having to do with the possession, control and distribution of water—without which he would die.

A Santa Clara Valley farmer at work, circa 1920.

Courtesy History San José

CHAPTER 1

Farmers Unite for Water Conservation

By David W. Rickman

Nature in all its abundance greeted the first human intruders who scrambled up the low hills to gaze upon the broad, peaceful valley below; the one we now call the Santa Clara. Yet, they would not know what the needs of future inhabitants would be, nor comprehend that mankind could actually harness nature to help meet those needs.

It looked like a good land, no doubt. Lying at the southern end of a great, calm bay, the valley's mouth opened to the waters and was edged by broad salt marshes. The valley contained flat grasslands, parklike fields and foothills clothed in scattered oaks. Embracing the valley floor were two low, steep ranges of mountains. The range to the east stood almost barren except for grass and an occasional laurel, but the one to the west caught the mists of the ocean and was covered by lush, green forests and crested with a stand of huge redwoods.

There was more water in this bowl-shaped valley than they could ever use. During the winter and spring, hundreds of ponds dotted the earth and the many rivers were bordered by the thickly grown willow, alder, laurel, cotton-wood and blackberry. The rainy season brought teeming flocks of wild birds and waterfowl into this valley. Runoffs welled a small lake in the southern region and helped to change the course of the rivers gradually over the span of years, or during torrential times, all at once.[3:154-161]

To the first inhabitants of the Santa Clara Valley, rain and floods could only have meant a cooling relief from summer's heat and perhaps the trouble of relocating their villages, for most were established along streams and ponds.[3:33] To a modern geologist, however, the abundance of water holds a different meaning. We now know that for eons, the waters of countless winters have rushed down the sides of the mountains enclosing the valley. These seasonal rains washing over the slopes worked tirelessly to erode them. In time, the water receded and exposed the mountains to the effects of the elements. Huge boulders tumbled down to the foothills while rocks, gravel, sand and, finally, clay swept through the valley as runoff waters found their way to the sea. Whenever the streams changed course, they deposited new beds of eroded stone until a network of gravel

For eons, the waters of countless winters have rushed down the sides of the mountains enclosing the valley.

One day in late January

of 1854, the first well

was sunk in San José.

crisscrossed the valley floor and was covered by clay and later by topsoil. Only in a relatively few places did these veins of debris reach the surface. It was here that water from rain and floods could seep through the soil and down into the gravel. These subterranean reservoirs, or aquifers, still reach several thousand feet below the ground surface. In some places they are capable of storing enough water to provide for the needs of all of the valley's flora and fauna even during periods of drought.[25:13-14] In other places, the aquifers reach the ground surface and act like windows that allow water to be conveyed from the surface to the ground-water basin.

Like the plants and trees, man can and does use the water stored beneath the ground by digging wells to tap this supply. At one time there was such an abundance of water under pressure that it flowed freely from the wells, sometimes spouting several feet above ground (artesian wells).

An Ohlone village.

Courtesy Santa Clara County Parks & Recreation Dept. and Markus Lui

Although aquifers have always been a common source of water throughout the world, it was not until the middle of the 19th century that man used those of the Santa Clara Valley.[8:12]

The Indians who lived near the seashore, rivers and ponds for thousands of years made very little impact upon the environment. They subsisted by hunting, fishing and gathering nuts and berries. Without knowledge of agriculture, the Indians' numbers depended directly upon the availability of wild food; thus, they never taxed the water supply to the point of having to dig for it.[7:115]

Just over two centuries ago, the rhythmic pace of life in the valley was rocked by the precipitous arrival of the Spaniards. Gaspar de Portola's first reconnoitering expedition in 1769 was followed by several others until, finally, in 1776 Colonel de Anza secured the great Bay of San Francisco for Spain. A pueblo and mission were then planned for northern California, and Governor Felipe de Neve chose a location near the Guadalupe River in the Santa Clara Valley because of the abundance of pasture, wood and water, as well as natives who could be converted to Christianity.[28:6]

Plans were made almost immediately for a system of controlling the river's water. In April 1778, Governor Neve reported that an earthen dam had been constructed across the Guadalupe and an irrigation ditch dug to take water to the small fields. That same month, however, spring floods broke through the dam and entered the pueblo.[2:313] So frequent were these floods that before the end of the century both the pueblo and the mission not far away had to be moved to higher ground.[28:7]

Damming rivers for use in irrigation was common in most of Spain's colonies in the New World. The technique originated in the Old World, however, and was used in the Santa Clara Valley more from tradition than necessity. As long as the ponds and rivers were plentiful, the fruit trees, grain and vegetables grown by the Spaniards seldom needed watering and the livestock even less.[3:37] Nevertheless, the same water system continued in use, in various states of repair, throughout the Spanish and Mexican periods.[28:21]

During the Mexican era (1822 to 1846), the growing population and the increase in livestock did not disturb the groundwater of the valley. Trade with the East for hides and tallow brought prosperity to the Californians. Ranchos spread over the valley, each with its own water source. While agriculture continued in a de-emphasized role, there was naturally an increasing amount of planting to feed the 900 whites and many more Indians who now lived in the valley, but there was still no need for wells.[24:7]

Not until the conquest of the territory by the United States in 1846 did the burden of increased agriculture and human numbers force man to draw upon the groundwater. The broad, flat floor of the Santa Clara Valley was found to be fine farmland by the newly arriving settlers. This fact, as well as the temporary status of San José as state capital and the city's location on the main highway of north-south traffic in California, seemed to make the valley an attractive target for new settlers. By 1850, the city of San José boasted a burgeoning population of 3,000. The now inadequate groundwater system led to the next logical step in searching for water. One day in late January of 1854, the first well was sunk in San José, and water was struck at just 80 feet. There was an ensuing eruption of water that reached ten feet above the ground.[5:263-5]

Artesian wells and the wells which drew water to the surface by windmill pumps became such a common necessity that they were a hallmark of the Santa Clara Valley by the 1870s.[4:65-66]

Windmill pumps were such a common necessity they became a *hallmark* of the valley.

The Williams Ranch as depicted in the 1876 "Thomspon and West Atlas" shows the typical use of windmill-powered water pumps. Before electricity, such pumps were commonly used to pump water from shallow wells. Through an ingenious arrangement of gears and connecting rods, the rotary motion of the mill or fan was changed to a perpendicular stroke of the pump-shaft; water was thus lifted by a piston to a storage tank raised some distance above the area of use. A check-valve on the lower end of the well pipe kept the water from returning to the well, and thus each stroke of the pump raised the water another few inches. Where wind was generally reliable, this proved a very satisfactory source of economical power for early farms.

Courtesy Martin Luther King Library, San José

Soon after this event, the most memorable artesian well was drilled in San José. Called "Dabney's" after the well's owner, it released a spout of water that reached nine feet in height, and created a stream four feet wide and six inches deep. After flowing uncontrollably for six weeks, the well was finally declared a public nuisance by the city because its stream ran down busy Fourth Street. William Campbell, seeking water for the city of San José, also struck a gusher, this one at First and Santa Clara streets. It flooded the streets and was drained by a crooked trench down what thereafter became known as "Fountain Alley."[1] After much time and money, the well was finally brought under control.[5:265]

Artesian wells soon disappeared.

Courtesy Santa Clara University Archives

Capped artesian well on the University of Santa Clara-owned farm near Guadalupe Creek and Bayshore Freeway, circa 1910. Until 1915, artesian wells were sufficient. Thereafter, the heavy demands of increased orchards and the introduction of gasoline and electric pumps decreased the groundwater supply and pressure. Artesian wells soon disappeared.

A new era in water use commenced. By 1865, the number of artesian wells in the valley was close to 500, and even at this early date, the potential for misuse was evident. Indiscriminate drilling of wells would exhaust the water supply. Clearly, some means of conservation was needed. In the valley's newspapers, a series of editorials and letters appeared which complained in concert that farmers and others who left their wells uncapped, allowing water to flow freely to the bay, were to blame for the shortage of water and for erosion damage to the lowlands.[8:14 15]

The public complaint had little effect upon the farmers who continued to sink new wells throughout the valley. New settlers demanded water, and if water meant the difference between a cash crop and surviving versus debt and starvation, who could argue against them? Conservation seemed especially futile when everyone knew that the water lay right beneath their feet.

Initially used to meet human and animal needs, the wells were not used at this time for agricultural purposes. Until the mid-1860s, farmers concentrated on raising cattle and wheat, which was dry-farmed, that is, not irrigated. Following this was a decade in which wheat alone dominated the farmers' efforts. It was the railroad which made fruit growing profitable so that orchards and vineyards grew in number, and an increasing variety of table vegetables were cultivated as the century drew to its close.[3:60]

Although for some twenty years, irrigation in the Spanish and Mexican sense was attempted by the newer arrivals, it was with little success. Farmers from the East had none of the Latin traditions nor any real inclination to gain their expertise. Consequently, most of them continued in their own tradition of mulching.[3:115] A few, whose lands were located along running water, would divert winter and spring floodwaters into their orchards. Ditches of importance were the Statler, Sorosis and Calkins ditches, which irrigated approximately 4,000 acres and took water from Campbell and

Los Gatos creeks. The Pioneer Ditch diverted water from Almaden (Alamitos) Creek and irrigated 900 acres.[27:83-5] The Duncan Ditch and Kirk Ditch both took water from Los Gatos Creek, one irrigating the north bank and the other the south bank. Theophilus and Socrates Kirk came to the Santa Clara Valley in 1853. They purchased land along the south bank of Los Gatos Creek and by 1859 had formed the "Kirk Ditch Company,"[24] which was still functioning as an irrigation system until the late 1960s under the direction of Clarence H. Kirk, grandson of Socrates Kirk.

George W. Page came to Santa Clara County in 1889 and developed two ditches on the west side of Los Gatos Creek, which became important for irrigation of vast acreages in the Campbell area.[24] Other ditches included Masson Ditch on the east of Los Capitancillos (Guadalupe Creek) and the Auzerais Ditch on Penitencia Creek. However, the prevailing sentiment ran against this technique, and it was especially disputed by real estate agents who did not wish to foster the belief that the valley's land needed irrigation.[6:8]

Several dry years, especially from 1897 to 1899 when the valley received scarcely half the average rainfall, caused farmers to become genuinely concerned about irrigation.[3:116] Winter and spring flooding was used more often, but the dry winters posed serious problems and soon land along running water was difficult to acquire. As a result, more and more wells were sunk so thirsty crops could be watered.

With the development of more efficient transportation networks and the growing demand for fruits and vegetables, a general agreement was reached that irrigation was indispensable. After two more dry seasons, 1903-04 and 1907-08, Campbell and Cupertino alone had up to 14,000 acres under irrigation.[25:8-10] This trend of increased irrigation and well drilling continued until by 1915, 8.1 million gallons a year were taken by man from beneath the Santa Clara Valley. Because the water replenished itself at a much slower rate, the groundwater level dropped rapidly.[8:18]

An increasingly rapid rate of fall in the water table could only result in increasing costs for deepening wells. No precise figures exist for this era, yet it may have been comparable to the estimated $6 million spent during the decade following the First World War.[26:4] The pinch was doubtless being felt, but it would take another dry spell and some important misinformation about availability of federal funds to rouse the valley toward conservation after more than half a century of abuse.

During a particularly hot and dry summer in 1913, the thoughts of most of the Santa Clara Valley's residents must have turned often to the subject of water, its scarcity and abundance. Two years before, during the winter of 1910-11, the valley experienced some of its worst flooding on record. Yet, the following years were increasingly drier to the point that even a flood might have been welcome.[8:21-22]

A method for controlling such caprices of nature was eagerly sought. In June 1913, a conversation between a San Francisco irrigation expert passing through San José and some local farmers sparked the first attempt at organizing for conservation. He had noted the drought and asked if anyone had heard of the government funds which had been accumulated from the sale of public lands for the purpose of developing irrigation works on land in need of them. In effect, the federal government would pay for the conservation of water which irrigators could use for their own needs. The response was enthusiastic and a meeting of farmers and ranchers was called in Campbell for June 12. Lending their support and advice were two state assemblymen, Frank Benson and L. D. Bohnett, as well as state Senator Herbert C. Jones. All of these men would figure prominently in the conservation movement in the years to come.

Before the meeting could progress very far, a disappointing telegram arrived from the valley's congressman, E.A. Hayes. It explained that the money which they wanted

Indiscriminate drilling of wells would exhaust the water supply. But if water meant the difference between farmers having a cash crop and surviving versus debt and starvation, who could argue against them?

Uncontrolled flooding in *1911*
was one factor that made valley farmers aware of the
need for a managed *"water system."*

BOATING ON SAN FERNANDO ST.
NEAR VINE ST.   MARCH 7-1911.

*"No one can say, with any fore knowledge in the matter,
how much longer the present weather conditions are to continue."*
~ *San Jose Mercury, March 7, 1911*

was designated only for previously uncultivated lands in arid and semiarid regions. The Santa Clara Valley thus did not qualify. Small comfort was found in the fact that the valley, often called a "Garden of Eden," would need those funds to prevent its "reverting to a desert," as the meeting's secretary phrased it.[9:1]

Rather than allowing themselves to give up the idea of conservation, the landowners looked into a number of other possibilities. State, rather than federal, funds might become available with proper lobbying, it was thought, and a committee was appointed to investigate. In the meantime, the formation of their own irrigation district to look into possible reservoir sites might demonstrate their earnestness to the government. A motion to this effect was made and, while not universally favored, was adopted. Opposition to the plan stemmed chiefly from the fact that such investigations and even surveys would cost money.[25:22]

Had the majority of landowners been more seriously concerned about water shortages, these first efforts would have been more fruitful. Instead, the idea of gaining state funds was shelved as soon as federal opposition arose. Similarly, the search for possible reservoir sites floundered when complications arose. Los Gatos Canyon was considered but prior property rights, especially those of the Southern Pacific Railroad, discouraged the committee. Guadalupe Canyon was also a very likely location, but there was difficulty in raising the funds for a proper survey.

As an independent measure, Cupertino looked into creating its own reservoir on Stevens Creek, but the land that was needed would have to be purchased from the San Francisco-based Spring Valley Water Company. This plan was also abandoned. The Guadalupe Canyon plans were also scrapped after conflicts over property rights. Had there been a little more determination behind the conservation effort, any of these projects might have succeeded. Coyote Creek in the southernmost region of the valley was the last

and most feasible location for a reservoir, but a series of events occurred that halted even these plans.[25:23-26]

It can be well demonstrated that the two greatest hindrances to the conservation movement up to this time were the general belief that the water supply would soon replenish itself and a consequent reluctance to spend money to save water. To do so, one need only look for evidence of conservation efforts following the winter of 1913-14, which was one of the wettest in years; almost none appears in the newspapers. It is true that from 1916 to 1920 the winters were again mostly dry,[26:16] but by then the need to keep supplying an increasing demand for agricultural products, especially fruit, kept the farmers' minds off the subject, and they were far more willing to pump water out of the ground to keep up with the demand. A world war was in progress,

MONTEREY ROAD, MARCH 7-1911

"In many places the horses on the wagon were forced to swim and only two or three persons could be taken at a time on account of the depth of water."
~ San Jose Mercury, March 7, 1911

In the report was contained the conclusion that the water lost into the bay each year must be saved and distributed to the residents of the valley or percolated into the aquifers for storage below ground.

and the citizens were in a state of mind to care little for long-range resources until the job at hand was done.[8:23]

Not until November 4, 1919, seven days short of the first anniversary of the war's end, did the public's interest in water conservation again surface in the newspapers. On that day, a group of interested citizens proposed at a meeting of the San Jose Chamber of Commerce that a new study of the water problem be taken up.[10:1] The story made the front page, but little seemed to come of this proposal.

At last, a meeting of the Farm Owners and Operators Association on December 20, 1919 resulted in action on the conservation issue. A committee appointed by the organization began investigating the problem. Over the holiday season, a resolution was composed and presented to the Santa Clara County Board of Supervisors and to the press on January 22, 1920. The resolution expressed strong opposition to the waste resulting from the use of artesian wells, and ended by stating that the Association was responsible for raising the conservation question again and "with the cooperation of the farmers of this valley will keep on the job until we get water."[11:1]

The parochialism of this view of conservation responsibilities drew criticism from the Santa Clara County Consolidated Chamber of Commerce. It was not solely farmers' involved in the water problem, chamber members stated, and they demanded that broader representation be appointed to the committee. When members were then drawn from the chamber, the board of supervisors, and the Grange and trades unions, several farmers resigned in protest.[8:24]

Nevertheless, the enlarged organization, now titled the "Santa Clara Valley Water Conservation Committee," went ahead with plans to solve the growing water shortage. Charles E. Warren, an orchardist from Cupertino, was made chairman. He had been involved in the earlier efforts to organize an irrigation district, as had former Congressman E. A. Hayes, now serving on the finance committee.[12:4]

A Comprehensive Conservation Plan: The Tibbetts and Kieffer Report

An in-depth survey of the valley that could lead to the formulation of a comprehensive plan to conserve water was the primary goal of the committee. An engineer equal to the task had to be found. After some consideration, Fred H. Tibbetts of Campbell was chosen for his experience and enthusiasm for the project.[13:1]

Naturally, the next problem which presented itself was how to pay for such a survey. This was not so easily solved, for it was estimated that the cost of the survey would be between $25,000 and $30,000. The County Board of Supervisors was petitioned for $15,000, but reluctantly came up with only $5,000 out of advertising funds. With the balance still to be collected, the San Jose Chamber of Commerce offered to raise $10,000 by a membership drive if the committee would try to raise the rest through farmers' donations, thus splitting the cost between business and agriculture. By August, the chamber of commerce and the conservation committee had raised $8,060 and $8,195, respectively. With only $4,000 left to be raised, Fred Tibbetts was given his go-ahead.[15:1]

The entire undertaking took only eight months from survey to final presentation of a very complete report. By October, four parties of five men each were in the field measuring wells and looking for suitable reservoir sites.[15:11] The rest of the work lay in research into the average rainfall and water tables, the climate and geology, and the devising of a thorough conservation system. When the final report by Fred H. Tibbetts and his associate, Stephen E. Kieffer, was presented in March of 1921 under the title of *Report to the Santa Clara Valley Water Conservation Committee on the Santa Clara Valley Water Conservation Project,*[26] many persons on the committee and in the valley were not prepared for just how complete the report was.

An in-depth survey of the valley was needed,

and an engineer equal to the task had to be found. Fred H. Tibbetts

of Campbell was chosen for his experience and enthusiasm for the project.

Fred H. Tibbetts

When all of the many facts, figures and statistics were waded through, some thought-provoking information lay at the heart of it. As of 1892, some 100 new wells were drilled each year in the valley. Less than thirty years later, in 1920, the annual rate had reached 1,700. While in 1912, only 29 percent of the valley was under irrigation, by 1920, 67.5 percent was, including 90 percent of all orchards. In the 1904-06 period, land receiving water from diverted streams in winter and spring totaled 14,000 acres; by 1920 the acreage had declined to only 3,000. The sum of all these data was the hard fact that far more water was being pumped out of the ground than nature could replace, especially when up to 69 percent of the annual rainfall washed through the valley and into the bay each year.[26:44, 46, 58]

More distressing, probably, to the valley's residents than the amount of water wasted, was the cost of conserving it. In the report was contained the conclusion that the water lost into the bay each year must be saved and distributed to the residents of the valley or percolated into the aquifers for storage below ground. To this end, 17 large reservoirs must be constructed as well as low check dams, pumping stations in the lowlands to divert the runoff, and a system of concrete conduits to distribute the conserved water to its desired destinations. The engineers' estimation of the cost was an unprecedented high of $10.9 million.[26:11-17, 60, 210]

Plans to form a water district were already in the works by the time the report was presented. Water districts were not a new concept in California, for between 1887 and

1895, forty-nine of them had been formed in the state.[25:17] Yet, since 1890, most of them had been formed under the Wright Irrigation Act, a piece of legislation wholly inadequate for the needs of the Santa Clara Valley. It was intended for districts which would be formed around single sources of water, such as lakes and rivers, and this simply was not the case in the Santa Clara Valley. Furthermore, the conservation committee wanted an act with provisions for groundwater recharge.[25:43] Nothing remained for them to do but write their own act.

Two veterans of the water conservation movement were called to the task. Former state Assemblyman L. D. Bohnett, now legal counsel for the Santa Clara Valley Water Conservation Committee, was asked to draw up a new bill outlining the special conditions present in the valley and the manner in which the new district intended to organize. Herbert C. Jones, the other veteran and still serving in the state senate, guided the new bill through the legislature until, in June of 1921, it was accepted. Now termed the "Jones Act," the bill provided that a water district could be formed by a majority vote of all electors to be included within its boundaries. Bond issues for the district's conservation activities were to be voted on and paid for only by those who would receive conserved water. Both the number of votes and amount of payment would be apportioned according to the amount of water that one received. Citizens who did not benefit from conserving water would still pay a very nominal tax, about $0.023 per assessed hundred of their acreage, for the upkeep of the office and

Whenever large sums of money are to be spent by large numbers of people, there will be divisions in public opinion, and sometimes these are fatal to the plans in question.

staff. Admittedly, this was a cumbersome system, not designed so much for ease of understanding by the public nor ease of administrating, but for cost distribution equity: Those who benefited from water conservation would pay for it and would pay in accordance with the amount of benefits which they received.[8:26]

Whenever large sums of money are to be spent by large numbers of people, there will be divisions in public opinion, and sometimes these are fatal to the plans in question. Now that the Jones Act had been passed by the legislature and governor, it had to go before the voters of the proposed district for final approval. Support was not lacking in the community; farm organizations, business groups and labor councils for the most part favored the measure.[17:1] Opposition, however, was not long in presenting itself, especially in light of the $10 million-plus price tag. While water conservation was a worthy cause, most people had a strong reaction to appointing a body that could bond and tax on that scale.

Acceptance of the district did not necessarily mean acceptance of the Tibbetts and Kieffer plan, and too few voters realized this. Once again they fell back on the belief that all that was needed was another wet spell to set things right again.[25:58-59]

September 27, 1921 saw the proposed water district go before the people and fail. Indeed, it was a narrow margin. Only about 10 percent of the voters turned out that day, indicating that not enough had been done to strongly influence public opinion one way or the other. Out of 6,425 votes cast, only the narrow margin of 301 votes had caused the proposition's defeat.[18:1] The slight margin of defeat encouraged the water conservationists. They were mostly convinced that with another try, success might be achieved. Already engineer Fred Tibbetts had warned them that as a result of the defeat, as much as $5 million would be lost due to increased pumping, drilling and construction costs

before the plan would have a chance to be adopted.[8:29]

Less than a year and a half later, L. D. Bohnett submitted revised legislation to Senator Jones that might be more appealing to the voters. Morgan Hill, a community whose watershed area lay to the south, independent from most of the rest of the valley's, was eliminated from the legislation in hopes of avoiding their sentiments of dissent. Lacking any real opposition in the legislature, the revised bill was passed in 1923.[25:7]

Following the bill's passage, local opposition to the formation of any form of water district quickly mounted. Calling the bill "needless legislation," the County Board of Supervisors issued a resolution protesting its passage. Palo Alto's City Board of Public Works protested the bill as an unfair tax burden upon their city whose water is based on another watershed. As with Morgan Hill, Palo Alto was removed from the proposed district's boundaries.[8:29] Dissent from official bodies in the county convinced the less resolute supporters of water conservation that the bill had no hope for county voter support. While the men behind the plan, L. D. Bohnett, Charles E. Warren and others of similar determination were adamant in their convictions, Senator Jones and many others began to falter in the face of growing opposition. Among the valley's newspapers, most of which favored conservation, none was as strong in backing the movement as the *San Jose Mercury Herald.* Yet in the months prior to the election, campaign news seldom reached the front pages of this and other valley journals.[8:29-31]

Whatever new recruits might have come over to the conservation effort did so because of the elements. In 1923, there occurred only 39 percent of the average rainfall.[23:16] It was so dry the following spring that Morgan Hill hired a rainmaker for an advance of $1,000 and a promised $3,000 to $4,000 more when five inches of rain had fallen. Despite the generous terms, the gentleman was unable to influence the precipitation.[21:1]

Preceding the election date of April 11, 1924 were seven months of events destined to defeat the conservation measure. In October 1923, the San Jose Water Works, which happened to supply about half the valley's domestic water users, decided to raise the various rates by 35 to 66 percent.[19:17] Knowledge that a water conservation district would benefit the Water Works by lowering its pumping costs at public expense was reason enough to turn many voters against the proposal.[8:32]

Supporters and leaders of the conservation effort did not have a carefully devised campaign strategy, but the opposition did. Organized under the title of the "Growers' Protective Association," the opponents of the proposition conducted a well-planned and well-financed campaign. This group, composed mostly of farmers and ranchers but led by holders of large parcels of land in both urban and rural areas, was united chiefly by a desire to keep taxes from going any higher.[25:81-2] Full-page ads were bought up by this group in the various valley newspapers. Most, like one in March of that year in the *San Jose Mercury Herald,* denounced the plan as "unworkable" and "costly." The same ad stated that acceptance of the district would "merely result in the spending of huge sums of money for large salaries for directors and engineers, and fat fees for lawyers."[20:4]

There was no evidence that this was the conservationists' purpose, nor is there any evidence now that they benefited unduly from the creation of a water district. It was, however, an accusation almost impossible to deny without lending it credibility. Even the fact that the conservationists failed to advertise as strongly as their opponents (due to unavailable funding) led to suspicions of the conservationists' motives.[8:24] Also, the bill was so heavily worded, in order to achieve the carefully researched water system outlined in the Tibbetts and Kieffer plan, that the proposition was difficult for the layman to understand. This, too, was capitalized upon by the opposition who were

quite willing to explain what they felt the bill intended to those unable to find out for themselves.[24:75]

Perhaps the strongest accusation hurled in this bitterly divided campaign came in the last week before voting when it was too late for the bill's proponents to answer effectively. It was claimed that the unprecedented expenditures of the district would cause banks to foreclose or demand early payment of mortgages. This, while not necessarily true, was weakly denied by bank officials.[21:1]

An unexpected lack of support came at the last moment from long-term conservationist, E. A. Hayes. He was quoted in the papers, at a time when only the most positive statements would help, as being rather surprised that the bill contained some provisions about pipe and ditch lines and electrical generation that he found rather objectionable. Nevertheless, he was certain that these areas could be deleted by amendment after the measure was adopted and urged a "yes" vote.[21:1] Coming from a member of the movement's leadership, such faltering could only be disastrous.

Earlier in the campaign, the basis of a very promising counter-argument for the conservationists was advanced by an officer of the Federal Land Bank. He favored the measure because his organization was refusing to advance loans to landowners in areas where the amount of groundwater used exceeded the supply which was replenished. This was, in his opinion, certainly possible in the Santa Clara Valley, but the argument lacked widespread attention.[8:33-34]

The cruelest blow against water conservation efforts was delivered by nature itself. In the past year, the rainfall had reached 94 percent of normal and more than double that of the year before.[23:16] Although this hardly affected the water table, nor was it a sign of a wetter trend in the climate, it was sufficient to take everyone's mind off droughts.

As was to be expected, the second attempt to gain public acceptance of a water district was a failure. A good many more voters went to the polls that April 11 than had in the last election, and the result was harsher. There were 7,044 votes cast in opposition, compared to 6,084 in favor; a margin of 960.[22:1] Only the most devoted conservationists escaped discouragement to cluster around a small nucleus of leadership. One such leader was Leroy Anderson, an orchardist from Saratoga and former professor of agriculture. While not originally a guiding force, he assumed the role of water conservation incarnate for the next few years. The Santa Clara Valley Water Conservation Committee disbanded soon after the defeat.[8:35] ■

The creeks and rivers of the Santa Clara Valley have not only been a supply of water, but a resource to enjoy. Photograph circa 1925.

SOURCES, CHAPTER 1:

1. Anonymous, Artesian Wells, San José: Public Library Scrapbook, no date.

2. Bancroft, Hubert Howe. *History of California,* Vol. IV. San Francisco: The History of Company, 1886.

3. Broek, Jan Otto Marius. *The Santa Clara Valley, California: A Study in Landscape Changes.* Utrecht, Holland: publisher unknown, 1932.

4. Hare, George H. *Hare's Guide to San José and Vicinity for Tourists and New Settlers.* San José: Unknown, 1872.

5. Hill, Frederic. *History of San José and Surroundings with Biographical Sketches of Early Settlers.* San Francisco: publisher unknown, 1871.

6. James, William F. and McMurry, George H. *History of San José.* San José: Smith Printing Company, 1933.

7. Kroeber, Alfred Louis. "The Nature of Land Holding Groups in Aboriginal California," *Aboriginal California: Three Studies in Culture History.* Berkeley: University of California Archaeological Facility, 1963.

8. Martin, Richard G. *Water Conservation in the Santa Clara Valley.* Thesis. Department of History, University of California, Berkeley, 1949.

9. *San Jose Mercury Herald,* June 12, 1913.

10. Ibid, November 4, 1919.

11. Ibid, January 22, 1920.

12. Ibid, February 28, 1920.

13. Ibid, March 16, 1920.

14. Ibid, April 28, 1920.

15. Ibid, August 12, 1920.

16. Ibid, October 7, 1920.

17. Ibid, March 28, 1921.

18. Ibid, September 27, 1921.

19. Ibid, October 30, 1923.

20. Ibid, March 9, 1924.

21. Ibid, April 7, 1924.

22. Ibid, April 11, 1924.

23. *Santa Clara Investigation.* California Department of Public Works, Division of Water Resources. Sacramento: Bulletin No. 42, 1933.

24. Sawyer, Eugene T. *History of Santa Clara County, California.* Los Angeles: publisher unknown, 1922.

25. Smith, Everett Eldon. *The Organization of the Santa Clara Valley Water District.* Thesis. Department of History, Stanford University, 1961.

26. Tibbetts, Fred H. and Kieffer, Stephen E. *Report to Santa Clara Valley Water Conservation Committee on Santa Clara Valley Water Conservation Project*, 1921.

27. U.S. Department of Agriculture, Office of Experiment Stations, Annual Report of Irrigation and Drainage Investigations, 1904. Washington: U.S. Government Printing Office, 1905.

28. Winther, Carl Osburn. *The Story of San Jose 1777-1869.* San Francisco: California Historical Society, 1935.

Second Edition Note: Specifically in this chapter, the citation number may include the referenced page numbers. For example, the citation "8:33-34" indicates that this information was taken from pages 33-34 of source #8.

With a train system in place, fruit from the valley easily reached eastern markets, and fruit production—
such as the dried apricot operation shown in this 1920s postcard—became highly profitable.

Courtesy History San José

CHAPTER 2

Organization for Water:
Rise of Economic and Political Interests

By Kevin Fish

With the completion of efficient railway lines and the formation of growers' associations, agriculture became big business in the 1920s. To meet market demands, growers organized to work for more efficient agricultural methods. While eastern markets beckoned for their goods, crop damage caused by the inevitable presence of drought and seasonal flooding confronted the farmers with intolerable economic risks. It was also obvious that post World War I industrialization was encouraging the rapid growth of the San Francisco Peninsula. Industry made it clear that cities such as San José would not be attractive unless they could "guarantee" a water supply. Thus, the farmers and the Chamber of Commerce were to band together to meet the challenge of water resource needs of the twentieth century.

On November 22, 1926, the first successful major steps toward a countywide effort for water conservation were taken when approximately fifty farmers met to establish an association for water conservation. On December 1, the Santa Clara Valley Water Conservation Association

incorporated and a board of directors was elected. Management was vested in a board of 12 directors, each of whom was to stand for election annually. The board was comprised of Leroy Anderson of San José, Max Watson of Agnew, James E. Wiesendanger of Cupertino, Karl E. Bracher of Santa Clara, Edwin Howes of Los Gatos, S. N. Hedegard of Campbell, W. K. Roberts of Sunnyvale, Nelson Barton of San José, Lloyd Gardner of Campbell, John A. Fair of San José, Warren E. Hyde of Cupertino and R. P. Van Orden of Mountain View. West Side Water Conservation Committee Chairman Leroy Anderson and the secretary to that committee, Max Watson, were elected president and secretary, respectively.[2, 20, 24] Confident of the association's future, Max Watson, manager of the Agnew branch of the Skaneateles Teasel Company of Passaic, New Jersey, made the following comments:

The farmers of the entire valley are enthusiastic over the association, which has culminated many

Agriculture became big business. Drought and seasonal flooding confronted the farmers with intolerable economic risks.

The most effective

conservation method

would be to store the

floodwaters underground

by enabling water to

percolate into the gravel

beds of the streams

of the valley.

years of effort in this direction. Not only the far-mers, but also the entire valley will benefit, and we are expecting to find active support in San José and other cities as well. Anyone is eligible for membership and a campaign will be announced soon. The election issues failed to provide the conservation program that was needed, and this association, similar to the Tri-Counties Water Co. in the southern part of the state, offers the best solution. It has worked successfully elsewhere and promises to solve our problems here.[20]

As stated in the Articles of Incorporation, the goals of the association were as follows:

1. To conserve the surface and subsurface waters of Santa Clara Valley, State of California, by spreading the floodwaters of said Valley over such lands adjacent to the stream channels of said Valley as may be available for that purpose, and to that end—

2. To secure control of such land as may be necessary or desirable for such spreading, by purchase, lease, gift, donation, license or other methods, as may be found most desirable and feasible;

3. To construct, maintain and operate thereon such works and structures as may be found most advantageous and desirable for water conservation purposes;

4. To prevent waste of artesian and subsurface waters by the enforcement of the law of the State of California prohibiting the waste of such water and by securing evidence of such violation and by the prosecution of the violators of said law;

5. To use such other methods of conserving the flood-waters of Santa Clara Valley as the Board of Directors of the Association shall determine, none of the purposes of the Corporation being in anywise for pecuniary profit or financial gain of the Corporation or of any of its members;

6. To buy, hire, lease and accept gifts and donations of such necessary machinery, tools and equipment as shall be required in order to efficiently accomplish the purposes of water conservation.

On February 26, 1927, Max Watson announced publicly that the prosperity of the valley depended directly upon the profits of its agricultural interests. As Watson put it:

If the water level continues to fall for the next 10 years as rapidly as for the past 10, it will mean that thousands of acres of orchards will die for lack of water, resulting in a tremendous loss in values. That cannot be allowed to happen.[17]

Watson stated that the sole purpose of the association was to prevent such a disaster. He favored conservation to check the falling water level and to save thousands of acres of valley orchards. According to Watson the means to conserve valley floodwaters involved three factors: cost, time and volume of water to be conserved.

Based upon the advice of the best geologists and water engineers in the state and highly successful projects in other localities, the association decided that the most effective conservation method would be to store the flood-waters underground by enabling water to percolate into the gravel beds of the streams of the valley.

The initial task of the new association was to continue the use of water percolation, which was being carried out by the West Side Water Conservation Committee. Major funding went into the development of an extensive system of sack dams, many along the Guadalupe Creek. Six sack dams were constructed in the west valley between 1926 and 1927. The dams served to spread the water over the gravel creek beds providing maximum replenishment to the underground strata, and thereby replenishing wells.

Orchardists of the vicinity were enthusiastic over the effectiveness of the dams. They met the night of July 7, 1927, at the Valley View School, where they decided to install permanent dams before the fall rains. Leon Athenour, who acted as chairman of the meeting, gave figures on the depth of water in his well over various years which, he contended, proved conclusively the value of the sack dams. In 1912, he said, depth to water in his well was 72 feet, but by 1919, the level had dropped to 96 feet, and, in 1925, to 118 feet. Despite the heavy rains of the 1925-26 season, the water level in the well rose only to 96 feet. In 1927, he stated that although there was less rain than the previous year, the water table had risen to within 73 feet of the surface, within a foot of what it was in 1912. He attributed the rise in the water table to the recharge seepage induced by the sack dams.

A committee to raise funds for financing construction of permanent concrete dams was created at the July 7th meeting. Nelson Barton was appointed chairman and the group voluntarily assessed its members fifty cents per acre. N. B. Galbraith, Thomas Armstrong, C. A. Scott, Ernest Matasci, E. Kittrill, M. Raymond, John Withers, H. W. Ogden and Max Watson also attended the meeting and spoke favorably of the project.[29]

Formation of the
Santa Clara Valley Water Conservation District

In the latter 1920s, groups organizing for water conservation gained additional impetus at both the state and local levels. Senator Jones had written the bylaws of the water conservation association, and had been active for years promoting water legislation in Sacramento. Finally, with the passage of the Water Conservation (Jones) Act of 1929, the creation of water conservation districts, with limited powers and jurisdiction, was made possible.

By 1927, six *sack dams* were constructed to spread water for *percolation* into aquifers.

The first countywide effort for water conservation began with the formation of the Santa Clara Valley Water Conservation Association in November 1926. Led by pioneer Leroy Anderson of San José, the association developed an extensive system of sack dams. In this collage, men are constructing a sack dam along Page Creek in Los Gatos, circa 1927.

Farmers Unite

In the meantime, alarm over the critical water conditions continued to rally the orchardists around the conservation cause. Even prior to any campaigning for the water conservation district's establishment, farmers sought cooperative assistance. On November 21, 1928, the farmers of the McKinley and Jackson school districts organized the Project Four Water Conservation Association. The new Association elected John A. Fair as president and Charles C. Derby as secretary-treasurer, and collected $325 of the $850 needed to complete the first experimental water conservation project on Coyote Creek. It was also at this meeting that Max Watson stood up to propose a water consumption tax to be based on the quantity of water pumped from each well. Watson argued that such tax funds would be used in extending conservation measures, and so established the basic principle of the present-day pump tax.

The Pre-Election Campaign

With nearly all the water used in Santa Clara Valley being pumped from the underground reservoir, we have seen this supply drawn upon more rapidly than it is being replenished by the natural absorption from the various streams entering the valley. That nature may be materially assisted in replenishing our water supply from creek flow has been demonstrated to be practicable here as well as on many other streams in California where gravel beds at the surface have been used as percolating areas to force greater absorption of the floodwaters. However, an organized district is essential to manage the enterprise and raise sufficient funds to do the work properly.
Four years ago the Santa Clara County

Consolidated Chamber of Commerce appointed an active committee on water conservation and has always shown a keen interest in the need for a more adequate water supply. We therefore heartily approve the plan to organize a district under the provisions of the Water Conservation (Jones) Act of 1929. We understand that the district proposed is to include the entire Valley floor from the lower gorge of the Coyote north to San Francisco Bay and that the annual assessment levy is not to exceed 15 cents of each $100 of assessed land value.
~ August 6, 1929, Santa Clara County Consolidated Chamber of Commerce

As the fall 1929 election approached, governmental officials and citizens whose economic future depended upon available water resources rallied together to campaign for the passage of the water conservation district measure and the updated version of the Jones Act. All evidence illustrating the critical need for an assured water supply came forth. Members of the Santa Clara County Consolidated Chamber of Commerce were major campaign contributors, funding a series of educational radio broadcasts in cooperation with the Santa Clara Valley Water Conservation Association. Beginning August 15, Radio Station KQW granted the association fifteen minutes each Tuesday night to assist its appeal for public support.

Also helpful to the association's cause was the August 26th report of F. M. Budlong of Campbell and Budlong, local manufacturers of deep well turbine pumps. In a letter to the association, statistical information of the company revealed the expensive consequences of declining groundwater levels:

When we first engaged in the manufacture of deep well turbine pumps in 1919, our average pump setting in the territory from Coyote Narrows to Los Gatos, northerly to Mountain View and easterly to Milpitas, was approximately 70 feet from the surface. By the spring of 1924, the average depth of pump setting was 100 feet, and in the spring of 1928 it was 120 feet. From January 15, 1929 to July 1, the average depth has increased to about 150 feet.

In the basin filled by flow of Coyote Creek, the pump setting in 1924 was 70 feet; at the present time the average depth is 120 feet and deeper to keep pump bowls in the water. In the Campbell district, our average pump setting in 1920 was 120 feet while this season it is 200 feet deep.

In the district between Alviso and Mountain View, the average pump setting in 1920 was 60 feet and now it is 140 feet. During the time we have been lowering pumps, the maximum capacity of all these wells has decreased an average of over 35 percent in the amount of water that it is possible to take now over the year 1923. We estimate that the cost to our customers of lifting the same number of acre-feet of water or the same number of gallons has increased over 50 percent in the last five years.[37]

During the election month, saltwater seepage from San Francisco Bay became another issue. The Santa Clara County Board of Supervisors received a letter from San José City Engineer J. R. Byxbee. Because the saltwater threat was already evident, Byxbee asked the county to pass a law to seal wells that became brackish. Supervisor Joseph McKinnon argued in favor of sealing the wells and stated that Gus Hunter of Agnew Road was already the county's official "well plugger."[36] Orchardist R. P. Van Orden also addressed the saltwater problem speaking out in favor of the water conservation district as a means of

saving valley orchards that bordered the Bay. In an October 30 statement, he said that if the Jones Act and the water conservation proposal were approved at the polls November 5, it would mean more work with better results for each dollar expended than any other law then on the statute books and would cause real estate values to become stabilized. He said that such values would surely decline if the act and the proposal were defeated, and that the opposition to the act came from those who had solemnly sworn to vote against all taxes and bonds, and from those who, through ignorance, could see no direct benefit to themselves.

During the month preceding the election, the campaign reached its height. Senator Jones, home from Sacramento, addressed the San Jose High Twelve Club at the Hotel Sainte Claire and later, the San Jose Lions Club, at all times making the appeal for his water legislation. Also speaking out in favor of the conservation measures were the Santa Clara Valley Water Conservation Committee and the Farmers Education and Cooperative Union of Santa Clara County. Resolutions were passed and individual farmers stood up and publicly announced their fears over the scarcity of water and the rising costs of pumping.

Election Results

By election day, November 5, 1929, virtually all opposition to the water conservation measure had disappeared. The Water Conservation (Jones) Act was adopted, and the proposal to create a water conservation district was approved. Voters in the area of the proposed district in the central section of Santa Clara County voted in favor of the proposal by a vote of nearly nine to one. With only 13 percent of the registered voters casting their ballots, the final vote tally was 5,389 in favor to 604 against the proposal. Organized under the Jones Act, seven directors were elected

State Senator Herbert C. Jones

Great bursts of joy and enthusiasm were expressed the night of the election. Stated Senator Jones, "No community can be greater than its water supply."

The 1929 measure

for a Water District

passed with 5,389

voters in favor;

604 against.

from regional areas within the newly formed district. The district had been divided into seven divisions, each of which was to have a director. The seven directors elected were: Division 1, S. D. Farrington; Division 2, Leroy Anderson; Division 3, R. P. Van Orden; Division 4, J. Fred Holthouse; Division 5, Edgar Jackson; Division 6, John A. Fair; and Division 7, C. D. Cavallaro. No opposition names were placed in nomination, but a few were written in on the ballots from various districts. After the election, the Board of Directors elected Leroy Anderson as president and R. P. Van Orden as secretary, and hired Senator Jones as district counsel, while Fred H. Tibbetts was retained as chief engineer.

Members of the Santa Clara Valley Water Conservation Association, San Jose Chamber of Commerce and business and farm organizations were enthusiastic over the huge majority vote rolled up by the water conservation district measure. Great bursts of joy and enthusiasm were expressed the night of the election. Senator Jones applauded the results especially for its future impact upon the valley's economy. "No community can be greater than its water supply," he said. "Here is a step to save this indispensable requisite to our growth in the Santa Clara Valley." He particularly credited the *Mercury Herald* for its "efforts in laying the facts before the public," and praised the newspaper for having "fought for the preservation of the waters of the valley ever since the days of the Bay Cities Water Company lawsuits a quarter of a century ago."[48]

On November 19, 1929, the Santa Clara Valley Water Conservation Association officially disbanded and passed the burden of future water resources to the new district. The following properties that belonged to the association were turned over to the new district: state appropriative rights to 10,000 acre-feet of water per year; conservation projects on the Los Gatos and Almaden creeks; 12 acres of land and property valued at $6,000 on Los Gatos Creek, Page Ditch and Santa Clara Valley Water Company Ditch; and other

dams and culverts constructed by the association. The association also transferred a five-year lease to the district that had been granted by the Southern Pacific Railroad Company on gravel beds in Almaden Creek, on which spreading dams were located.

The Question of Water Rights

The original district boundaries followed those of the groundwater basin underlying the lands that would benefit from the works of the district.[63:4] Thus, its jurisdiction extended from Adobe (San Antonio) Creek in Palo Alto in the north to the town of Coyote to the south, and from the foothills in the east to the foothills in the west. The entire Santa Clara Valley floor within these confines under a 200-foot elevation was included. In 1953, some 4,000 acres of land in the Evergreen area of the eastern foothills were added. In 1954, the 14,000 acres comprising the central region of the Santa Clara Valley Water Conservation District, extending from Coyote to the southern limits of Morgan Hill, were formally annexed to the district.

The goals of the original district are stated in the Water Conservation Act of 1929 (later amended as the Water Conservation Act of 1931). Under "Powers and Purposes," now Section 74500 of the California Water Code, the goals are to appropriate, acquire and conserve water and water rights for any useful purpose; to preserve, store, spread and sink water for such purposes; and to acquire or construct dams, dam sites, reservoirs and reservoir sites. The district would operate works, drill wells, operate pumps, sell and distribute water and do related activities. In other words, the district would endeavor to direct the winter storm flows into the subterranean reservoir of the valley and thereby raise the rapidly lowering water level, insuring sufficient water for irrigation and domestic purposes. Thus, since its formation, the district's goal was to make sufficient water available to meet the ever-increasing needs of Santa Clara Valley.[63:5] The initial task of the new district was to enact its water conservation policies, using the latest engineering technology, and to solve the many legal problems associated with implementing the recommendations of the Tibbetts and Kieffer Report (see Chapter 1). The selection of sites for dams, canals and reservoirs meant immediate confrontation with landowners, publicly-held water agencies and communities who feared the impact of large dams upstream from their locales.

The district directors rapidly learned that to meet the challenge before them, their powers had to be enlarged. Lobbying began, and in 1931, Senator Jones convinced the state Legislature that it was necessary to amend the Water Conservation Act of 1929. Under the proposed amendments, the district would be able to raise necessary funds by bringing bonds before the vote of the people, approve annexation of additional territory, take sewage or other wastewater from cities, treat it and sell the effluent for any useful purpose, and levy special assessments. Because of the protest of the Pacific Gas and Electric Company, a provision to permit the district to invest in electric power generation was removed before the bill was submitted to the voters on November 17, 1931.

The major opposition to the amended act was represented in the Farmers and Homeowners' Protective League. The League campaigned actively against the amendments to the 1929 Act, predicting that dam construction would obstruct and limit the amount of water normally available to farmers for irrigation purposes.

Fearing an invasion of their water rights, some farmers opposed the impounding of floodwaters as planned in the Tibbetts report.[†] C. H. Johnson, spokesman for the League, also questioned the expense of the $6 million conservation district bonds, instead, favoring the use of ditch irrigation. Still opposed to the bonds as late as January 1932,

In November 1931, voters were asked to expand the powers of the Water District and fund reservoir construction with a $6 million bond issue.

Local residents examine campaign literature at the San José election headquarters, 1931.

he said, "The solution of the water problem is to take the muddy water from the streams by ditches and pumping and distributing it over the land, particularly over the gravel strata. This fertilization and revitalization of the land is worth thousands of dollars."[61]

The Great Depression was the backdrop to the state-wide 1931 election and to the district's efforts to gain the taxpayers' support for financing the $6 million necessary to carry out the recommended construction of dams and reservoirs. The frightening state of the economy nation-wide explained, in Senator Jones' opinion, the defeat of the bond measure by a vote of seven to one.[19][††] However, the amendments passed, increasing the powers of water conservation districts statewide. The amended act became known as the Water Conservation Act of 1931.

Suits and Countersuits

The question of extending the district's legal powers soon became evident in several lawsuits that also occurred in the 1930s. There was a general suspicion over extending the power of an agency that could so dramatically affect the economic future of the valley's farmers.

One case involved Harry L. Haehl, owner of the extensive Laguna Seca Ranch in the South County. Haehl obtained the holdings following the 1913 legal suit between the Coyote Valley, Santa Clara Valley farmers and the privately-owned Bay Cities Water Company. The local farmers opposed the company's efforts to transport water out of their valley to the East Bay cities. As a result of the suit, Bay Cities Water Company went out of existence, and Haehl, its chief engineer, acquired most of the company's holdings.[21]

When the new Santa Clara Valley Water Conservation District planned to percolate water through the Coyote Valley in the 1930s, Haehl and other local farmers opposed the plan saying that it would flood them out. In order to overcome the objections, the district built the Coyote Canal to bypass the Coyote Valley. The Coyote Canal terminated at Metcalf Road, where it discharged into the Coyote Percolation Reservoir. After the District started releasing water from the Coyote Reservoir in 1936, Haehl filed suit against the district, claiming that by raising the groundwater level at the lower gorge of the Coyote River, where Metcalf Road is located, the district was raising the underground water level under his ranch to the surface of the ground. The district claimed that Haehl's flooding problems were due to surface runoff from the hills. The case was settled out of court when the district acquired the 486-acre Haehl Ranch as part of the final settlement and gave Haehl some money and some surplus land above Calero Reservoir.[62]

The fact that the district had filed with the State of California for appropriative rights for floodwaters that

---

[†] For historical reasons, California water law is complicated by the existence of two kinds of water rights: riparian and appropriative. The former is a part of ownership of land adjacent to a stream; the latter is secured by simply beginning a beneficial use with the necessary normal steps. Thus, a farmer who relied on his riparian status might fear that upstream regulation by an appropriator could deny him the full flow of his legal entitlement. The applicant who files his claim first has superior appropriative rights to those of another. However, the law is clear that reasonable (non-wasteful) riparian diversions have absolute priority over any appropriator; also, during water shortages, according to the California Water Code, domestic water use is superior to that of irrigational water use, thus supplanting this rule.

[††] In another election July 1, 1934, voters approved a bond issue in the amount of $2 million. In addition, voters approved a second bond issue of $400,000 on July 1, 1936.

normally wasted into San Francisco Bay via regional creeks caused new conflicts with farmers. Already established along the creeks were privately owned and developed systems that diverted water into various water courses, such as man-made ditches or canals, during the spring and early summer months. Agricultural land was irrigated by such diversion systems.

Even before the district entered the picture, there were battles over creek water. Farming families had developed the Kirk and Page ditch systems along Los Gatos Creek. There were diversion dams along Guadalupe and Stevens creeks, used primarily for irrigation. Battles had already taken place along Guadalupe Creek because people upstream of the lower diversion systems were taking too much water.[9]

Direct confrontations with landowners became particularly evident with the proposed construction of the district's reservoirs. The design of Vasona Reservoir, explained in Chapter 3, was determined by the issue of the preemptive water rights of farming families such as the Doetsches, Lesters and Kirks. Many conflicts had arisen among these families over the rights to Los Gatos Creek water.

As a continuation of this conflict, when the Vasona Reservoir was proposed, these families at first opposed the project, especially the Doetsches and Lesters, who owned land within the proposed reservoir site. The Lesters and Doetsches were representing other owners of riparian and appropriated water along the Los Gatos Creek. Should they sell their lands they would, in effect, be eliminating their appropriated rights. Also, if they granted easements, they would be, in effect, fee owners of the land and thus could effectively represent themselves and the appropriative water users to whom they were providing water. Considerable legal conciliation was necessary as the Lesters and Doetsches wanted to protect their water rights by not selling their property. The district obtained an easement over their lands and also rehabilitated the wells as the

Vasona Dam was constructed directly over the existing wells. As a result of such opposition, a galley system was used in the design of the reservoir to insure the rights of owners downstream.[9]

Another source of conflict over water rights occurred with the San Jose Water Works. The Water Works, having begun pumping water in 1866, should not have conflicted with the district, whose purposes were to recharge the ground with water. However, with the Lexington Reservoir proposal, the question over the rights of the Los Gatos watershed arose.

The San Jose Water Works claimed the rights to two sources of water. One was the Los Gatos watershed where the company had diversion and storage facilities in the foot-hills above the town of Los Gatos. The company collected runoff during the rainy seasons, some of which was stored and some of which was used immediately. Their second supply of water was from wells, which they had drilled. The water was pumped from the groundwater basin and served to Los Gatos, Saratoga, San José and a portion of Campbell. As the city of San José grew, the San Jose Water Works grew along with it. The company attempted to develop its mountain water, which was only approximately 10 percent of its supply, the balance of which was obtained from the underground basin.

As the Santa Clara Valley water table subsided, the Water Works experienced a serious threat to its supply of available water. In the latter 1940s, when the district proposed to locate Lexington Reservoir downstream from the Water Works' Austrian Reservoir, it conflicted with the Water Works' appropriative rights. Having filed for the unappropriated water before the district, the Water Works had legal priority. So that the Water Works would not incur damages from a loss of water caused by the construction of Lexington Dam, the Water Conservation District had to relocate all of the company's facilities that would be affected.[5]

The proposed construction of reservoirs led to direct confrontations with landowners; this was complicated by California's water rights system. Considerable legal conciliation was necessary.

It was during these trying formative years of the 1930s that the Santa Clara Valley Water Conservation District pioneered the working design of an effective program of water conservation.

The issue of the district's right to take immediate possession of lands needed for rights of way and reservoir purposes plagued the agency's formative years, and posed serious complications to any major conservation efforts. Once again, Senator Jones, the attorney for the district, worked on a measure that would benefit water conservation. This time, Jones sponsored an amendment to the State Constitution, and in 1933, the legislature approved it. A statewide campaign was launched to obtain the voters' endorsement of the Water District's rights of immediate possession, and, with the aid of farmers' organizations and other interested citizens, the amendment was adopted in November 1934.

With substantial new power, the district initially worked with a board of three realtors to negotiate for the lands required for reservoirs and canals. This board consisted of Frazier O. Reed, W. L. Atkinson, and Arthur Moore. In 1934 and 1935 and immediately thereafter, this committee was instrumental in acquiring lands for the first five reservoirs. Frazier Reed, with a thorough knowledge of condemnation proceedings, soon became a full-time consultant to the district, and conducted important negotiations with landowners and participated in policy decisions. According to Richard Garland Martin, Reed possessed a rare engineering skill although he had never been trained as an engineer.[19] Reed insisted from the beginning that a criterion or yardstick be established for a consistent evaluation of similar properties.

The challenges that the new district faced in its efforts to carry out an efficient conservation system on the valley floor were similar to those being experienced throughout the state. On June 2, 1930, Harold Conkling, Chief of the State Division of Water Resources; state Senator Jones; local Grange members; and farmers met in Gilroy to discuss the water situation in the South County. At that time, Jones reported that Los Angeles had recently voted $40 million to increase its water supply, and San Diego was proposing the transport of water from the Colorado River over an elevation of more than 4,000 feet to meet its needs. The state had appropriated $500,000 for the study of the water problem statewide.[11]

At the same meeting, the Morgan Hill and Gilroy Grange committees and the Gilroy Chamber of Commerce wanted to work directly with the state program of water conservation to develop their water plan. Chairman A. A. Martin of the Gilroy Grange Committee proposed a plan to take the excess waters of Uvas Creek over to Llagas Creek, where it could be percolated into the underground reservoir rather than being permitted to flow to the Pajaro River and thence to the ocean.[11] In view of the suggested project, Jones outlined the measures already being undertaken by the Santa Clara Valley Water Conservation District north of Coyote, emphasizing that tax dollars were being well spent. He stated that tests had shown that practically no water reached the underground reservoir of the valley by percolation from the surface except where that water is directed to relatively small gravel areas. This statement was upheld by Conkling, and it was emphasized that the storage of water through dams was the only solution for the valley in order to conserve a maximum amount of water.[11]

Leroy Anderson, president of the Santa Clara Valley Water Conservation District, was also at the meeting. He told farmers that eventually the valley would have to resort to storage of winter floods by a system of reservoirs. Jones' and Anderson's ideas were first realized in 1934, when the voters approved the first bond issue for the construction of the district's first six reservoirs. It was during these trying formative years of the 1930s that the Santa Clara Valley Water Conservation District pioneered the working design of an effective program of water conservation.■

SOURCES, CHAPTER 2:

1. Anderson, Leroy. Letter to the editor, *San Jose Mercury Herald,* Feb. 15, 1926.

2. Anderson, Leroy. Report to the Santa Clara Valley Water Conservation Association, 1927.

3. Articles of Incorporation of the Santa Clara Valley Water Conservation Association.

4. Beaudet, John. Interviewed by Kevin Fish, July 19, 1976.

5. Clarke, John H. (Jack). Interviewed by Kevin Fish, July 12, 1976.

6. "Committees Will Study Conservation Problems," *San Jose Mercury Herald,* May 2, 1926, p. 2.

7. "Conservation of Water Planned," *San Jose Mercury Herald,* May 2, 1926, p. 1.

8. Doetsch, Sr., Ralph. Interviewed by Kevin Fish, August 23, 1976, Dec. 15, 1976.

9. "Dropping Water Level in County Bared by Survey," *San Jose Mercury Herald,* Oct. 9, 1930.

10. Enander, Violet V. Interviewed by Kevin Fish, June 18, 1976.

11. "Gilroy District Begins Move to Conserve Water," *San Jose Mercury Herald,* June 3, 1930.

12. Henley, Albert T. Interviewed by Kevin Fish, June 18, 1976; July 12, 1976; Aug. 2, 1976.

13. Henley, Albert T. "The Evolution of Forms of Water Users Organizations in California," *California Law Review,* 45:5 (December 1957), p. 669. Reprint.

14. Henley, Albert T. "Rights to Beneficial Use," *California Farm and Ranch Law; California Continuing Education of the Bar,* 1967, p. 294. Reprint.

15. *The Hollister Advance.* Nov. 17, 1927.

16. Jones, Herbert C. *Water For the Valley; A Quarter-Record of the Santa Clara Valley Water Conservation District;* 1929-1954, pp. 13-14.

17. Kriege, Daniel F. Interviewed by Kevin Fish, July 20, 1976.

18. Lester, Will W. Interviewed by Kevin Fish, Dec. 11, 1976.

19. Martin, Richard Garland. *Water Conservation in Santa Clara Valley.* Unpublished Master's thesis. University of California, Berkeley. 1949.

20. "New Association Is Organized to Conserve Water," *San Jose Mercury Herald,* Nov. 23, 1926.

21. Roll, J. Robert. Interviewed by Kevin Fish, Aug. 3, 1976.

22. Smith, J. Winter. Interviewed by Kevin Fish, June 28, 1976.

23. Spiers, Alfred R. Interviewed by Kevin Fish, July 28, 1976.

24. *San Jose Mercury Herald.* November 20, 1926.

25. Ibid. Jan. 13,1927.

26. Ibid. Feb. 16, 1927.

27. Ibid. Feb. 27, 1927.

28. Ibid. March 8, 1927.

29. Ibid. July 8,1927.

30. Ibid. July 2, 1928.

31. Ibid. July 11, 1928.

32. Ibid. July 15, 1928.

33. Ibid. Nov. 22, 1928.

34. Ibid. Feb. 5, 1929.

35. Ibid. July 17, 1929.

36. Ibid. Aug. 6, 1929.

37. Ibid. Aug. 27,1929.

38. Ibid. Oct. 5, 1929.

39. Ibid. Oct. 22, 1929.

40. Ibid. Oct. 24, 1929.

41. Ibid. October 27, 1929.

42. Ibid. Oct. 28, 1929.

43. Ibid. Oct. 30, 1929.

44. Ibid. Oct. 31, 1929.

45. Ibid. Nov. 1, 1929.

46. Ibid. Nov. 2, 1929.

47. Ibid. Nov. 3, 1929.

48. Ibid. Nov. 6, 1929.

49. Ibid. Nov. 19, 1929.

50. Ibid. Nov. 20, 1929.

51. Ibid. Nov. 26, 1929.

52. Ibid. Nov. 27, 1929.

53. Ibid. Dec. 1, 1929.

54. Ibid. Jan. 5,1930.

55. Ibid. June 3, 1930.

56. Ibid. June 30, 1930.

57. Ibid. Dec. 7, 1930.

58. Ibid. 1934.

59. *San Jose News,* Aug. 28, 1929.

60. Ibid. Nov. 20, 1929.

61. Ibid. Jan. 16, 1932.

62. Minutes of the Santa Clara Valley Water Conservation District, March 7, 1939; June 8, 1943.

63. Santa Clara Valley Water Conservation District. *30 Years of Progress,* Annual Report, Fiscal Year Ending June 30, 1960.

64. Santa Clara Valley Water Conservation District and Santa Clara County Superintendent of Schools Office. *Water: Our Buried Treasure,* 1960.

65. SCVWD files: Lexington Dam and Reservoir Bond Election Material 1947. Anderson Dam and Reservoir Bond Election Material 1949.

66. San Jose Water Works.

67. Peck, Willys. "This Historic Landmark A Biggie," *San Jose Mercury News,* Feb. 22, 1976, p. 27.

68. "Valley's Water Shortage Acute, Says Geologist," *San Jose Mercury Herald.* Oct. 14, 1930.

69. Martin, Hal. "Water Conservation District Honors Founders Who Began Job in 1926," *San Jose Mercury News,* Dec. 1, 1946, p.8.

70. "Water Election To Be Held November 5th," *Santa Clara Journal,* Oct. 15, 1929.

71. "Water Shortage For Fire Alarms Peninsula Cities," *San Jose Mercury Herald,* July 3, 1930.

72. Watson, Max. Memorandum from Max Watson to Leroy Anderson, Feb. 8, 1928.

At work on the Upper Page concrete and steel dam, 1932.

CHAPTER 3

Dams and Reservoirs—Engineering Landmarks

By Kenneth E. Dickey, Sr.

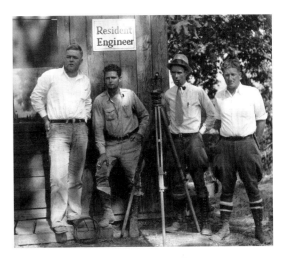

Engineers employed in the valley during the Depression era worked to oversee the construction of six reservoirs: Stevens Creek, Vasona, Guadalupe, Almaden, Calero and Coyote, all of which were built between 1934 and 1936.

When voters in the Santa Clara Valley approved the formation of the Water Conservation District on November 5, 1929, little if any thought or attention was directed to the economic soundness of the nation.[3:342] It was not selfishness; it was concern for immediate problems—local conditions that had to be corrected, and corrected soon, if the Santa Clara Valley was to grow and prosper. A vote for water conservation was a vote for insuring the valley's agriculture and economic growth. The vote meant that more industry would locate in the metropolitan area. Factories would be built, and more and better jobs would result. An increasing population would cause new homes to be constructed, also creating more and better jobs. Everything would be improved when ample water was made available. However, this bright, positive outlook when the Santa Clara Valley Water Conservation District was born would soon darken, for negative factors would shortly grip the nation and a period of uncertain reality would have to be endured.

The Economic Backdrop

The year 1929 was one of both progress and decline. That year, Herbert Hoover became the thiry-first president of the United States. The nation had been prospering since 1922, and the Gross National Product (GNP) had increased each year. Industry led the way with Henry Ford and his new "assembly line" production of automobiles. Thanks to Thomas A. Edison, all types of electrical home appliances were being introduced and manufactured at an accelerated pace. New chemicals, such as dyes which were formerly imported and the new synthetic "rayon fiber," had increased in production from 3 million pounds in 1919 to 33 million in 1929.[2:526-7] Across the nation, industry was producing at an all-time record. On the surface, the indicators of the time revealed prospects for a healthy, stable future, but the fact was that the country's financial institutions were unsound.

In the early half of October 1929, the stock exchange began showing erratic actions of unreasonable proportions, and for over a month stocks were up and down like a teeter-totter. On Tuesday, October 29, 16 million shares of stock were traded, and the market stopped wobbling and crashed. Stocks dropped to their lowest point and many became worthless. President Hoover's efforts to halt the downward trend of the economy were futile, and even the creation of the federal Reconstruction Finance Corporation (RFC) in 1932, with its power to lend money to financial institutions (later expanded to business and industry) did little to alleviate conditions.[3:342]

Despite the Depression, in Santa Clara County six dams and reservoirs were constructed; canals for transferring water were finished; and many other facilities were completed. Approval of the 1934 Water District bond measure for $2 million helped. But the economic conditions during this period continued to decline until 1933, when the Roosevelt administration and Congress provided aid in the form of public work programs, which helped somewhat in the agricultural areas. In the large cities of predominantly industrial areas, however, these programs did little to ease the hardship and suffering.

At this time, there was no unemployment compensation or other form of welfare as there is today. Church-sponsored missions and veterans' organizations provided food for as many as contributions would permit. Some were able to provide a cot and warm shelter against harsh rains and winter cold. Soup kitchens sponsored by local governments ladled out soup and bread to long lines of the unemployed at local fire and police stations or other designated places throughout the country. Shacks and shanties quickly appeared on vacant public and private properties. Constructed of scrap lumber and corrugated fiber boxes, these shanties became the only shelter for hundreds of thousands of the destitute. Vast armies of the homeless and jobless hopped freight trains going from place to place around the country seeking work and sometimes living in empty railroad cars along the way. So-called "hobo jungles" close to running water and railroad switching yards were common during the Depression years. The inhabitants of the shanty towns were not hobos or bums, or too lazy to work; they were respectable, unemployed persons who were the unfortunate victims of the times. It became a way of life for them during the early and mid-1930s.

Foundations for an Engineering Landmark

In spite of the adverse effects of the Depression on the nation, agricultural Santa Clara Valley continued to apply the latest engineering skills to its water conservation effort. The plan of action for the construction of a complete system of dams and reservoirs had been established in the 1920s by the Santa Clara Valley Water Conservation Committee. Known as the "Tibbetts and Kieffer Report" (see Chapter 1), the plan outlined the necessity for containing the water which is normally lost into San Francisco Bay.

Following extensive research, engineers Tibbetts and Kieffer recommended the construction of a combination of large reservoirs, low check dams and pumping stations in the lowlands to catch the runoff, and a system of concrete conduits to distribute the conserved water.[4:225-37] As described in Chapter 1, Santa Clara County residents voted down the 1921 proposal to form a water conservation district, but farmers began to implement the findings of Tibbetts and Kieffer on their own. Led by pioneer orchardist, Leroy Anderson, local farmers formed the Santa Clara Valley Water Conservation Association to begin construction of small sack dams. Donations totaling $10,000 were accepted from farmers and corporations to finance the association's conservation measures (see Chapter 2).

The association first experimented with water percolation through the construction of various types of dams that had been recommended by Tibbetts and Kieffer. Practical experiments were conducted along the gravel beds of Almaden Creek that were leased from the Southern Pacific Railroad. Spreading dams and percolation ponds formed from old irrigation ditches were put into use during the winter months when there was sufficient rainfall. Such facilities would retard the flow of creek water, causing "spreading" and the increased percolation of water into the underground aquifers for storage. Such dams, which successfully raised underground water levels, were financed and built by the concerned farmers. It would be these early conservation measures which would later work with the system of reservoirs to complete the conservation plan.

The following types of dams were constructed by the Santa Clara Valley Water Conservation Association:

Sack dams. Sack dams were used in the early experiments. The sack dams were merely burlap sacks filled with whatever earth material was available, laid snugly side by side, layer on layer, at irregular intervals over the gravel streambeds. These dams served the purpose in the first year or so of experimentation, but due to deterioration by the elements, the high replacement cost caused their discontinuation in about 1928 or 1929.

Sausage dams. Sausage dams were constructed of rock and strips of heavy gauge "box type" construction wire. Strips of wire matting were laid across the stream, then rock was placed on and between layers of the wire matting. This method of construction provided a stable dam and served the purpose of spreading water over larger areas for percolation, but this method was also expensive and was later discontinued.

Rock dams. Experiments with rock dams proved successful and less expensive than sausage or sack dams. A mound of rocks spread across the stream about one or two feet high was sufficient to retard the flow of water, thereby providing for spreading and percolation. Eliminating the cost of sacks and wire was a much needed dollar savings for the water association.

Check dams. Check dams are small structures of loose rock, logs, brush and occasionally concrete, built in a series of mountain canyons to regulate and prolong the flow of rainwater descending the watershed.[5]

Before work could begin, the financial requirements were outlined and loans secured. According to the provisions of the Water Conservation Act of 1929 (Jones Act), under which the district was created, the board could incur an indebtedness which could not exceed an amount of 25 cents for each acre of land in the district, and could only be incurred before the collection of the first tax assessment. The directors agreed upon $25,000 as the amount of incurred indebtedness. Warrants of the district would be issued for this sum bearing interest at the rate of 7 percent per annum from the date of issue to the date assessed funds from taxes became available.[9:47-50]

Construction of Early, Temporary Dams

Directors of the Santa Clara Valley Water Conservation District conducted an all-day inspection of dam sites on November 18, 1929, and they agreed that immediate construction of a series of temporary dams was necessary in the short time remaining before the winter rains. Additional dams of the same simple type of construction would be built along the Guadalupe, Almaden and Los Gatos creeks, and a series of new dams was tentatively planned for Saratoga and Stevens creeks.

During this period, the board of directors operated the district on a "shoestring." Income for district operations was based upon land values only ($0.15 per $100.00 assessed land value), taxed by the county assessor during the years

The early dams built by concerned farmers followed the Tibbetts and Kieffer plan, and provided a foundation for the valley's water conservation system.

33

From 1933 to 1939, the PWA spent nearly $6 billion on 37,000 projects that provided jobs for some 500,000 persons.

from 1929 to1934. However, by careful management, the district was able to acquire land through purchase or lease. It was conscientiously involved with the work of developing percolation ponds at locations where the underground deposits of gravel and sand reach the valley's surface. Property for the Upper Page Pond, at the intersection of Santa Clara-Los Gatos Road and Hacienda Avenue, was purchased in 1930. The following year the district purchased the land for percolation ponds at the intersections of Almaden and Coleman roads and put this percolation area to use.[7:6]

The November 1931 bond election for issuing $6 million in bonds to carry out construction of the facilities outlined in the Tibbetts and Kieffer Report failed (see Chapter 2), so the district continued its low budget activity of small construction projects. In 1932, the district developed a percolation area on Coyote Creek, constructing a removable flashboard dam to spread the stream flow over a 60-acre area. Periodic well measurements in 1934 indicated that water levels were at an all-time low, nearing a 140-foot depth. The early percolation program had a limited effect on the water table as it operated only during the winter months when streams were flowing. The district recognized that a system of dams and reservoirs in the runoff areas would capture much of the winter rainfall that was now washing into the bay. With a system of dams, this water could be contained and released as needed for delivery to areas prepared to percolate the water into the underground reservoir. This was supported by the Tibbetts and Kieffer Report.

Role of the Public Works Administration

By the time President Franklin D. Roosevelt was inaugurated on March 4, 1933, the national economy was near rock bottom. Some 15 million jobless and their families (close to a third of the nation) were suffering hardship and hunger. "What I am asking," later wrote President Roosevelt, "is the abolition of relief."[†] In this frame of mind, President Roosevelt's "New Deal" administration anxiously searched for ways and means to alleviate the problem. One means of combatting unemployment and relief was creation of the Public Works Administration (PWA) under the authority of the National Industrial Recovery Act of 1933. The PWA was administered by the Department of the Interior, and headed by Secretary of the Interior Harold Ickes.[3:908] The purpose of the PWA and similar organizations created during this period was to increase employment and business activity and to act as "pump priming," thus aiding the overall economy by stimulating the private sector through the use of public funds.

In general, the PWA made grants to state and local agencies who would hire private contractors to construct the projects. While workers would never become rich, this stop-gap measure did provide for basic necessities of life. Receiving a check for relief left a bad taste in the mouth of millions of unemployed, but here was a check that was earned through hard, morale-boosting work. The program and the administration received much criticism, but from 1933 to 1939, the PWA spent nearly $6 billion on 37,000 projects that provided jobs for some 500,000 persons. Ironically, it was the federal funds made available during the Depression era which would enable the construction of the Santa Clara Valley's first reservoirs. The Board of Directors of the Santa Clara Valley Water Conservation District applied for a PWA grant of $683,000 on November 7, 1932. This grant would be a federal contribution of 30 percent of the total construction cost of six dams, reser-

---

[†] **Second Edition Note:** In the 1930s, "relief" was the term used for welfare.

District folks *celebrated* the final PWA payment. With a *$683,000* grant, the district was able to *employ* many otherwise *jobless* people.

Celebrating receipt of final P.W.A. Payment, May 22 1937... Barbecue at home of Herbert C. Jones

Standing, left to right: Kenneth R. Malovos, assistant attorney; Joseph E. Russell, Guadalupe inspector; W. F. Noethig, former director; Eugene Blair Grattan, assistant attorney; R. L. Parry, director; S.W. Pfiefle, director; Arthur Moore, right-of-way agent; John Fair, former director, Walter Hunt, Calero and Coyote engineer; T. T. Tourtillot, director; Edgar Jackson, former director; Frazier O. Reed, right-of-way agent; Herbert C. Jones, attorney; W. L. Atkinson, right-of-way agent; Walter Keene, "Mountain View Register Leader"; Harold I. Wood, supervising engineer; Robert S. Shover, auditor.

Seated, left to right: W. E. Wiesendanger, director; Mary McConnell, attorney's office; Emlyn Dahlberg, attorney's office; S. D. Farrington, president; Fay Griffiths, secretary; Fred H. Tibbetts, chief engineer; Janice Bohnett, attorney's office; R. P. Van Orden, director.

Absent: H. G. Mitchell, director; Leroy Anderson, former director, president and secretary; Fred Holthouse, former director; Ralph F. Simmons, former director; C. D. Cavallaro, former director; Lloyd A. Mason, assistant attorney.

Table A. Daily Pay Rates on Reservoir Construction
(per PWA agreement)

Class of Work	Prevailing Daily Rate
Asphaltic plant platform lab	$ 7.20
Blacksmith	8.80
Carpenters	8.80
Cement finishers	8.80
Concrete mixer operator, small	7.20
Electrical workers	9.00
Engineers — Hoisting, portable, quarries, tractors 50 HP or over, rollers, mixers, asphalt plants, material yards	9.00
Engineers — Bridge and structural	10.00
Engineers — Pile drivers, derrick barges, cable ways	10.00
Engineers — Firemen and apprentices	6.00
Engineers — Portable compressor	6.00
Gradermen	7.20
Iron workers — Reinforced concrete	9.00
Iron workers — Bridge and structural	11.00
Laborers — Building, cement, common, muckers	5.20
Miners — Powdermen, timbermen, tunnelmen	6.00
Painters	8.80
Pile Drivers	9.00
Plumbers	10.00
Roofers	8.80
Sheet Metal Workers	8.80
Shovel operators — up to and including 1/2 yard	8.80
Shovel operators — from 1/2 yd. up to and including 1 yd.	10.00
Shovel operators — 1 yd. up	11.00
Shovel operators — underground	12.00
Shovel operators — Cranesmen	9.60
Shovel operators — Cranesmen, underground	10.80
Shovel operators — Oilers	6.72
Teamsters — 1 and 2 horse drivers	6.00
Truck drivers — up to and including 6-1/2 tons	6.00
Truck drivers — over 6-1/2 tons	7.20
Tractors — 30 HP up to 50 HP	8.80
Tractors — under 30 HP	6.00
Trouble shooter (mechanic)	8.80

Overtime — one and one-half times the above rates.

The prevailing rate for Sundays and the following legal holidays—January 1st, February 22nd, Memorial Day, July 4th., Labor Day, Admission Day, Thanksgiving Day and December 25th—shall be double the above set out respective rates (except for watchmen, guards and flagmen).

voirs and necessary canals for Almaden, Calero, Coyote, Guadalupe, Stevens Creek and Vasona reservoirs.

John D. Crummey, founder of John Bean Corp. (later to become Food Machinery Corp., or FMC) in Santa Clara, was appointed by the Santa Clara Valley Water Conservation District to serve as liaison with PWA in processing the application, and was authorized to speak for the district board of directors. The application for the grant had to be processed by various staff sections within the PWA, such as legal, engineering and fiscal. As Mr. Crummey had long been an ardent supporter of water conservation and actively supported the projects under consideration by the PWA, he would be of invaluable assistance during processing of the application. The legal section dealt with verification of public need and conformity with all legal requirements of aid. The soundness of the project and implementation of standards of acceptable engineering principles, design, quality of materials, technique of construction, and overall procedure for quality control and safety of the project were the responsibility of the engineering section. The fiscal section was responsible for disbursement of public funds in an orderly manner consistent with the progress of the many and varied PWA-approved projects.

As previously mentioned, in the June 1934 election, voters approved issuance of $2 million in bonds by the water conservation district. After approval and sale of the bonds, the PWA could act favorably on the application for the grant. Official confirmation by PWA that the grant for $673,000 had been approved was received on June 30, 1934. The following conditions were agreed upon:

1. PWA was to have final approval of the construction plans of the project. This included design, materials and methods of construction.

2. Local contractors were to be given preference in bidding for the project contracts. All classes of workers were to be recruited for employment through the local offices of

state employment agencies. This was to ensure that the locally unemployed would benefit and, so far as possible, keep money circulating in the local area.

3. Employees would work, so far as practical, three days a week, 10 hours a day. Two groups were set up, one working Monday through Wednesday, and the second working Thursday through Saturday. This would provide income for the necessities of life to a maximum number of unemployed and their families.

4. Employees were to be paid each week to ensure an even flow of federal money into the local economy.

5. Rates of daily pay, then prevailing, were agreed to by the Santa Clara Valley Water Conservation District Board

of Directors and incorporated in "Minutes of the Board on August 23, 1934."

The federal government, except for the actual work and necessary supervision of the construction, had complete jurisdiction over the project. In furnishing 30 percent of the construction cost, it was judge, jury and "workers' union" all in one. The PWA would need to approve the project from start to finish. It would have to approve any unforeseen changes made in design, materials or methods of construction, and any change in the number of hours to be worked, number of days in a week to be worked, rates of pay per day, rates in classes of work, or agreed-to "work conditions."[8:66] Public indignation and outcries of "social-

Construction in progress on Calero Dam, September 12, 1935.

Table B. Reservoirs Constructed by the Santa Clara Valley Water Conservation District*

	Almaden	Calero	Coyote	Guadalupe	Stevens Creek	Vasona	Anderson	Lexington
Year Constructed	1935	1935	1936	1935	1935	1935	1950	1952
Capacity of Reservoir** (acre-feet)	1,586	10,050	22,925	3,228	3,465	400	89,073	19,834
Capacity of Spillway (cubic feet/second)	7,000	5,000	33,000	6,000	10,000	12,600	24,000	20,000
Reservoir Area (acres)	62	329	688	75	95	79	1,600	450
Reservoir Length (miles)	1.1	2.2	4.8	1.1	1.1	.08	7.8	2.5
Type of Dam (fill)	earth	earth	earth & rock	earth	earth	earth	earth & rock	earth
Dam Crest Height (feet above streambed)	105	90	120	129	120	30	240	195
Dam Crest Elevation	615	490	802	627	545	305	640	665
Dam Crest Length (feet)	460	840	990	650	1,000	1,000	1,385	830
Dam Crest Width (feet)	20	20	100-160	20	20	20	40	40'
Dam Base Width (feet)	545	495	945	650	620	153	1,100	1,370
Cubic Yards of Fill	250,000	550,000	1,060,000	530,000	70,000	3,320,000	2,124,000	8,424,000
Outlet Pipe Diameter (inches)	36"	36"	50"	36"	50"	42"	49"	50"
Outlet Pipe Length (feet)	690	450	900	690	680	20	1,160	1,410
Cubic Yards of Concrete	3,000	4,000	3,000	4,000	5,000	2,000	5,214	5,450
Tons of Steel	130	170	120	130	200	150	264	182
Spillway Weir Length (feet)	123	82	110	80	127	220	191	150
Type of Spillway	Side channel	Chute	Chute	Chute	Side channel	Concrete buttress & radial gate	Chute	Chute
Freeboard (feet)	8	6.5	25	10	8	5	15	15
Resident Engineer	J.W. Smith	R.P. Bryant	G.W. Hunt	T.D. Sawyer	F.W. Moore	J. W. Smith	J. R. Roll	J. R. Roll
Contractor	Bohnett & McDonald	Bohnett & McDonald	Macco Construction	Teichert & Son Inc.	Bohnett & McDonald	Carl N. Swenson Co.	Guy F. Atkinson Co.	Guy F. Atkinson Co.

Second Edition Note: As a result of merging with the Gavilan Water District in 1987, two more reservoirs, Uvas and Chesbro, would be added to the district system. See Chapter 9.

**Second Edition Note*: SCVWD surveys its reservoirs every five years to update the true capacity given years of sediment buildup or improvements. The reservoir capacity on this chart was updated to reflect known capacity as of February 2004.

ism and favored treatment" were common during the PWA years. In numerous instances, workers on PWA projects received more money for like work in a 30-hour week than employees in the private sector who worked 45 to 55 hours a week. This bred contempt in many areas, especially when heads of families employed in the private sector were having great difficulties providing necessities, in spite of working longer hours, while their neighbors who worked only 30 hours a week were able to spend money in the local taverns.

The major dams constructed during the Depression were the Almaden, Calero, Guadalupe, Stevens Creek and Vasona, all of which were completed by 1935. Later dams included Coyote in 1936; Anderson, completed in 1950; and Lexington, completed in 1952.

Major Dam and Reservoir Construction

Actual construction of a dam is sometimes delayed if the dam site is in a remote or inaccessible area. Improvement or construction of roads and bridges permitting access of extremely large and heavy construction vehicles, equipment and materials is often necessary. Also, safe areas must be prepared for storage of petroleum, oils and lubricants (POL), and explosives. A first aid station is of paramount importance with so many workers and so much varied activity and movement of giant vehicles, machinery and materials. Fresh drinking water must be available, and sanitary facilities must be established and maintained. Temporary structures for containment of active streams must be constructed. Somewhere close to the dam site, millions of gallons of water (depending on the size of the dam to be constructed) must be stored for use in construction of the dam. All of this and much more must be accomplished before the first shovel of dirt is removed that signals the start of actual construction.

When the first six dams were constructed in the 1930s, both the ways and means of dam construction were much different from today. In 1935 and 1936, the axe, pick and shovel, combined with a long day of physical labor, were very much in vogue—and very inexpensive, too. Ditches were dug by human labor, and trucks were often loaded in the same manner. When a scoop shovel was used, it often required about a dozen shovels of dirt to fill a dump truck. The largest trucks had a hauling capacity of less than 10 cubic yards as compared to today, when we have earth-moving equipment that is capable of transporting 100 cubic yards of earth at one time. Bulldozers were new pieces of equipment in the 1930s, capable of cutting and pushing only about 1 cubic yard or less at one time, while today, large dozers move 5 yards at once. Road graders (or scrapers) have not changed much in design or characteristics but are much more powerful and easier to operate today. Trucks with 15-foot beds were about the maximum length and trailers were of about 20- or 24-foot maximum length, as compared to today's trailers which may be over 40 feet long, or run in tandem and measure 50 feet or more. Hydraulic lifts, commonly referred to as "fork lifts," had not yet begun to be used in heavy construction, so most equipment and supplies were loaded and unloaded manually, sometimes with the aid of rollers and skids, or block and tackle, and a hastily assembled tripod. Occasionally, a large sturdy tree was used in lieu of a tripod at construction sites. "Sheeps-foot rollers," commonly called "tamper rollers," are about the same now as they were in the 1930s. Much of the time you may see them connected in tandem; two tampers are pulled by one tractor for more work and efficiency. A few teams of horses were used at the construction sites, but this was only for light utility work.

This brief review of the mechanical equipment used for dam construction in the 1930s shows the conscientious effort and hard work required to accomplish the tremendous

The equipment used for dam construction in the 1930s shows the conscientious effort and hard work required to accomplish the tremendous task of moving 2,980,000 cubic yards of fill.

Of all the sound engineering principles involved in dam construction, proper sealing of the cutoff trench (combined with grouting) is possibly the most important phase.

task of moving 2,980,000 cubic yards of fill. This figure refers to fill material only, and when one considers the earth material that had to be excavated to first reach bedrock and then to excavate the cutoff trench, the accomplishments are even more remarkable. For example, if each truck that transported fill material carried the maximum of 8 cubic yards at one time, it would have required 372,500 round trips for the trucks to move only the fill material.

Construction of the core of the dam always precedes construction of the "up and down" stream sides until the specified height of the core is reached. Then the sides are brought up even with, or exceeding, the impervious material of the core. The core may be topped with soil material and vegetation or, if it is a large dam, a roadway may cross the crest of the dam. Each dam has its own individual characteristics. Geological and engineering data, tests, and survey, have to be designed according to the specifics of the particular dam. The geographic location, terrain, size of reservoir, distribution outlet, conditions of precipitation,

Construction of the outfall pipe on Calero Dam, 1935.

and shifting of underground strata due to earthquake potential are all carefully taken into account. The construction process is then able to proceed in the following manner:

Grubbing and clearing. The first phase of dam construction is grubbing and clearing. Grubbing is derived from the word "grub," which means to root out or uproot it; trees are cut and removed, then stumps and roots are grubbed out. Grubbing includes removing large, long-rooted vines, which must also be uprooted and cleared away. Trees are removed to safe areas, and firewood is made available free to the public or burned.

Stripping. The next phase of construction is a combination of cutting, breaking and removing soil. This may be 10, 20, 30 or more feet in depth. Stripping is the term given to removal of all soil down to a suitable foundation. For simplification, we will assume the suitable foundation is solid rock. An area the length and width of the base of the dam is stripped down to solid rock, sometimes referred to as bedrock.

Construction of outfall pipe. The outfall (outlet) pipe is incorporated into the dam for the purpose of releasing water at controlled rates as conditions require. These outfall pipes are from 36 to 50 inches in diameter. The lengths of the pipes vary from a mere 20 feet at Vasona Dam to 1,410 feet at Lexington Dam. The outfall pipes are steel, with some sections as much as 60 feet long. A steel collar welded to adjoining ends of pipes secures one section to the other for the total length of the assembly. In addition, the pipes are "laced" together by means of circular and longitudinal heavy steel bands. A trench is dug downstream from the dam, and cradles are constructed at specified intervals in the floor of the trench to provide for alignment of the pipe. A wooden form is constructed at the outfall end and concrete is poured into the form which is reinforced with steel resulting in outfall housing. The trench is then filled with concrete, completely encasing the pipe.

Excavating cutoff trench. As crews are completing construction of the outfall pipe system, preparations are made for constructing the cutoff trench. The cutoff trench will provide for positive sealing of selected material (clay) that provides an impervious core. The cutoff trench is cut out of solid rock or other suitable foundation. Explosives are used in the initial process of trench excavation, and heavy engineering construction equipment breaks the solid rock to form the trench. The cutoff trench, when later filled with impervious material, provides a seal that prevents seepage of water. Without this sealing, water would find its way beneath the dam. Tremendous pressure from water backlogged in the reservoir would certainly cause deterioration and soil movement, and would eventually undermine the entire dam structure if not found and corrected. Of all the sound engineering principles involved in quality dam construction, proper sealing of the cutoff trench, combined with grouting, is possibly the most important phase of dam construction. Continuing inspections were made by contractor engineers and Water District engineers throughout construction of the trench. When approval is given by state engineers, further stages of construction may be continued.

Inlet pipe and housing. The steel inlet pipe contained in an inlet housing is located at the base of the dam on the upstream side. The inlet pipe is connected to steel pipe of a specified diameter that runs under the base of the dam and joins with the outfall pipe. The inlet pipe is positioned at a predetermined height above the streambed. A concrete foundation, reinforced by steel bars, is poured into wooden forms. Concrete sides reinforced with steel are joined in a similar manner to the foundation to form the inlet housing. Grate openings in the housing permit water to come in but filter out debris that might otherwise enter. Thus, a means has been constructed for transferring water from the reservoir through the inlet pipe, then through pipe under the dam

to the outfall pipe, then through canals and streams in the system to on- and off-stream percolation ponds for storage underground. This controlled release of water provides a means of supply to areas where well depth levels indicate a need for replenishment.

Grouting program. Geologists and engineers are well aware of the normal shifting of the subsurface strata that compose our earth, often causing cracks in the impervious strata. As earthquake faults are located adjacent to the eastern and western borders of the Santa Clara Valley, it is only natural that cracks exist within the surfaces of the dam sites. In addition, the tremendous force created by the use of explosive charges as well as cutting and pounding to excavate the cutoff channel is almost certain to produce cracks. A grouting program has been developed to insure that water cannot seep through these cracks and undermine the dam. Through soil sampling and other geological tests, the data obtained reveals to engineers exactly what is to be done and how it should be done. The program is divided

After a day's work on August 29, 1935, Joe (last name unknown) emerges from the upstream cast iron flange after pouring the inlet pipe structure on Calero Dam.

41

into three phases: drilling, grouting and filling the cutoff trench with selected clay. Holes are drilled throughout the suitable foundation (or bedrock) of the dam site and adjacent areas. Depth and number of holes drilled are determined by the geological data obtained from continuous tests. Phase Two is grouting the subsurface cracks. A thin mixture of water and cement is prepared, called "slurry." Large quantities are pumped into the holes under high pressure. This assures that the slurry will find its way into all chinks, cracks and crevices and perform the function of sealing, thereby assuring a solid foundation.

Raising the dam. Raising the dam refers to placing of materials that will be used to fill (build or raise) the dam. In all earth-filled dams constructed by the district, the cutoff trench and core of the dam is a fill (or building up) of selected clay. Clay is an impervious earth material that, when tightly compressed, provides a watertight seal.

First, the core is filled with layers of clay, then rolled, watered and re-rolled numerous times to form a tight, compact fill. Under engineering supervision, moisture in the proper amount is added to the clay. It was mentioned earlier that millions of gallons of water had to be made available close to the dam site for use in construction. This stored water may be sprayed under high pressure over large areas by means of a large hose, or may be sprayed on the clay by means of large water transport trailers, or both. Dry clay is deposited on the dam site area in layers, and water is added as heavy rollers and tampers roll the clay. Thus, the properly moistened clay is compacted into a firm but pliable layer forming the basis of the dam. This process continues, layer upon layer of clay being tamped and rolled as the core takes on a semi-pyramidal shape. As the core is formed, other crews and equipment are busy filling the upstream and downstream facings of the dam with earth and rock.

Earth dams. Material used for filling the sides of the dam is either earth or a combination of earth and rock. In the earth-filled dams, construction and materials differ from that of the earth- and rock-filled dams. The sides of the earth dam are filled with soft earth materials which may include clay, then they are tamped and rolled in the same manner as for the clay core. Water is added as necessary, as tampers and rollers perform their function in compacting the soil layer upon layer, as the dam is formed. A layer of reinforced concrete or asphalt about a foot thick is then poured on the upstream side of the compacted earth fill. The concrete or asphalt surface protects the earth fill and core from the wave and wind action that lashes against the exposed surface of the dam. The downstream surface of the dam may contain some rock as fill material. Trees, shrubs and plants are common in the vicinity of the dam and may be planted on the downstream surface of the fill to prevent erosion.

Earth and rock dams. A variety of materials is used as fill for the sides of dams. Both up- and downstream sides are, for all practical purposes, the same in material, size and method of construction. Some sizing of rock fill, with more of the larger, boulder-type rock, may be used for the upstream side to protect the earth fill and core from waves and severe wind. With the exception of substituting rock for the concrete or asphalt slab, the earth and rock dam is similar to the earth dam.

There is one major difference in the method of construction, however. The earth substances used for fill are of various specified materials such as soil that includes sand, gravel and rock of various sizes. This combined material is deposited in layers on top of the bedrock surface and adheres to the core of clay. As the fill material is tamped and rolled, water under high pressure is sprayed on the fill, in conjunction with the tamping and rolling operations, causing the smaller particles of earth, sand, gravel and smaller rocks to settle and compact beneath and around the larger rocks. As the buildup of layers of earth and rock continues to rise, the materials become compact sides that protect the dam core and cutoff trench. Additional soil on the downstream side may be added where needed for the planting of trees, shrubs and plant growth to combat erosion.[11]

Coyote Dam and Reservoir

The Coyote Dam and Reservoir was one of the original six systems approved for construction by voters in the May 1934 bond election. Construction of the dam systems began in 1934, after the PWA approved a grant for $673,000. The original goal was to have all the dams completed by 1935, in time for winter rains, and the Water District accomplished this task except in the construction of Coyote. After finding that Coyote Dam straddled the active Hayward Earthquake Fault, the construction plans had to be redesigned. Major changes were necessary, such as the base thickness of the dam, which had to be changed from 500 to over 900 feet. These changes delayed the start of construction on Coyote until May 1935.

Other unavoidable and unforeseen difficulties plagued the project, the most notable delay being finding suitable rock for fill. Such rock for the two faces of the dam was not available in the immediate vicinity of the construction site as geologists had predicted. Consequently, it was necessary to purchase the rock (sandstone) from a quarry located over a mile east of the site in an inaccessible area called Larios Canyon. By December 1935, a road to the quarry was completed, which rapidly increased the rate of construction. However, all the rock had to be dynamited out of the hillside. It took a month just for crews to carve out the large explosive chambers within the cliff. Twenty tons of explosives were placed in these chambers for an initial explosion that brought down a section of the cliff over a quarter of a mile in length. This would provide over 100,000 cubic yards of rock for the two facings to be placed over the earth fill, providing protection from normal wave wash and lashing during high winds. In December 1935, the PWA granted a six-month extension, and the completion date was rescheduled for July 1, 1936.[6]

There were 231 men working on construction of district dams as of May 25, 1935. Of these, 99 were working on the Coyote project and 132 on the other five dam systems. By July 1, a total of 573 men were employed—166 on Coyote, the remainder on the other dam systems. And by October, 663 men were employed, of which 250 were at Coyote. In the past, men had been transported by truck from various points, mostly San José, and traveled 30 miles each way to and from the dam site, causing much loss of time. Therefore, the Santa Clara Valley Water Conservation District Board of Directors requested and received permission to work six days at 40 hours a week. In addition, a "Tent City" was constructed by the contractor at Coyote, with crews living as well as working at the dam site. Three crews, working three shifts around the clock for six days a week, caused increased efficiency and production.

The Coyote Dam site took on the appearance of a well-lighted stage at night. The work shift at the site was six hours and 40 minutes with an hour off for lunch. Facilities for lodging, a kitchen, combination dining room and lounge facilities, and a shower were made available in about 30 tents. Outside washing basins were available for fast cleanup or laundering of clothing. By October 1935, a million dollars in machinery and 250 men were working on the project when a new piece of equipment called a "carry-all" (earth mover) was brought to the job by the contractor. This carry-all could carry 28 yards of rock at once, or as much as about five or six truckloads, and in less time. It was powered by an 80 horsepower diesel engine. Later, a second carry-all was made available at the site.

Following the added unforeseen expense of obtaining rock and road construction, the Water District board of

A quarter-mile section of a cliff in Larios Canyon was brought down with 20 tons of explosives. This would provide 100,000 cubic yards of fill for the dam's two facings.

After the first six **reservoirs** were completed, *groundwater* levels started to *rise*.

"Santa Clara Valley's first true artesian well in a score of years engages the interest of Satoru Kawashima, who farms the J. R. Wattrous ranch on Zanker Lane, and Fay Logan, secretary of the Santa Clara Valley Water Conservation District. They are examining an outflow from the well on the Wattrous property. Inset: The well itself, flowing between eight and 10 gallons a minute from the rising water level beneath the flat land ranch near Alviso."
~ March 24, 1938, San Jose Mercury Herald

directors applied to the government for an additional grant of $375,000, which would also allow for cost overruns on the other dams. The application was denied with various reasons given, but it boiled down to differences of interpretation of regulations between the Santa Clara Valley Water Conservation District and the federal bureaucracy.

Pending appeal to the PWA, and because of the winter rains in December 1935 and early January 1936, construction on Coyote was shut down and did not resume for over a month. Work resumed on Coyote in late January, but the appeal was denied by the PWA and construction was halted again in late February. A letter from the PWA in reference to appeal of their decision on this application for a $375,000 grant revealed that not only was the request for the additional grant denied, but nearly $300,000 of the original grant would not be forthcoming until the project was at completion stage, or until sufficient money was made available by a bond election.[13]

The board of directors called an election on May 12, 1936, for a bond issue of $400,000 to complete the project. It was approved by a margin of more than three to one. When the voters approved the bond issue, it was a signal that construction could be resumed when the bonds were sold. Actual work on the construction site got under way in July, but disputes over the right of way worsened and plagued efforts to complete the dam. Farmers and ranchers individually and sometimes in groups would close roads with barricades, causing harassment and delay. As soon as one right of way settlement was reached, another problem would crop up. This continued until September when final right of way agreements were reached.

In August, the PWA reduced the work week for truck drivers to 30 hours. This caused a shortage, and finally a 40-hour work week was reinstated. The second carry-all had arrived in August, but 22 trucks were idle because private industry was increasing production at this time, and a 48-hour week was normal. Eventually, the employment situation was normalized and production was in full swing until December. The final construction work on Coyote was officially completed on December 3, 1936. A group of about 50 men from a local Civilian Conservation Corps was made available for planting trees, shrubs, plants and rye seed on the face of the dam to prevent erosion by rain and wind. At last, Coyote Dam and Reservoir, along with Almaden, Calero, Guadalupe, Vasona and Stevens Creek, were completed as major engineering landmarks toward the realization of the countywide water conservation plan.

Lexington Dam and Reservoir

Before the first bond election in 1931, the water conservation district had furnished the state highway department with a map indicating a possible future dam and reservoir near Lexington on Los Gatos Creek. In 1933, it was learned that a new highway was to be built through the planned reservoir site, and necessary surveys were already being made. The district pleaded with the highway department to build the road at a higher elevation, but to no avail. The objections were overridden on the grounds the chosen line was the most direct, and the highway was constructed accordingly, even though the Water District offered to pay the cost of that part of the old two-lane highway which would be submerged by the dam and reservoir.

In the first part of the century, most people traveled between Santa Cruz and San José by means of the Southern Pacific Railroad (via Los Gatos). Special weekend trains to Santa Cruz beach and boardwalk provided fun for commuters and revenue for the railroad, and remained popular until 1935, when the new Los Gatos-Santa Cruz highway was completed. In 1938, when Southern Pacific abandoned its route to Santa Cruz, the major obstacle to construction of a dam on the valley's west side was removed. Plans

Signage at Lexington Dam site, 1952.

were drafted, and an interested public started to push for construction of the dam and reservoir in the area south of Los Gatos. As plans were completed and public support increased, the entire project was brought to an abrupt halt, as necessary labor and materials were unavailable for the duration of World War II.

After World War II, the thoughts of individuals and all echelons of government turned from war production to peacetime production and consumption of civilian goods. For nearly four years, the War Production Board (WPB) had exerted extraordinary power over civilian industry. The WPB established priorities for the scarce raw materials and channeled them into the war production effort. From very small companies to the largest corporations, industrial plants had been converted from producing nonessential civilian goods to production of war material. Most restrictions were lifted immediately following the war, but in some cases, release of raw material was reserved for manufacture of certain types of goods. Priorities shifted from WPB to the Civilian Production Administration (CPA) in November 1945. State and local governmental agencies held priority spending for materials in construction of roads, public buildings, utilities, and necessary construction for the public health, education and welfare; industry soon provided these materials. Some manufacturers were working three shifts to meet the demand for consumer goods. It took nearly four years for industry to meet the demands for automobiles, home appliances, farm machinery and many other civilian items for comfort and convenience. Home and business construction was running from high to average until the late 1960s.

During the war years and long afterward, the Santa Clara Valley grew and prospered. Economically, the valley benefited because of the demand for food throughout the world during the decade from 1940 to 1950. But with growth and prosperity, the demand for water increased. Winter rains for the seasons 1939 to 1946 averaged a lower-than-normal 13.61 inches. Water levels were lower than at any time since the dams and reservoirs had been constructed, except in 1939. Reserve water available in the six reservoirs was seriously low as the new year of 1947 became reality. It was time to take the plans for the proposed Lexington Dam and Reservoir off the shelf; it was time for action.

A delegation headed by state Senator Byrl R. Salsman of Palo Alto and former state Senator Herbert C. Jones (attorney for the Water District) called on Governor Earl Warren (later to become Chief Justice of the U.S. Supreme Court) with a request that he sponsor an appropriation bill to move a part of the Los Gatos-Santa Cruz Highway to allow construction of a proposed dam and reservoir south of Los Gatos. It was further requested that the governor declare the bill an emergency measure and recommend the legislature give it consideration prior to taking up the 1948-49 budget. The governor told the delegation he must deny the request. He objected to the bill on the ground that unless it could be proven that the state erroneously constructed the highway in the present location, the Water District would have to pay for its relocation.[10]

Assemblymen John F. Thompson and Robert Kirkwood, both of Santa Clara County, co-authored the appropriation bill in the amount of $2,475,000 for construction to realign the highway and introduced it on April 10, 1947. Assemblyman Ralph Bills of Compton told his colleagues the bill should be approved on the grounds that an injustice had been done to the people of Santa Clara County when the highway was built in its (then) present location, and that the expense of relocating the highway should be borne by the state. After brief discussion, the Assembly passed the bill by unanimous vote.[12]

In a letter to Assemblyman John Thompson, dated January 1947, state Senator H. Ray Judah of Santa Cruz objected to the proposed realignment and construction of the highway because it would adversely affect the flow of traffic. Surveys showed that 16,000 to 18,000 vehicles traveled the highway daily, and this interruption of traffic would be a serious detriment to business in Santa Cruz. Senator Judah explained that the letter was not aimed at interference with the water project itself, but simply a notice that in the planning of the project, if it went through, the road change should come first and the dam and reservoir last. Assemblymen Thompson and Kirkwood assured Judah this would be the case, and their bill contained the provision that the highway was to be completed before construction of the dam. Senator Salsman had introduced a Senate bill identical to the bill already passed by the Assembly. When the bill reached the floor, a provision had been added by Judah that the Senate Finance Committee consider a proposal that the Santa Clara Valley Water Conservation District pay part of the cost of highway moving. Judah had been chairman of the State Highway Commission at the time the highway division constructed the four-lane road.

Herbert C. Jones protested that the road had been constructed without consideration of pleas by the Water District.

Also, the district had offered to pay part of the cost of the old two-lane highway that would be submerged by the dam. He stated that this offer had been made several years prior to rebuilding the four-lane highway. The senate passed the bill unanimously, but the governor had stated earlier that he would hold a hearing to satisfy himself if the legislature approved the bill.

Governor Earl Warren signed the bill on July 17, 1947, after a two-hour hearing attended by both proponents and opponents. In concluding the hearings, the governor declared that the appropriation of general fund money to move a highway to permit construction of a dam represented a departure from policy. The bill, an emergency measure, became effective immediately on signing; however, the money would revert back to the state's general fund unless the state engineer approved plans and specifications of the dam, and Santa Clara Valley Water Conservation District voters approved a bond issue within two years.

A group of citizens from Los Gatos had opposed the bill in hearings before the legislature and governor. Although small, the group was an annoyance, making statements and proposals to block approval of the bill. It was necessary for the district to send qualified people (costing time and money) to Sacramento to counter the opposition. Fortunately, the legislature and the governor could see the opposition's play for what it was—harassment—and fully understood the valley's need for additional water.

After the Emergency Appropriation Bill was signed into law, the Board of Directors of the Santa Clara Valley Water Conservation District prepared a campaign to educate the voters. In March, about four months earlier, Owens-Corning Fiberglass Corp. announced that it had purchased 43 acres of land in Santa Clara upon which it would erect a $7 million plant that would employ 800 people to start, and increase to 1,000 or more with an annual payroll of $1.5 million.[14] In September 1947, the city council of San José expressed concern over the amount of industry moving into the Santa Clara Valley.[15] Since 1943, 70 new industries had settled in the valley, using large quantities of water. Each of them meant an increase in population and this meant more subdivisions and the need for additional water.

The Board of Directors of Santa Clara Valley Water Conservation District declared an election for a bond issue to be held on October 7, 1947. The directors, local chambers of commerce, civic organizations, radio, newspapers and television combined to make the voters aware of the decline of water due to the rapid growth of population, industry and agriculture. The times were good, jobs were plentiful and though prices had risen, so had wages. Families were living better than ever before, and savings accounts were the order of the day. What conveniences or luxuries families didn't yet have, they were saving money to purchase. Homes were being built and sold briskly. The G. I. Bill and FHA had made home buying much easier, and housing construction would be booming for years to come.

The desire to keep the valley growing and prospering was prevalent among most of the older residents and newcomers, and more water was needed for continued growth and prosperity. When voters went to the polls on October 7, over 72 percent approved the bond issue with a vote of 16,375 for the bonds and only 6,314 votes against. The $2.5 million needed to build the dam was available for dam construction and acquisition of land.

Initially, the dam was referred to by different names, primarily "Windy Point Dam," because the location of the proposed dam was near an obscure spur known as Windy Point. It was said that some might think that Windy Point referred to the long and bitter verbal battle that took place at Sacramento, so about August 1, 1947, the directors of the Santa Clara Valley Water Conservation District forestalled that contingency by naming the dam and reservoir for Lexington, a small nearby community.

The Lexington project experienced almost every possible obstacle. When completed in 1952, the increase in population density had already made the reservoir a critically important facility.

The communities of Lexington and Alma were to be casualties of the Lexington Dam and Reservoir. In Lexington, there were fewer than a dozen families living a peaceful semi-rural life. The Lexington Elementary School was located in Alma, where about fifty families lived in a small community with a post office and a handful of small businesses. Naturally, the people of the two communities were unhappy about leaving. They deplored the necessity of selling their homes and leaving a peaceful spot where clear air and some of the most beautiful scenery of Santa Clara County surrounded them. However, the residents understood the need for the reservoir and dam and finally accepted what was to be.

Geological exploration at the Lexington dam site began in early 1948 just after the bond election. Nine tunnels were dug at various heights into the canyon wall on both sides, the longest being 153 feet. The results of the exploration indicated an excellent foundation for the dam. These exploratory tunnels and an associated geological survey were completed by May. State geologists and two consulting geologists then conducted extensive exploratory work relating to safety factors, soil types, foundation prospects, slopes and other factors, and submitted their reports.

The state engineer approved plans for construction of Lexington Dam on August 12, 1948. It was thought that the state highway engineers were working on plans for detouring traffic, and actual work would start on the detour route in early 1949, taking a year to complete. It would then take a year to construct the dam, meaning the reservoir would not be operational until late 1950. A season of much needed water would be lost. That doubled, when on December 16, 1948, it was learned that the work of relocating the highway would not start until 1950, as surveys for rerouting the 1.9-mile stretch of highway had not yet begun. This was a surprise and a disappointment to the district. Political bureaucracy at the state level had certainly cheated Santa

Signage near Anderson Dam site, 1949.

Clara Valley Water Conservation District users out of two years of rain that could have been saved—along with the increased costs of construction, which would not be fully known until the highway was nearing completion and the cost of land acquisition was known.

By 1949, the issue of purchasing the San Jose Water Works property was faced. Because the Water Works demanded what was considered to be an exorbitant price of $1,254,000, the Water District appealed to the state Public Utilities Commission to fix a value on the property. This was accomplished, and a fair price was established that was agreeable to both parties. The highway was rerouted by December 1951. Construction of the dam commenced in the spring of 1952, and was completed by fall. The more than four years intervening between the estimated and actual construction of the project, and the increased costs for labor, materials and properties, necessitated an additional voter-approved bond measure for $850,000. The Lexington project had seen almost every possible obstacle block its completion. By 1952, the increase in population density had made the reservoir a critically important facility.

Leroy Anderson Dam and Reservoir

By 1948, when no progress had been made on the relocation of the Los Gatos-Santa Cruz Highway despite the passage of a bond issue four months earlier, Water District authorities began to search for an alternative reservoir site.

The site chosen would later become Leroy Anderson Dam and Reservoir, named after the key founder and first president of the Water District.

A long, deep, natural gorge located three miles east of and parallel to Highway 101 in South County, near Madrone, provided a suitable dam site. The Santa Clara

Anderson would store more than all the other district reservoirs combined . . . nearly everyone agreed it was necessary due to the rate of population growth.

Raising the girders at Anderson Dam, 1951.

49

Valley Water Conservation District Board of Directors met and directed Chief Engineer G. Walter Hunt to prepare within sixty days a full report on the site proposed. The proposed plans were submitted to the board in April 1949, resulting in the scheduling of a bond election for the following summer. The total cost for land acquisition and construction was estimated to be $3 million, and the reservoir would store an estimated 75,000 acre-feet of water—more than all the other district reservoirs combined. Despite some questions raised by concerned groups, nearly everyone agreed that the large capacity was necessary due to the rate of population growth. The valley's population had grown from 30,000 in 1940 to 90,000 in 1948 along with a parallel growth in farming and industry.

The bond issue was approved in the summer of 1949, and preliminary surveys were immediately initiated. Once approval had been given by state engineers, and plans and surveys had been evaluated, construction began. Because no federal or state funds were involved and control was maintained at the local level, the new dam and reservoir was completed in record time, between the last rains of spring and the first rains of autumn of 1950.[16]

Central Santa Clara Valley Water Conservation District

On December 19, 1949, citizens in the Coyote Creek narrows near Morgan Hill formed the Central Santa Clara Valley Water Conservation District. Its boundaries touched the southern boundary of the Santa Clara Valley Water Conservation District to the northwest and the South Santa Clara Valley Water Conservation District (founded on August 1, 1938) to the southwest, bridging the valley floor between the two districts. The purpose of the Central District was to try to obtain water rights on the Coyote Creek for a supplemental water supply because the underground water basin was decreasing rapidly. Members of its governing board of directors were: Ed Acton, Joseph Chiri, Andrew Costa, John Reynolds and Harold Thomas. Secretary of the board was Superior Court Judge Harold Holden.

Upon investigation, the Central District learned that no water rights were left within its boundaries, and to obtain a supply from the Uvas or Llagas creeks was too expensive. They decided to contact the Santa Clara Valley Water Conservation District for a supplemental supply of water, as plans for Anderson Dam and Reservoir were already under way. Negotiations led to the annexation of the Central District on August 19, 1954. Meanwhile, voters in the district approved bonds with which to purchase lands for the Main Avenue Percolation Ponds near Morgan Hill, and as a condition for annexation, paid a pro-rata share of bonded indebtedness to the Santa Clara Valley Water Conservation District. While hundreds of smaller annexations of parcels of land to the Santa Clara Valley Water Conservation District occurred over the years, this was the only case where a total district was annexed.[††] A local election was held and was approved overwhelmingly.

~

Even though the water conservation district faced a tragic national economy during its first years, it was, ironically, the Great Depression which enabled the construction of the county's first six reservoirs. The PWA provided the district with financial support, manpower and a timeline, enabling the agency to construct a brilliant conservation system. Conceived by Fred Tibbetts and Stephen Keiffer in the 1920s, the system of dams and reservoirs was

---

[††] **Second Edition Note:** More agency mergers would take place in later years. See Appendix A.

recognized in 1976 as an historic landmark by the San Francisco Section of the American Society of Civil Engineers. At a ceremony at the Villa Felice Restaurant, overlooking beautiful Lake Vasona, district officials and staff, and those who had worked so hard to accomplish the seemingly impossible task, heard the Santa Clara Valley project cited as the first and only instance of a major water supply being developed in a single groundwater basin involving the control of numerous independent tributaries to effectuate almost optimal conservation of practically all of the sources of water flowing into the basin.■

The valley's *water system* is a *landmark . . .*

James J. Lenihan, chairman of the board of the Santa Clara Valley Water District, receives from James E. McCarty, president-elect of the San Francisco section, American Society of Civil Engineers, a bronze plaque designating the district's water conservation system as a California Historical Engineering Landmark. The presentation was made on February 25, 1976 in ceremonies at Villa Felice. The water system was the first such landmark to be designated by the ASCE section. Nearly 200 persons attended the ceremonies.

SOURCES, CHAPTER 3:

1. Transcript of Proceedings relating to the formation of Santa Clara Valley Water Conservation District, and to the first issue of bonds therein aggregating the principal sum of $2,000,000.

2. *Encyclopedia of American History*, edited by Richard B. Morris. Harper and Row, 1970.

3. *Family Encyclopedia of American History*. The Reader's Digest Association, 1975.

4. Report to Santa Clara Valley Water Conservation Committee on Santa Clara Valley Water Conservation Project, "Tibbetts & Keiffer Report," 1921.

5. *San Jose Mercury Herald*, Oct. 21, 1930 and Oct. 26, 1930.

6. *San Jose News*, Dec. 10, 1935; also, *San Jose Mercury Herald*, Dec. 10, 1935.

7. *"30 Years of Progress"* Annual Report, SCVWCD, 1960.

8. Minutes of the Board of Directors, SCVWCD, Aug. 23, 1934. (Vol. 2)

9. Minutes of the Board of Directors, SCVWCD, Dec. 18, 1929. (Vol. 1).

10. *Santa Cruz Sentinel News*, Feb. 26, 1947.

11. *San Jose Mercury Herald*, May 11, 1947, p. 26.

12. *San Jose News*, April 10, 1947.

13. *San Jose Mercury Herald*, March 1, 1936.

14. Ibid, March 10, 1947.

15. Ibid, Sept. 20, 1947.

16. Ibid, April 26, 1951, pp. 1, 4.

Second Edition Note: *Specifically in this chapter, where the author used a source more than once, the citation number includes the referenced page numbers. For example, the citation "3:66" indicates that this information was taken from page 66 of source #3.*

Men assist a family in evacuating their Alviso home in December 1955. The infamous "Christmas week floods" caused devastation in many areas of the valley and throughout California.

CHAPTER 4

Post-War Problems: Struggles for Authority

By Charles K. Hart

Santa Clara County, the "Valley of Heart's Delight," evolved more rapidly during the World War II years. What had been a predominantly agricultural economy became a combination industrial-agricultural economy. The county had grown as a market and shipping center with a related industrial network of plants for food processing, food packaging and the manufacturing of food machinery. It was also known as the world's canning center as well as a major center for wine production. The cities of San José, Santa Clara, Sunnyvale, Mountain View, Palo Alto, Gilroy and Morgan Hill stood as independent communities surrounded by agricultural land, basically dependent upon their own local groundwater supply. This was also true for other smaller towns in the county. Most of the roadways were two lanes wide except for Bayshore Highway, which was slowly being converted to a freeway. Highway 17 was yet to be built through the county and San José.

Into this relatively restricted area came thousands of servicemen and war workers during the war years. Many were employed in the San Francisco-Oakland area, but Santa Clara County also felt the impact in several ways. Moffett Field was the largest military installation in the county. Joshua Hendy Iron Works in Sunnyvale employed 7,500 people. It was one of the nation's major suppliers of naval landing boat engines. Wartime industry was adding to the already expanding number of agricultural producers and food processors, placing new demands upon the valley's housing and water resources.

Many of the newcomers liked the Bay Area climate and saw it as a good place to live. Housing shortages, already existing during the active war years of 1942 to 1946, became more critical as veterans brought their families to settle in the area permanently. Construction of new housing, which was restricted by the war, began to pick up in the late 1940s, and by 1954, the building boom had exploded into action.

The building pressures on all public services, including water needs, mounted as the population increased. In

What had been a predominantly agricultural economy became a combination industrial-agricultural economy.

Sunnyvale led the valley by growing 442 percent, from 9,800 residents in 1950 to 53,000 residents in 1960.

the decade from 1940 to 1950, the growth in Santa Clara County's population increased by 66 percent to 291,000; between 1950 to 1960, an increase of 121 percent to 642,000 took place. The north county cities were responsible for most of the phenomenal growth during the 1950s, with Sunnyvale leading the way. It grew 442 percent from 9,800 to 53,000 residents in the brief 10-year period. There were four industries in Sunnyvale in 1946 and by 1956, there were 44. Not all of the cities expanded this rapidly, but a typical pattern of growth was established which continued past the 1950s.

More and more industries moved into Santa Clara County during the 1950s to utilize the growing labor force and expanding markets. A partial listing indicates the scope and variety of movement: IBM Corporation located its main computer manufacturing plant in south San José in the early 1950s; Ford Motor Co. built a major assembly plant in Milpitas in 1952; in Sunnyvale, Lockheed Corporation located its Polaris missile plant, and the U.S. Air Force established its Missile Tracking facility, while Westinghouse Electric Company bought the Joshua Hendy Iron Works to produce large marine gears; General Electric Company built the first facility for production of nuclear power plants in San José; and FMC Corp. expanded its production capabilities throughout the valley. The industry that would have the greatest impact on Santa Clara Valley's population and urban growth started at the Stanford Industrial Park in Palo Alto. The electronic industry, led by Hewlett-Packard Company and Varian, Inc., was soon to send its offshoots throughout the Santa Clara Valley.

As more and more industries moved into the county, all of the problems of urbanization began to demand attention. Tracts of houses appeared almost overnight, and the beginnings of large centralized shopping areas started with the Valley Fair complex on Stevens Creek Boulevard.

As orchards and farmland were covered with houses,

shopping centers, industries and parking lots, the environment was affected in three major ways. New complications were added to the existing problems of insufficient groundwater storage, land surface subsidence and control of surface water runoff.

Agricultural needs had already overdrawn the limited supply of groundwater. As discussed in Chapter 2, water shortages had already resulted in the formation of the Santa Clara Valley Water Conservation District in 1929. Even before urbanization got rolling, the population demanded 42,000 acre-feet of water in excess of the underground supply, producing an all time low in the water table.[5:7]

Mean annual precipitation in Santa Clara County varies from a maximum of about 70 inches in some areas of the Santa Cruz Mountains to a minimum of about 13 inches at Alviso near the bay.[10:IV-1] The measurable rainfall generally occurs from November through March, and storms can be frequent and severe, particularly in the mountains.

Infiltration of runoff into the underground water storage basin varies across the valley floor. A high rate of infiltration occurs next to the foothills where very deep, sandy or gravelly soils are found adjacent to streams and rivers. As soil types change to clays or shallow soil over rocks or hard core, the rate of infiltration is drastically reduced. Rainfall that exceeds infiltration rates runs off toward the bay through regular channels.[10:IV-3]

Mountain ranges which mark the east and west boundaries of the county are divided into three distinct rainfall and drainage patterns. South County land drains into the Pajaro River and Monterey Bay. As South County remained agricultural, it was not as severely affected by the water conditions of the 1950s. The eastern foothills of the Diablos and Mt. Hamilton drain into Alameda County and then into San Francisco Bay. Central and northern Santa Clara Valley drain into southern San Francisco Bay, crossing through the most densely populated area in the valley.

Mid-Century Floods

Prior to 1952, there was no flood control district or any other agency which had responsibility for clearing or improving streams. The stream beds were in private ownership, and floods were the only force that periodically cleaned out the beds.[1]

Minor flood flows in 1945 did not clear much of the debris in the creeks, so when the 1955 Christmas week floods occurred, there was a particularly heavy accumulation of debris and vegetative growth. The floods uprooted trees and brush, carrying them to lodge at bridges, which were plugged almost solid along Saratoga and Calabazas creeks. Drag line cranes were used to clean the creek beds where possible. Where Calabazas Creek paralleled El Camino Real, it took over a month to clean out the log-jam.[1] San Francisquito Creek, which forms the boundary in Palo Alto between Santa Clara and San Mateo counties, was badly flooded back to the Stanford University Golf Course.[7] The area just westerly of Bayshore Highway had considerable residential damage from mud and silt carried by the floodwaters.[7] The flooding was caused in part by a lack of adequate drainage outlets to the bay. A single five-foot pipe through the bay levee was the only outlet for the floodwaters from Stevens, Permanente, Barron, Matadero and Adobe creeks. Dikes of the Leslie Salt ponds held the water captive until low tides let it drain into the bay.[7] Land surface subsidence of eight to 10 feet at the north boundaries of Sunnyvale further contributed to the flooding, where creek mouths were below the normal bay tide level.[6:3]

In the town of Alviso, flooding was particularly a problem. In Alviso, drainage from Saratoga, San Tomas Aquino and Calabazas creeks joined the Guadalupe River, which also received water from Los Gatos Creek. Land surface subsidence in this area was about six feet by 1950. A series of dikes had been built to hold the bay waters

Flooding typically involves not only water but a load of mud and debris. This photograph shows Homestead Road in the city of Santa Clara, flooded by Saratoga Creek, December 1955.

under control, but many times the heavy storms also co-incided with abnormally high tides. This combination raised the level of floodwaters and they overflowed stream banks and then drained into Alviso. The stream overflow caused occasional dike breaks on the Coyote drainage channel and along the Guadalupe River, adding to flooding of the southern tip of the bay.[7]

A storm in 1952 flooded the Silver Creek area in Evergreen causing damage to a primarily agricultural area. Another flood on the lower Guadalupe River in 1953 was confined to an area north of Montague Road. The Uvas/ Llagas watershed also was severely flooded in 1955 and 1958. The lack of natural channels and a fairly flat terrain spread the water over a large, primarily agricultural area called Soap Lake.[7]

Damage from the 1958 flood would have been disastrous had not Anderson and Coyote Dams on Coyote Creek been finished in 1952. Lexington Dam was completed just

Main Street, Gilroy, December 23, 1955.

days before the 1955 Christmas flood. These dams, along with others, had been built by the Santa Clara Valley Water Conservation District for the main purpose of collecting water for irrigation and percolation. They were not designed as "dual purpose facilities." However, the reservoirs did aid flood control, although operating procedures did not provide for saving any flood control capacity as they filled.

The third environmental problem—closely related to lack of groundwater storage and poor control of excess runoff, causing flooding—was land surface subsidence, which occurred primarily in the north valley. Blue clay deposits forming the pressure areas of underground water reservoirs and mud flats of the San Francisco Bay can be traced to geological action during a period about 25,000 years ago. The blue clays lie under and alongside the present stream beds.[5,7] Artesian wells were plentiful in these areas as late as the early 1900s.[1] A direct consequence of continued overdrafts from these aquifers without equal infiltration of surface water was a compression of the blue clay. Weight of the overlying sediments squeezed water out, and the clay further compressed as more water was pumped out. The compressed clay permanently loses its water absorption capacity, and does not "rebound" during wet years. The end result was irreversable land surface subsidence. Alviso is the most visible evidence of this condition (see Chapter 6). In addition, a high water table also acts as a barrier to saltwater intrusion of the bayshore lands.[5,7]

Establishment of the Santa Clara County Flood Control and Water Conservation District

John F. "Jack" Thompson was a native Santa Clara County son, a longtime farmer, an active member of farmers' co-operatives and a state legislator. He served in the assembly from 1943 until his election to the senate in 1950, where he served subsequent terms beginning in 1954 and 1958. As a farmer, he was well aware of water supply, conservation and flood control problems.[3:77] In 1951, he authored the legislative Act that created the Santa Clara County Flood Control and Water Conservation District.[†] By that time, 12 flood control districts had been established in other parts of California, so a precedent was available.[8:2]

The Act was effective July 10, 1951, but was challenged immediately by the already existing Santa Clara Valley Water Conservation District. In 1951, the district owned and operated an extensive system of dams, canals and water percolation ponds for water conservation. The district wanted to protect these assets, and indicated its opposition to the flood control group unless the Water District's interests were assured. Accordingly, Senator Thompson inserted an amendment into the enabling Act that protected the original water conservation district's "properties, structures and works then existent or later constructed or acquired."[8:3] This amendment became effective April 18, 1952, and the two districts existed as separate entities through the 1950s and early 1960s. Management of the Flood Control District was determined by the Santa Clara County Board of Supervisors, acting in an ex-officio capacity.[8:5]

As originally formed by Thompson's enabling act, the Flood Control District's primary responsibility was flood control. The Santa Clara Valley Water Conservation District had not addressed itself to this problem except as it affected its own facilities. Some conflicts arose throughout the county when the Flood Control District was given drainage control over the entire county and its watercourses. After the Santa Clara Valley Water Conservation District's prior rights were protected by the 1952 amendment, the Flood Control District began its task in earnest.

Control of flooding had been a fragmented operation before the district was formed. Stream channel improvements to control flooding had been established for Permanente Creek in Mountain View, and for Coyote Creek in San José from 13th Street (then known as the Oakland Highway) to the San Francisco Bay in the 1880s.[7] San José had experienced periodic flooding in the Canoas Gardens and Willow Glen areas. Handling of storm water in the San José city limits was only partially successful since flooding on Coyote Creek, Guadalupe River and Los Gatos Creek was uncontrolled in areas upstream from the city limits. Each city handled its own drainage differently, based upon its past needs, until rapid urbanization began. Subdivisions were often constructed with only the streets to act as storm drains. This sometimes caused serious flooding when large volumes of water collected in the low spots. These were the conditions confronting the new Flood Control District in 1952.[1]

Vicinity of Vahl's restaurant in Alviso, December 23, 1955.

[†] **Second Edition Note.** The act was entitled the Santa Clara County Flood Control and Water Conservation Act.

Flooding could *stretch for miles* over the *flat lands* of the valley.

Aerial of Alviso, April 4, 1958.

Prior to the 1955 flood, the north valley had been divided into about 30 small zones, each of which was a drainage area embracing residential developments in the still unincorporated areas. This was before cities (primarily those in the north and west valley) began the push for land annexation to acquire unincorporated territory. Storm drains for the unincorporated areas were designed, and preparations were made to hold bond elections within each of the small zones since no drainage fees had been collected from the developers. Most of the people then living in these areas had not been bothered by flooding, so didn't see the need for additional taxes to install a drainage system. After bond issues in two small zones had been defeated, the county board of supervisors, which was then the board of directors of the Flood Control District, decided that the small drainage zone approach should be abandoned.[1]

Five flood control zones are formed. After abandoning the small drainage zone concept, the district decided to form five large zones whose boundaries were based upon watersheds of major streams. These zones were made permanent by approval of the Secretary of the State of California, and each was set up as a separate taxing unit to more equitably distribute the cost of flood control in each local area.[1]

The Northwest Zone embraces Palo Alto, Los Altos, Los Altos Hills and Mountain View. It covers the watersheds of San Francisquito, Matadero and Adobe creeks and their tributaries.

The North Central Zone includes Santa Clara, Sunnyvale, Saratoga, Cupertino and portions of Los Gatos and San José. Natural creeks in this zone are Saratoga, Calabazas and San Tomas Aquino, but two artificial channels were constructed by the district to provide a drainage outfall for a large area in Sunnyvale between Calabazas Creek and Stevens Creek. They are called Sunnyvale West

Channel and Sunnyvale East Channel and empty into Guadalupe Slough and Moffett Channel, respectively.

The Central Zone handles drainage from San José and Los Gatos with Los Gatos and Alamitos creeks, plus Guadalupe River drainage basin defining the zone boundaries. The Coyote Creek watershed limits determine the boundaries of the East Zone, which includes Anderson and Coyote reservoirs. The South Zone covers the Llagas and Uvas-Carnadero creek watersheds of the Pajaro River.[1]

The 1955 flood focused attention in Santa Clara County on the real need for action in controlling water runoff if future floods were to be averted.

Financing Flood Control Improvements

Plans and reports were drawn up for flood control improvements in the Northwest, North Central and East zones. Based upon the studies, the Board of Supervisors held public hearings and explained their proposals. They passed resolutions declaring their intentions to construct the improvements and announced the need for bond elections to provide financing. The bond election held in the Northwest Zone in October of 1956 carried with the necessary two-thirds majority, and $6.4 million in construction funds were authorized. The Northwest bond election was the only one held in the 1950s.[1]

The bonds were sold in yearly increments in order to keep the property tax rate as level as possible during their amortization. There was no way to obtain revenue from unsold flood control bonds, so the construction projects were spread over a period of six years.[1]

Unfortunately, the collection of hydrological data needed for flood volume computation had not been done prior to the mid-1950s. Information needed to prepare a reasonably accurate estimate of flood flows was scarce to nonexistent. As a result, many of the original improvements in both the Northwest Zone and North Central Zone were underdesigned, later proving to be too small.[1]

Work on the South, Central and North Central zones continued as data was collected, but the bond measures were not put on the ballots until the 1960s. Urban development had not progressed very far in the East Zone during the 1950s. There were numerous large dairy farms on the valley floor and cattle ranches on the hillside grazing lands. A full page ad was prepared by the dairymen and cattlemen who opposed the issuance of flood control bonds that would not directly benefit them. The day before the October 1956 bond election, the ad was run in the local newspaper, and because there was no opportunity for the proponents to reply, a 2-to-1 defeat of the bond issue resulted. In face of the defeat, several pay-as-you-go improvements were planned, but progress was slow since the East Zone tax base was next to the lowest in the county, and funds were slow to accumulate for flood control projects.[1]

Toward the Formation of One Water Authority

When state Senator Jack Thompson sponsored the formation of the Flood Control District in 1951, he had already envisioned its future merger with the Santa Clara Valley Water Conservation District.[1] Sentiment for the merger grew for several years, hence the original name of Santa Clara County Flood Control and Water Conservation District. Assemblyman Bruce Allen, who served with Thompson, was worried about the duality of the districts. He lobbied for the merger, and introduced AB2242 on March 25, 1959, asking for dissolution of the Water Conservation District. However, the directors of the Water Conservation District were not ready for a merger, so, with the help of Assemblyman Clark Bradley, they lobbied against the bill, and it was defeated.[3:110] It was questioned whether the bill was a valid exercise of legislative power.

While efforts supporting a merger were underway, it was evident that a new imported water source was needed.

Many legal questions were raised, and an opinion was difficult because there was no precedent on which to base a decision.[9:2]

While such efforts were underway, it was also increasingly evident that new sources for augmenting the water supply were needed. The precedent of importing water into the county began in the early 1950s, when several northern towns began to draw upon San Francisco's Hetch Hetchy water system. In 1913, Congress had passed the Raker Act, authorizing rights of way for the aqueduct and pipeline which would transport water from a reservoir on the Tuolumne River north of Yosemite to Crystal Springs Reservoir, for use by the San Francisco Public Uitlitics Commission. This resulted in a connecting pipeline which served Palo Alto, Sunnyvale, Milpitas and Mountain View, but had limited application because it could not be used for agricultural purposes.[7]

Tri-County Water Authority studies water importation.
In 1955, at the urging of Santa Clara Valley Water Conservation District and adjoining counties, the state legislature recognized the need for new sources of imported water, and authorized the formation of the Tri-County Water Authority to research and study the problem. The Authority was to have a five-year life during which it was authorized to levy taxes to cover research costs. The taxes collected enabled the Authority to continue for two years past the original five, at which time it disbanded.[7]

Santa Clara Valley Water Conservation District, San Benito County and Alameda County Water District composed the Authority's first membership. Alameda County had its own water supply, so it dropped out of the Authority during the first year. Santa Cruz and Monterey county districts then joined, but Monterey soon dropped out, leaving Santa Cruz with Santa Clara and San Benito as the final trio of the Authority. (Monterey later rejoined in 1964.)

The State Water Resources Control Board was estab-

lished in 1947 to make a statewide inventory of water resources and, in 1955, projected future requirements. These two studies were incorporated into the statewide California Water Plan of 1957.[2] Consultants working with the Tri-County Water Authority prepared an estimate of future water needs, which exceeded by a considerable amount the planned delivery from the South Bay Aqueduct of the California Water Plan. They concluded that the best way to serve the area, particularly San Benito and Santa Cruz counties, was through the proposed San Felipe project.[7] This future water needs study was written in the late 1950s and formed the basis of bond elections which would later be held in the 1960s.

An attempt was made in early 1959 by Senator Thompson and Assemblyman Allen to repeal the Tri-County Water Authority Act. The authors' intentions in this regard were not announced, but their efforts were not successful.[9:2] The struggle for political control within Santa Clara County, described below, may have been a motivating force.

Wastewater reclamation studies were quite limited in the 1950s; however, both the cities of Campbell and Cupertino tried to set up plans for disposing of treated sewage in streambeds near their northerly city limits. Both cities were growing rapidly and had no central treatment plants, and when their disposal plans were denied by the state Department of Health, they were forced to negotiate contracts with San José to use its plant.

Campbell proposed construction of a sewage treatment plant near Los Gatos Creek, planning to discharge the treated effluent into the creek. The Santa Clara Valley Water Conservation District supported the concept, but the public was against using reclaimed wastewater and, as stated above, the health authorities feared that the underground basin would become polluted. Other sanitation districts were also against Campbell's proposal, so the proposal was abandoned.[7]

Health authorities were not convinced that a process existed which could filter out viruses, even though bacteria could be filtered out. The pH factor (hardness of water) and dissolved solids also posed a problem. Groundwater is already hard as compared to imported surface rain water, and percolation or pumping it back into the ground as treated effluent compounds the hardness.[1] Cupertino negotiated a contract to hook into the San José-Santa Clara sewage disposal system.

As previously mentioned, the Tri-County Water Authority had recommended the San Felipe source for additional water, but it also recognized that South Bay Aqueduct water would be available sooner. The California Water Plan had been drawn up in final form in 1957, but statewide bond elections were not held until 1960. However, the state—with general revenues from state funds— started construction of the South Bay Aqueduct in 1959.[7]

The Santa Clara County Flood Control and Water Conservation District and the Santa Clara Valley Water Conservation District were struggling for political control to determine which should be the one to import water. The Flood Control District favored the South Bay Aqueduct, primarily because it was under construction and the water was badly needed. The San Felipe project was favored by the Santa Clara Valley Water Conservation District, a member of the Tri-County Water Authority. San Felipe would be part of the Central Valley Project, which had been developed by the federal Bureau of Reclamation to transfer water from the Sacramento and Trinity river basins into the water-deficient areas of the San Joaquin Valley and Southern California.[2] After transport down the Sacramento River and across the Delta, the water is raised into the Delta-Mendota Canal to flow south into the Mendota Pool on the San Joaquin River. Part of this water is stored during surplus periods in the San Luis Reservoir west of Los Banos. It was from this source that the Tri-County Water

Authority recommended additional water be secured and transported into the Pajaro River watershed and northerly into Santa Clara County.[7]

The San Felipe project authorization did not take place until 1967. Congressman Charles Gubser was the persistent spark plug who, in the 1960s, consistently worked for this project in the House of Representatives.■

SOURCES, CHAPTER 4:

1. Bums, Malcolm. Interviewed by Susan Mathews, California History Center, August 1976.

2. *California Almanac*. San Jose Mercury, 1971, pp. 288-292.

3. *California Blue Book*, 1954.

4. *Standard Industrial Survey Summary Report*, Statewide Industrial Development Committee, California State Chamber of Commerce. November 1960.

5. Preliminary Studies for General Plan, City of Sunnyvale, 1955.

6. *The Sunnyvale Story*, City of Sunnyvale, Fall and Winter 1973.

7. Currlin, Donald. Interviewed by Susan Mathews, California History Center, July 1976.

8. Henley, Albert Thomas. Declaration of Superior Court of the State of California for the County of Santa Clara No. 341743, n.d.

9. Henley, Albert Thomas. Excerpt from Report Re: Allen and Thompson, Attempt to Repeal Tri-County Authority Act, n.d.

10. Johnson, Morgan. *Water Resources in Santa Clara County, A Plan for Conservation*, 1973.

11. League of Women Voters of San Jose. *A Citizens' Guide to Government in Santa Clara County,* brochure, 1958.

Second Edition Note: Citations in this chapter may include the referenced page numbers. For example, the citation "9:2" indicates that this information was taken from page 2 of source #9.

Morning fog on Uvas Reservoir.

Jim McCann

CHAPTER 5

Vision of the Future—Total Water Management

By Lynn Longa

"He who controls the waterhole controls the range." This popular quote from the West's frontier days held very true in the changing setting of Santa Clara County in the late 1950s. The struggle over the waterhole symbolizes man's economic dependence upon the evasive life source. As post-war industry expanded and diversified, the valley's population continued to increase and the contest for water intensified. Like the increasingly complex society the resource was to accommodate, the management of water became serious business. The floods of the 1950s had resulted in the formation of a county flood control district, while subsequent water shortages made the search for alternative supplies imperative.

There were now two distinct agencies with different functions: the Santa Clara County Flood Control and Water Conservation District (directed by the Santa Clara County Board of Supervisors) and the Santa Clara Valley Water Conservation District (directed by locally elected citizens). During the 1960s, both agencies were to struggle over the control and management of the vanishing commodity.

In addition to the battle over which agency should contract for water, there was conflict over the best importation plan for supplemental water supplies. The Santa Clara Valley Water Conservation District supported the Pacheco Pass Project—now called the San Felipe Division of the Central Valley Project, whereas the Flood Control District supported the South Bay Aqueduct. Both factions agreed to hire a review panel to determine which agency should import water and which project was the more feasible.

This blue ribbon panel was made up of three men: The Flood Control District appointed John S. Longwell, a former chief engineer who had served fifteen years as manager of the East Bay Municipal Utility District. Samuel B. Morris, who had served as consulting engineer and former chief engineer and general manager of the Los Angeles Department of Water and Power, was appointed by the Tri-County Water Authority (see Appendix A). The third man, Professor S. T. Harding, a professor of engineering at the University of California at Berkeley, and one of the outstanding men in the water field, was chosen by the other

The management of water became serious business.

two appointees. The purpose of appointing this board of consultants was to have them review all available data and information affecting the local water situation, and recommend a plan of action for Santa Clara County.[22;4,12] Their final report indicated that eventually both sources of imported water would be needed, but the Flood Control District decided to firmly support the South Bay Aqueduct. The county supervisors who directed the district argued that because the facility was part of the State Water Project under the jurisdiction of the state Department of Water Resources, execution of the water supply contract and financing of the project were guaranteed. Further, the project would furnish sufficient water to Santa Clara County until the early 1970s. Therefore, they deemed the aqueduct as more feasible than the Pacheco Pass project, which was still under study.

However, no matter what the source of the imported water would be, both agencies—the Flood Control District and the Santa Clara Valley Water Conservation District—wanted sole authority over importation.

Basically, the county supervisors saw water as a means of revenue. The supervisors included such men as Howard Weichert, Ed Levin, Wesley (Bud) Hubbard, Sam Della Maggiore and Sig Sanchez. The Santa Clara Valley Water Conservation District, which was formed by local farmers, wanted to keep water a low-priced item as long as possible. As the 1960s began, it was represented by such men as Ed Mirassou, a well known wine producer; Hermann Gerdts, who was associated with the prune industry; Frank Polak and Joe Chiri, farmers from the Morgan Hill-San Martin area; and S. W. Pfeifle, J. J. Mariani, Jr., Vernon Holthouse and Frank Wilcox, all of whom represented the farming community. Later, in the 1960s, Robert T. Sapp and James J. Lenihan replaced Mariani and Holthouse, and began to represent the business interests of their respective districts.

Water Commission to decide who imports water. In order for the county to implement water importation via the South Bay Aqueduct, the Board of Supervisors instituted the Unified County Water Plan. The plan was prepared by Supervisor Bud Hubbard; James Pott, director of public works; and Donald Currlin, manager counsel of the Flood Control District. The plan would establish a Santa Clara County Water Commission. The commission was to be initially composed of one member from the Santa Clara County Board of Supervisors; one member from each water conservation district in the county; one member from those cities that were actively engaged in importing water; plus one representative from San José, because of its large population. It was this countywide Water Commission that would make the final determination of who would import water, and who would be the contracting agency for the entire county.

After the formation of the commission, the question arose as to whether it fully represented all the interests within the county. Cities that were not represented on the commission felt they should have a voice in such an important matter and they requested equal representation. After some debate, the commission was eventually comprised of one elected representative from each city in the county, one elected member from the Board of Supervisors, and one elected director each from the Flood Control District and from the Santa Clara Valley Water Conservation District.

After lengthy discussion, the Water Commission recommended that the Flood Control District be the contracting agency with either the state or federal system, or anyone else who could supply water to the county. It was felt that the district, under the Board of Supervisors' purview, represented overall county interests, whereas the Santa Clara Valley Water Conservation District represented only the area on the valley floor north of Morgan Hill, excluding Palo Alto and parts of Milpitas.

Following the decision that the Flood Control District would be the contracting authority, Donald Currlin was assigned the responsibility of determining the pros and cons of each project. He explained that there were difficulties with each project. The South Bay Aqueduct could not supply all of the water necessary to serve the county for the next fifty years, nor could the San Francisco-owned Hetch Hetchy Aqueduct.[†] Although the San Felipe project could have been built large enough to supply all of the county's water needs, it had not yet been authorized as a federal project.[††] Donald Currlin met with Patrick Creegan, consulting engineer for the Tri-County Water Authority, and J. Robert Roll, engineering manager for the Santa Clara Valley Water Conservation District. According to Currlin:

The end result was that since four cities within the county had separate contracts with San Francisco for the use of Hetch Hetchy water, we felt that it could not be eliminated. The cities' physical distribution facilities had been built to take deliveries from the Hetch Hetchy Aqueduct, and so possibly would not fit into either the South Bay Aqueduct or the San Felipe systems.[6]

The result of the commission's analysis was that the county supervisors should sign the contract with the State of California for the use of South Bay Aqueduct water, with the use of Hetch Hetchy water to continue in the north county. These two projects would resolve the immediate problems until the San Felipe project could eventually be built.

With the county's role in water management greatly expanded, its first step was to obtain financing for the South Bay Aqueduct linkup, treatment plants, conveyance and distribution facilities. In order to construct the In-County Distribution System and the first water treatment plant, two bond elections were held. The first vote, held November 9, 1962, received only 65 percent instead of the 66.66 percent needed to pass the issue. It failed mainly due to opposition by the city of Sunnyvale, which used Hetch Hetchy water. Officials of that city were concerned about paying both district taxes and Hetch Hetchy fees. The second bond election passed on June 11, 1963, after compromises were made with Hetch Hetchy importers, including Sunnyvale, regarding water pricing.

Financing was thus provided for construction of the Rinconada Water Treatment Plant to be located in Los Gatos. From this plant, distribution systems would take treated water to Cupertino, Santa Clara and Campbell. Water would reach the treatment plant from the South Bay Aqueduct on the valley's east side via a 72-inch pipeline laid across the valley floor. The In-County Distribution System would be designed in such a way that the San Felipe project, when completed, would effectively combine with the other facilities in an effort toward achieving total water management.

The magnitude of the task of implementing the new distribution systems and integrating them with existing water systems, challenged the effectiveness of the Santa Clara County Flood Control and Water Conservation District. It was obvious that although this district was to be the sole agency for importing water, it needed the complementary

The South Bay Aqueduct could not supply all of the water necessary to serve the county for the next fifty years, nor could the San Francisco-owned Hetch Hetchy Aqueduct. Both these sources and a third source, the CVP, would be needed.

[†] The Hetch Hetchy Aqueduct was serving the north county cities of Palo Alto, Milpitas, Sunnyvale and Mountain View with water that could only be used for municipal purposes, not for agricultural purposes, pursuant to federal law.

[††] Final authorization for the San Felipe Division was given by Congress in August 1967. The first 1.8 miles of the Pacheco tunnel were constructed under the act authorizing the San Luis Unit of the Central Valley Project.

Water *imported* from the State Water Project through the
South Bay Aqueduct would be processed at the
valley's first water treatment plant, built in *Los Gatos*.

Governor Edmund G. (Pat) Brown, the visionary force behind the State Water Project (SWP), stands alongside the South Bay Aqueduct, May 11, 1965.

Water from the South Bay Aqueduct traveled through the Central Valley Pipeline to reach the Rinconada Water Treatment Plant (above). The plant, completed in 1967 by the Santa Clara County Flood Control and Water Conservation District—a predecessor to today's SCVWD— was built with a capacity to treat 80 million gallons of water per day (mgd). In the early 2000s, the capacity was upgraded to 100 mgd (see Chapter 14).

skills of the Santa Clara Valley Water Conservation District. A compromise was needed, and it wasn't long before the two agencies were assisting each other.

There were some very real practical problems which arose after delivery of the first water from the South Bay Aqueduct in July 1965. These problems related to the implementation of the water pricing policy. A program of well registration was undertaken, and in 1964, the Santa Clara County Flood Control and Water District began construction of the Central Pipeline and instituted a groundwater extraction charge (pump tax). At the same time, the Santa Clara Valley Water Conservation District converted its revenue source from property taxes to groundwater charges.[6] The county body collected the water charges for both agencies and turned the appropriate amount over to the conservation district. In exchange for its collection services, the conservation district provided the county with its data on groundwater levels. The cooperation between the two agencies was a major factor leading to an eventual merger.

The 1968 Merger

The expanded activities of the Flood Control District became such a burden on the board of supervisors, it was evident that the two districts should be consolidated and governed by a separate board. However, as Supervisor Sig Sanchez said, before a merger could take place, the political climate had to change. Several compromises were worked out to bring about the changes necessary to make the merger possible. The Water Commission was effective in advocating a merger, and the two districts set up a joint committee to effect consolidation, while a special Water Pricing Subcommittee hammered out an equitable pricing policy.

One very important compromise written into the Consolidation Act was the formation of the Agricultural Water Advisory Committee. This committee was mandated to advise the new board of directors regarding the needs of the farming community. It would be specified in the legislative act creating the new district that the committee would be made up of farmers.

Another compromise had to do with composition of the board of directors for the new district. The Santa Clara Valley Water Conservation District was governed by a seven-member elected board, and the Flood Control District was governed by the five-member Santa Clara County Board of Supervisors. The question now was: Who will compose the new governing board of directors? Violet Enander, clerk of the board for the Water Conservation District, explained the compromise:

> *The political compromise was that there would be seven board members, five elected from the supervisorial districts, and two members who would represent the public at-large, appointed by the board of supervisors. It was specifically designated that one of the appointed members live within the boundaries of the old Santa Clara Valley Water Conservation District, and one from the South Santa Clara Valley Water Conservation District, because it was believed that the south district would also merge at the same time. There was no controversy with the Santa Clara Valley Water Conservation District; its board was strictly for the merger, and on the basis of its own power agreed to the merger without having to go to the public for a vote. But the south district did go to a vote in April 1968 on the merger question.[9]*

However equitable the board's representation would be, the budget for the new district would have to be approved annually by the county board of supervisors.

On March 7, 1968,

consolidation of

the two districts

became a reality.

These board directors and managers would set the *newly merged* Water District on the path to *integrated water management*.

Standing, left to right, are staff members Donald K. Currlin, Violet V. Enander, Glenn F. Dodson, Albert T. Henley, J. Winter Smith, Lloyd C. Fowler, Charles G. Wilson, Ronald R. Esau and Ben C. Francis.

Seated, left to right, are board directors Victor F. Corsiglia, Will Lester, R. Jack Sturla, Frank A. Wilcox, Robert T. Sapp, James J. Lenihan and Joseph Chiri.

In order to help put the merger together in an amicable manner, the Water Conservation District brought in Glenn Dodson as general manager. As a distinguished member of the community, the board believed that Mr. Dodson would be able to bring the opposing sides together. At that time, the chief engineer and general manager was J. Robert Roll, who continued solely as chief engineer, and later took advantage of early retirement. His stepping down was one of the compromises that helped make the merger possible. It is interesting to note that after the merger was completed, Mr. Dodson also stepped down.

Another compromise regarded the attorney. Albert Henley had been with the Water Conservation District, and he continued as legal counsel for the new district while Donald Currlin, the Flood Control District's manager-counsel, became general manager of the new agency. Then there was the matter of the new department heads. Of the four department heads that formed the new district, Ronald R. Esau as director of public services and Violet Enander as clerk of the board came from the Water Conservation District. Lloyd Fowler, director of engineering, and Charles G. Wilson, director of administration and finance, came from the Flood Control District.

On March 7, 1968, consolidation of the two districts became a reality. The new agency would be called the Santa Clara County Flood Control and Water District.[†††] The first board of directors as appointed by the Board of Supervisors was as follows: District 1, Joe Chiri; District 2, Victor Corsiglia, Sr.; District 3, Robert Sapp; District 4, Maurice Dullea; and District 5, James Lenihan. These appointments were confirmed by the electorate in June of 1968. At-large appointees were Jack Sturla and Frank Wilcox. Chiri, Sapp, Lenihan and Wilcox had been serving as directors of the former Santa Clara Valley Water Conservation District. Mr. Sturla resigned his board position with the South Santa Clara Valley Water Conservation District to accept appoint-

ment to the new board. Mr. Dullea, a Santa Clara city councilman, had been a member of the Water Commission, and was the key architect to the water pricing policy it had developed. Mr. Corsiglia, a local businessman, had been an active supporter of both districts.[8]

Water Pricing Policies

One of the important issues to face the new Santa Clara County Flood Control and Water District would be the establishment of "Water Pricing for Total Water Management." The necessity for effective water pricing had been recognized by the county as early as 1964, when, at the recommendation of the Water Commission, the Board of Supervisors levied a 5 percent tax on land and improvements to finance the studies that would be necessary to bring the water program into existence.[6] The Water Commission determined that the tax should be sufficient to pay for the continuing capital costs and interest charges for importation facilities of both the South Bay Aqueduct and the future San Felipe Water Project. All other costs would be borne by those who actually used the water. In order to place a tax on water users, it was necessary to obtain legal rights from the state legislature to charge a price per acre-foot for all water extracted from the groundwater basin. With legislative approval, the County Flood Control and Water District was authorized to levy what is now known as a groundwater charge, or pump tax.

Thus, the early pricing policy, as recommended to the board of supervisors by the Water Commission, and agricultural users. The treated water price would consist of an equivalent to the groundwater and agricultural users. The

---

[†††] The Santa Clara County Flood Control and Water District retained this name until January 1, 1974, when it changed to the Santa Clara Valley Water District.

treated water price would consist of an equivalent to the groundwater price plus the cost of constructing and operating the water treatment plants and their delivery networks.

Research findings after the merger found the old water pricing method ineffective, so the new Santa Clara County Flood Control and Water District made the following changes: The five-cent countywide property tax would still finance capital costs and interest for importation facilities, but the rest of the cost would be paid by what was called the "basic water users charge." This charge would consist of total costs of treatment plants, treated and raw water pipelines, and the maintenance and operation costs for the total water system. A "treated water surcharge" would be levied on users of treated water.

The economic and political issues that faced the new district were one reason why the South Santa Clara Valley Water Conservation District would not—and still hasn't—merged with the district.[††††] In the merger of 1968, the district grew from the boundaries of the old conservation district to cover the whole of the Santa Clara County, overlapping the area of the South Santa Clara Valley Water Conservation District. An election on the question of whether or not to join the merger was taken to the voters of the south district, which owns Chesbro and Uvas dams.[2]

In spite of the fact that the south district's board of directors favored the merger, opposition developed through the almost single-handed efforts of Alfred Angelino, a local farmer, and on April 30, 1968, the people voted to remain a separate entity. However, the question still remained: How long will the independent-minded people of this farming community remain separate? Stated Sig Sanchez:

I don't think there is any question that the merger has to take place. What will force it will be the cost, if nothing else. Hopefully, the people who are responsible for running the South Valley Water Conservation District will recognize at the appropriate time that the merger should take place, before getting to the point where it will be very costly for their constituency.[17]

The challenge of designing a system for total water management that would meet conceivable future water needs was enormous. The fact that the south district did not merge with Santa Clara County Flood Control and Water District was not the agency's most vital concern. With the In-County Distribution System in operation and the resources of the South Bay Aqueduct at optimum use, the directors became increasingly concerned over when the San Felipe project would be approved. Much to their dismay, the unforeseeable financial burden of the Vietnam War would bring a rapid halt to federal water projects in the 1960s. Daniel Kriege, assistant operations and maintenance manager for the district, explained: "The fact that something like five billion dollars a month was going into supporting the Vietnam operation precluded Congress from spending monies for public works projects."[15]

The burden of the war was still felt in the 1970s, as the district entered a new chapter in its history. With the San Felipe project at a standstill, it would require the latest scientific and technological skill to fully utilize the valley's water resources. ■

[††††] **Second Edition Note.** The South Santa Clara Valley Water Conservation District changed its name to Gavilan Water District in 1981—see Appendix A. As explained in Chapter 9, voters in the south district would not approve a merger until 1987.

The newly merged agency

was focused on one enormous challenge:

designing a system for total water management

that would meet future water needs.

SOURCES, CHAPTER 5:

1. Angelino, Alfred R. Interviewed by Lynn Longa, Oct. 13, 1976.

2. Burns, Malcolm E. Interviewed by Lynn Longa, Sept. 3, 1976.

3. Campen, Alden. Interviewed by Lynn Longa, Aug. 13, 1976.

4. Campen, Howard. Interviewed by Lynn Longa, Oct. 18, 1976.

5. Currlin, Donald. Interviewed by Lynn Longa, Oct. 21, 1976.

6. Dullea, Maurice E. Interviewed by Lynn Longa, Oct. 19, 1976.

7. Dunn, William G. Interviewed by Lynn Longa, Oct. 4, 1976.

8. Enander, Violet V. Interviewed by Lynn Longa, Sept. 23, 1976.

9. Fowler, Lloyd. Interviewed by Lynn Longa, Aug. 23, 1976.

10. Gill, David. Interviewed by Jim Bates, Oct. 29, 1976.

11. Henley, Albert. Interviewed by Lynn Longa, Nov. 23, 1976.

12. Hyde, Homer H. Interviewed by Lynn Longa, Nov. 10, 1976.

13. Korbay, George. Interviewed by Jim Bates, Oct. 29, 1976.

14. Kriege, Daniel F. Interviewed by Lynn Longa, Aug. 27, 1976.

15. O'Halloran, John T. Interviewed by Lynn Longa, Aug. 27, 1976.

16. Roll, Robert J. Interviewed by Lynn Longa, Aug. 9, 1976; also, "Effect of Subsidence on Well Fields," *Journal,* American Water Works Association, Vol. 59, No. 1, January 1967.

17. Sanchez, Sig. Interviewed by Lynn Longa, Oct. 15, 1976.

18. *San Jose Mercury News,* Feb. 4, 1960, p.12.
San Jose Mercury News, Feb. 11,1960, p. 3.
San Jose Mercury News, March 14, 1960, p. 23.
San Jose Mercury News, March 18, 1960, p. 24.
San Jose Mercury News, April 27, 1960, p. 7.
San Jose Mercury News, Jan. 25, 1963, p. 1.
San Jose Mercury News, June 12, 1963, p. 1, 6.

19. *San Jose News,* May 22, 1963, p. 1.

20. Santa Clara County Flood Control and Water Conservation District, Minute Book No. 3, p. 49, Minutes of November 13, 1962. Also, Santa Clara County Flood Control and Water Conservation Minute Book No. 3, pp.189-190, Minutes of June 24, 1963.

21. Santa Clara County Flood Control and Water District. *Rinconada Water Treatment Plant,* no date.

22. "Combination Pacheco Pass and South Bay Aqueduct Routes to Import Water, Presented to Water Commission," Santa Clara Valley Water Conservation District, *Water Conservation News,* Vol. 5, No. 10, October 1961, pp. 4-12.

23. Wade, Jeptha A. Interviewed by Lynn Longa, Oct. 12, 1976.

24. Wilson, Charles G. Interviewed by Lynn Longa, Nov. 8, 1976.

Groundwater recharge ponds alongside Los Gatos Creek, parallel to Highway 17, looking east.

CHAPTER 6

Toward the Twenty-First Century

By James R. Melton, Public Information Officer, SCVWD

A whole new era of public water management came to the valley in 1968. It was not that the programs were so new; they were, in fact, a continuation of long-applied, proven methods of water supply and flood protection. What was new was the application of water resources management on an integrated and countywide basis. Finally, after 40 years, people responsible for reservoirs and groundwater recharge could sit down on a daily basis with others responsible for imported water and flood protection. They could view the entire scope of programs as a single subject: water.

The timeliness of the merger of the countywide flood control district and the older water conservation district was overwhelmingly correct. It was a perfect setup, and it allowed some of the most experienced water supply and flood control engineers in the state to get on with their work in a new, vigorous style. To the extent that no other public agency in the state had such a varied, integrated system, the directors and staff were pioneers, and they faced several challenges.

Integrating Water Systems

Foremost in the minds of district board directors and their professional staff was the need to continue efforts to restore and preserve the invaluable underground water basins. There was a paramount need to stop land surface subsidence and intrusion of fresh water aquifers by saltwater. To achieve these goals and provide adequate supplies of water, the district already had a number of existing tools with which to work: an efficient groundwater recharge program, a working imported water program, an incomplete but functioning In-County Distribution System, one operating water treatment plant and another already approved by voters, support from both public- and investor-owned water retail agencies, and a supportive community.

They had roadblocks, too: a rapidly expanding population and industrial sector, no control over groundwater pumping, and continued delays with the San Felipe Water

Water supply and flood control engineers could get on with their work in a new, vigorous style.

Project. Another challenge was to overcome obstacles and secure a substantial, additional source of water supply for the future. In 1968 and, in fact, until 1970, the only source under serious consideration was the San Felipe project. The agency was living with Vietnam War budget delays, but a new force for delay—environmental issues—would later play havoc with San Felipe plans and schedules.

Another concern was flood control. Widespread flooding in 1955, 1958, 1963 and 1969 reminded many in the community (but certainly not all, as resistance to district-proposed construction programs later proved) that the valley was nothing more than a huge floodplain; and that the vast majority of homes, industry and commercial buildings were built where floodwaters had flowed for eons. The county Board of Supervisors had been dealing with the problem for 17 years and accomplished a lot. Now the new Santa Clara Valley Water District Board of Directors, not burdened with problems such as welfare, law enforcement and a plethora of other public issues, could take a look at the old flood problem with concentrated interest and fresh viewpoints. Again, economic and environmental issues would later have a great impact on flood protection plans.

Integration, management and development of local and imported water supplies, and flood protection—two missions with seemingly a million questions and sub-issues. These were the puzzle pieces facing the first board of directors as they took control of Santa Clara Valley water management. Interestingly, events several years prior to the 1968 merger would make the formal integration of imported and local supplies an easy process.

Conjunctive use begins. In 1962, the Tri-County Water Authority's consulting engineer firm, Creegan & D'Angelo, developed a plan for distributing both treated and imported raw water in the valley. Treated water from the plant in Los Gatos, proposed by the county Flood Control District, would be sent to west valley areas that didn't have enough

groundwater supply for their needs. Raw water, on the other hand, would be routed to the groundwater recharge ponds operated by the Water Conservation District.

Lloyd Fowler, chief engineer for the Flood Control District and later for the merged Water District until 1980, explained that the turnout system for releasing imported water in recharge ponds was designed into the Central Pipeline, which carries water from the South Bay Aqueduct in east San José to Los Gatos.

Some of us at the Flood Control District got together with some of the people at the Water Conservation District in 1963 and 1964. We had all studied the Creegan & D'Angelo report, but no one knew exactly how to implement it. There were no formal contracts between the two agencies to govern such a program, but all of us knew that a merger was going to happen. So we got together and worked it out. There were plans for studies by the U.S. Geological Service and the state Department of Water Resources to determine what the capacity of the north groundwater basin was and where the most deficient aquifer zones were. But the reports were so far from completion that we couldn't wait for them. At that point, we had to decide where the imported water would be recharged. We just had to make our best educated guess, so we did. In retrospect, we guessed right.[1]

While decisions were being made about where to recharge imported water, another decision had to be made about regulating this new supply. The planned Rinconada Water Treatment Plant in Los Gatos would have a maximum annual capacity that was far less than the capacity of the South Bay Aqueduct, so a regulating reservoir had to be developed.

The Flood Control District and state were negotiating the issue of where the South Bay Aqueduct would terminate; whether at the proposed Air Point Reservoir east of Milpitas, or elsewhere. Studies indicated that the reservoir site would be located in an active geologic zone and that construction costs would be astronomical.

A quick review of alternative regulating reservoir sites in the area was disappointing, so another approach, one of using the Santa Clara Valley groundwater basin, was pursued. Conclusions were soon reached that the groundwater idea would work, and necessary arrangements were made with the Water Conservation District. All the water available from the aqueduct that could not be treated at the Rinconada plant would be delivered to district recharge sites.

It was an excellent plan from the standpoint of economics. The Flood Control District would not have to pay for the costs of a dam, and at the same time the state agreed to extend the South Bay Aqueduct further south into east San José near Penitencia Creek. That meant the Central Pipeline would be shorter and less expensive. While the economics were good, the operational aspects were not as positive. By placing the water in the "pool" of the groundwater basin, costs would have to be recovered through a groundwater charge instead of simply holding up the flow of water at a reservoir and releasing it into a pipeline when appropriate for delivery to a treatment plant.

Nevertheless, the decision was made in 1964, and the plan for full integration of imported water with local water in a groundwater basin—conjunctive use—was set.

By June 1, 1965 the South Bay Aqueduct and Central Pipeline were completed and in use. From that year until completion of the Rinconada treatment plant in 1967, some 60,000 acre-feet of imported water had flowed through the Central Pipeline and another new conduit, the Almaden Valley Pipeline, to Water Conservation District recharge ponds. This massive dose of imported water and an additional 63,000 acre-feet between 1967 and 1968 dramatically increased north valley water levels.

It was in this environment of cooperation and the expectation of the future that the Flood Control District and Water Conservation District consolidated in 1968. Because the integration of local and imported water was already a reality at the merger, there was no dramatic change in the operation of valley water resources. The only immediate, tangible changes were with the seating of a new board of directors as described in Chapter 5, and the movement of a handful of employees from the Water Conservation District offices on Almaden Expressway to Flood Control District offices downtown on Martha Street. By and large, few employees were shifted, and flood control and water conservation efforts at the staff level continued much as before.

At the policy level (the board of directors), much of the first months' effort was devoted to key district personnel matters such as employee representation and retirement plans. Other effort, of course, was devoted to primary issues of flood protection and water supply.

Formation of the
Flood Control Advisory Committees

The matter of flood control advisory committees was an important issue because it was through these groups that project priorities would be set. Five flood control zones, each based on major watersheds, had been in existence since 1956. Now the new board needed advisory groups, and it was decided that each city with territory in a particular flood control zone would have representation on that zone's advisory committee. Hence, cities such as Santa Clara and San José would have representatives on more than one zone committee because city boundaries were located in more than one watershed. Additionally, the County of Santa Clara would be represented on all zone

Between 1965 and 1967, about 60,000 acre-feet of imported water had flowed to recharge ponds. This massive dose and another 63,000 acre-feet in 1967 and 1968 dramatically increased north valley groundwater levels.

In 1969, after more than half a century of gradual sinking, land surface subsidence in the Santa Clara Valley was halted.

committees. In the early 1970s, committee representation would be expanded to include private citizens.

The flood control zone advisory committees soon were entangled in the process of project prioritization, so a logical method of determining which projects should be funded first had to be developed. George Korbay, the district's flood control manager, described the solution:

The district formulated a priority ranking system based on factors to which numerical values of importance could be assigned. The primary one of these was the potential for damage to already existing development. Others were completing projects between previously completed reaches of a stream; maintenance costs; coordination with other projects; and the like. The district's advisory committees assisted in setting priorities for these factors. Each year, all the district's identified flood control projects (about 150 in number at the time) would be analyzed, and a planning and construction program for the next five years would be developed.[2]

Imported Water
Rejuvenates Groundwater Basin

With a flood control priority system in force alongside the imported water reimbursement program (cities receiving Hetch-Hetchy water were reimbursed for up to 60 percent of the property taxes collected by the district to support repayment of South Bay Aqueduct costs), the district was able to deal equitably with valley cities on both vital planes and concentrate on delivering services.

Water was flowing through the South Bay Aqueduct—in fact, more water was available to the district than the

delivery contract called for. This was because the entire State Water Project was not yet complete, but state water sources were available. So, the district took advantage of the availability of this "surplus" water and offered it to public and private water retailers at district cost. Acceptance was immediate, and the benefit to the district was further reduced reliance on groundwater.

The cumulative effect of increased groundwater recharge plus purchase of scheduled and surplus water by treated water contractors was that in 1969, after more than half a century, land surface subsidence in Santa Clara Valley was halted. It was a major achievement for the district, and it gave the staff and directors a heady optimism that planning and management could eliminate any future return to subsidence and its dire consequences. After all, it was a well known fact that groundwater overdraft was a major valley problem. It had caused tens of millions of dollars in obvious and subtle damages. Well casings had collapsed. Bridges, such as a major railroad link in Alviso, barely stood above high tide. Land surface had dropped below or near to sea level along the baylands stretching from Mountain View to Milpitas. Levees, once protective, became vulnerable to high tides. And flood channels, their banks sometimes standing high above surrounding land, posed great danger to urban homes and industry.

So, it was proven that subsidence could be halted. But it was well understood that future overdrafting of the groundwater basin through mismanagement or natural disaster such as severe drought could cause renewed subsidence. To the board and staff, "mismanagement" translated into not having adequate water available for groundwater recharge. The challenge, then, was to determine just what kind of growth could be expected in the valley in the future and plan accordingly for an adequate water supply. Thus, as the 1970s dawned, the district launched studies on population growth and sources of supplies.

Alviso, 1914 - The land is well above sea level. The South Bay Yacht Club building stands in the right corner of this photo.

Alviso, 1978 - The land is now 10 feet below sea level, and a broad levee rings the shoreline; note the stairs descending from top of levee. The South Bay Yacht Club building still stands in the same location—seen in the right corner of this photo.

In the 1970s, several studies were conducted to evaluate the potential use of reclaimed water from the area's wastewater treatment plants.

Obvious to all concerned was that the San Felipe Water Project was a front-runner. The Vietnam War with its funding demand was slowing down, and this was a good indication that the federal project might finally get off the ground. But since the late 1960s a major new social issue—environmental quality—had been gaining public attention. It was various ramifications of this issue that caused the district in 1970 to take renewed interest in water reclamation, sometimes called reuse or recycling. A vigorous board of directors and engineering staff both recognized the need to return to serious study of the potential of reclamation in the context of an alternative to San Felipe.

Reusing Limited Water Resources

It seemed only logical that the recycling of water could serve the needs of the growing population. "When your clothes get dirty you don't throw them away. So why don't we clean up water and use it again?"[3]

In 1972, the district hired the engineering firm of Consoer-Bechtel to provide an engineering and economic analysis of reclamation as an alternative to San Felipe. The first phase of study was to determine the viability of using reclaimed water to recharge the groundwater basin underlying San José and adjacent areas. Consoer-Bechtel concluded that "without grant funds . . . reclamation is 50 to 100 percent more expensive than the San Felipe project." However, the study indicated engineering viability of a large-scale reclamation project, and the board of directors decided to proceed with a study. Dave Gill, district water supply manager, explained:

We then moved to Phase Two to look into public health aspects, which were raised in Phase One. Phase Two concluded that the state Department of Health would not allow groundwater recharge

using reclaimed water, and that extensive research would have to be completed before authority would even be considered for such a recharge program. With the Phase Two results in hand, our next question was whether we could have a reduced San Felipe project combined with a reduced wastewater project. So, we went to the San Felipe Committee and asked them to fund a study of using reclaimed water from several areas such as San José, Gilroy, Hollister and Watsonville for agriculture. San Felipe water would be used exclusively for municipal and industrial (M&I) purposes.[4]

The San Felipe Committee agreed to the study. When completed, it found that most of the water for such a project would have to come from San José; in summer months, when most crop watering is done, agricultural requirements from Coyote to Hollister alone were greater than the output of the sewage treatment plants in San José and Gilroy. Plus, cost loomed as a major problem. Consoer-Bechtel's Phase Two study showed that water recycled for agriculture—without even knowing whether health requirements could be met—would cost from $80 to $90 per acre-foot without grants or other subsidies. These costs were later compared with San Felipe Project water costs of $61 for M&I water and $16.50 for agriculture. Even with grant funding of main distribution facilities (which the State Water Resources Control Board and federal Environmental Protection Agency were not then funding), treatment and local distribution would have cost a minimum of $25 per acre-foot for agriculture. Another idea was to provide reclaimed water just within the Hollister and Watsonville areas; that project would have resulted in $75 M&I water and $25 agricultural water.

The net result of the reclamation studies conducted from 1972 to 1974 was that because the district would enter a period of groundwater overdraft in 1978, all stops should be pulled to secure earliest possible delivery of San Felipe Project water. The Water District board of directors called on the new district general manager, John T. O'Halloran, to proceed and secure the contract for San Felipe water, which was accomplished in 1977. Mr. O'Halloran also knew the necessity of developing reclamation facilities. In fact, between 1974 and 1980, the district constructed two operational reclamation systems and conducted two more major reclamation studies.

Palo Alto wastewater treatment plant. In 1975, the district contracted with Jenks and Adamson consultants to design an advanced wastewater reclamation pilot plant in Palo Alto. The plant's primary purpose would be to provide hands-on experience with an advanced wastewater treatment plant and provide a base for advanced research into the changes in quality as reclaimed water moved through a confined aquifer. The facility was completed in 1977. Water from the plant is injected into an aquifer underlying Palo Alto in the Bayshore Freeway area. This aquifer, which in the past contained potable water but had been intruded upon by saltwater in past years, is no longer in use.

Reclaimed water is injected into the aquifer, and a mixture of reclaimed and saltwater is pumped out. The system allows extensive monitoring by researchers from NASA, Stanford University and the U.S. Geological Survey. Water is also available from the plant for golf course and landscape irrigation.

Gilroy wastewater treatment plant. A second district system was built in 1977 in Gilroy as an emergency measure to overcome groundwater overdraft during the 1976 and 1977 drought. Primary treated water from the Gilroy sewage treatment plant is given secondary treatment, aerated and then sent to area customers such as flower seed nursery stock growers. The system was built in conjunction with Gavilan Water District and the City of Gilroy.

In 1978, the district did a study on the potential of using reclaimed water in the Milpitas-North San José-Santa Clara areas. The study indicated that treatment, storage and pumping facilities could be built near the existing water pollution control plant near Alviso, and that the project could serve numerous industrial, agricultural and landscape irrigation customers. The conclusion was that if the three cities would require dual water distribution lines in the area and apply for grant funding, the project would have been feasible.

The last reclamation study undertaken by the Water District in the 1970s was in conjunction with the state Department of Water Resources (DWR). This study, conducted by DWR, was an extension of the district's September 1975 agreement with DWR. The district had agreed to take a substantial reduction in San Felipe Project water if, by the year 1990, it was shown that a major reclamation project (in the range of 60,000 acre-feet) would be feasible. Dave Gill explained:

> The DWR study was intended to develop a concept for an agricultural market for reclaimed water that would make use of 40,000 to 60,000 acre-feet. The study took a detailed look at water quality of the San Jose/Santa Clara sewage facility and the possible application of reclaimed water on crops grown in south valley soils. The study concluded that the sodium content of the reclaimed water would be too high to be applied to south valley soils, which have a high clay content. Several crops were identified as salt-sensitive, and this finding made the project quite marginal. The solution to the high sodium problem would be to blend the reclaimed water with a higher quality water, but that decreased the volume of wastewater, and substantially increased the unit cost of the delivered

reclaimed water. The dilution, which has to be 7,800 acre-feet of reclaimed water with 15,000 acre-feet of San Felipe project water, would result in agricultural water costing something like $530 per acre-foot, which includes distribution costs.[5]

Considerable limitations—economic, distribution and public health—were revealed in the drive toward large-scale use of reclaimed water in Santa Clara Valley. But in 1980, the Water District in no way considered reclaimed water to be outside its water supply plans. Additional investigations were being planned for the future. Also in late 1980, the San Felipe project continued to be a central feature of the district's future water supply plans because it was technically, economically and financially feasible.

The Great Drought of 1976 and 1977

One of the most dramatic and memorable periods in Santa Clara Valley water history was the historic drought that began in mid-1975 and continued until January 1978.[†] By the time the drought ended, valley groundwater levels had dropped severely; agricultural wells had gone dry; thousands of new wells had been drilled or existing wells lowered; deliveries from the State Water Project had been reduced (what was delivered could not be percolated because of high salt content); and nearly all surface reservoirs were bone dry.

Fortunately, most people in the valley were only slightly impacted by the drought; years and decades of good water supply planning—and execution of plans—had provided valley water users with a reserve supply that was envied by millions of people on strict rationing throughout the Bay

Area. The stage for this reserve supply had been set in the 1920s when the Santa Clara Valley Water Conservation Committee began an informal groundwater recharge program. Larger steps were taken as Water Districts were formed, reservoirs were built, and imported water flowed into the valley. Even Mother Nature had cooperated.

In the years 1973 to 1975, the valley received normal or near normal rainfall that was captured in reservoirs and recharged into the underground. The average depth-to-water had been raised from lows exceeding depths of over 200 feet in the 1960s to an average depth of about 70 feet in 1975. Not since 1945 had the groundwater index been less than a depth of 80 feet to water. In 1975, water supplies were excellent. The South Bay Aqueduct was providing the district with significant amounts of water—over 106,000 acre-feet were imported in 1975. Further, the city of San Francisco's Hetch Hetchy system was delivering about 55,000 acre-feet annually to the people of Santa Clara Valley.[6]

The Santa Clara Valley Water District was banking away its supplies for the future for good reason. In its "1975 Master Plan for Expansion of In-County Distribution Facilities," two key facts were revealed: first, because the San Felipe project would not be ready until the 1980s, there would be a period of groundwater overdraft caused by increased demand from new residents and industry; second, the report said that even with minimum growth the valley's total water supply planned for the year 2020 would be inadequate unless countywide water use was cut by 10 percent.

As a result of this requirement for conservation, the

[†] **Second Edition Note.** The writer of this chapter could not foresee that a far more dramatic and lengthy drought would descend on California, commencing in 1987. See Chapter 11.

Water District immediately launched a nationwide survey of conservation practices and called the community together for a series of conferences to discuss the issue.[7] By late 1976, a district conservation education program had been established and some elements already implemented.

Groundwater supplies had been reduced by heavy outdoor water use in dry 1976 by farmers and homeowners; in fact, more water was used in 1976 than in any year in the valley's history. But 1976 deliveries from the State Water Project were also greater than any previous year—some 112,000 acre-feet. The extra imported water was not enough to overcome the great demand in 1976, however, and the groundwater level index dropped to below an average depth of 80 feet.[8]

By February 1977, it was apparent that rains were not coming, and that a second year of drought was upon California and the valley. With San Francisco, East Bay, Marin and Contra Costa areas already operating under mandatory rationing, the Santa Clara Valley Water District Board of Directors called upon valley residents to immediately reduce water use by 25 percent. To back up its request for conservation, the Board of Directors authorized a comprehensive conservation education and outreach program that included: development of classroom education materials for all grades in public and private schools; presentations to classrooms and area service clubs and distribution of conservation films to schools and theaters; distribution of large quantities of literature, buttons and bumper stickers; release of print and broadcast news campaigns; promotion of building codes in cities and the county requiring installation of water conservation fixtures in new construction; "water service only on request" programs in restaurants; and other projects.

Public response to the call for voluntary conservation was overwhelmingly positive, and by the end of 1977 groundwater levels had dropped only a few feet. Almost unbelievably, though, little rain fell up to January 1978, and many people were seriously concerned about a third year of drought. The state told the district to plan on receiving little water in 1978 and the district made plans for a severe, mandatory rationing program; an all out effort would be made to limit groundwater overdraft and its disastrous consequences.

Fortunately, the rains—a deluge, in fact—came by the second week of January 1978. "The drought was drowned," said Betty Roeder, president of Great Oaks Water Company. Reservoirs in the valley and around the state filled rapidly, assuring adequate water supplies for 1978. Everyone sighed with relief, and the district was able to say "thanks" to the community for its voluntary conservation effort. Some 22 percent less water had been used in 1977 than in 1976. ■

SOURCES, CHAPTER 6:

1. Fowler, Lloyd. Interviewed by James Melton, October 1980.

2. Korbay, George. Interviewed by James Melton, October 1980.

3. *Report on Oxidation Ponds with Special Reference to the Santa Clara Valley Water Conservation District,* 1959.

4. Gill, Dave. Interviewed by James Melton, October 1980.

5. Ibid.

6. Kriege, Daniel F. Interviewed by James Melton, October 1980.

7. *Water Savings,* Metcalf and Eddy Consultants, 1976.

8. Kriege, Daniel F. Interviewed by James Melton, October 1980.

"It is a pleasure for me to come out here and help blow up this valley."

After making this comment, President John F. Kennedy, together with Governor Edmund G. (Pat) Brown, detonated the explosives at the San Felipe Water Project groundbreaking, August 18, 1962.

CHAPTER 7

The San Felipe Water Project: 1949-1980

By Albert T. Henley, General Counsel, SCVWD

Authorization in 1967 of the San Felipe Division of the Central Valley Project marked the end of one long process and the beginning of another.[1] The goal had been to find a feasible project by which supplemental water might be brought into Santa Clara Valley. At the urging of a local delegation headed by former state Senator Herbert C. Jones, a 1949 federal act reauthorizing the Central Valley Project to include works on the American River was amended to include this language:

> *The Secretary of the Interior, through the Bureau of Reclamation, is hereby further authorized and directed to conduct the necessary investigations, surveys and studies for the purpose of developing plans for . . . a conduit or conduits with necessary pumping plants and supplemental works extending from the most feasible diversion point on the Central Valley Project, California, to serve lands and municipalities in . . . Santa Clara and San Benito counties.*[2]

The Secretary of the Interior did not make his study at once. Water hungry interests in Santa Clara and San Benito counties therefore decided to go forward with local resources. An act to form the Santa Clara-Alameda-San Benito Water Authority (to be called the Tri-County Water Authority) was quickly drafted, and in 1955, it was passed by the state legislature.[3] This enactment permitted public agencies, upon a popular vote, to join their efforts in exercising limited powers—largely in order to make the preliminary feasibility studies the secretary was not making. These studies showed an unmistakable superiority in a tunnel under Pacheco Pass as the conduit for water importation.

Meanwhile, the giant San Luis Reservoir on the easterly side of Pacheco Pass was authorized by Congress for joint federal-state construction and use. This action recognized the interest of the central coastal counties in a Central Valley Project supply by directing the Secretary of the Interior to plan the San Luis works in such manner as to provide for eventual construction of the Pacheco Tunnel.[4] Congress also appropriated during the San Luis

Water hungry interests in Santa Clara and San Benito counties were intent on securing CVP water through the San Felipe project.

Many hurdles were crossed

before the contract signing

for San Felipe water in 1977.

cordingly, caution. Not enough is known of the effects on human health of long-term ingestion of the exotic chemicals, trace organics and rare metals our industries put in their sewers. Some use in agriculture is permissible for irrigation, but only on limited crops (usually those not for direct use as human food). And even so limited an agricultural use is feared by agricultural experts when the water is found to contain the levels of salt that unrestricted use of home-regenerated water softeners tends to produce. The result is detrimental to the soil. So while water reclamation will increasingly be done and will unquestionably be nec-

essary in the San Felipe service area, it was found not to be the hoped-for final rescue and solution—at least not for the period just ahead.

Delta water quality issues emerge. In July 1971, the State Water Resources Control Board issued Decision-1379, setting certain quality standards for waters of the Sacramento-San Joaquin Delta. As such standards are necessarily met in periods of low natural flow by releases from upstream fresh water storage, there was a recognized adverse effect upon local expectations from San Felipe. Upstream storage is, after all, the planned source of San

June 7, 1977 was a day of celebration and ceremony as the Santa Clara Valley Water District signed a contract with the U.S. Bureau of Reclamation for delivery of San Felipe project water. Nearly all of the district's 300 employees and many agency friends attended the event. Board Chairman Courtland Rush, seated center, signed for the district, and Regional Director Billy Martin, seated right, signed for Bureau of Reclamation. Clerk of the Board Violet Enander of the Water District certified signatures under the witness of other directors and staff.

Felipe supplies; but that water, when used for repulsion of salty tidal inflows, is not available for export. The Santa Clara Valley Water District, and indeed all four members of the San Felipe Committee, at once made the difficult decision to pledge by formal resolution that importations would be so conducted as to avoid a degradation of Delta waters.

This readiness to acknowledge a priority of right in another area of the state constituted an example of environmental sensitivity and general virtue which did not go unrewarded. When, in the following year, the newly elected governor, Edmund G. Brown, Jr., took office, some opponents of San Felipe assumed that his administration would oppose the project as, among other things, a damaging theft of necessary Delta waters. Instead, acting in conformance to the prior pledge, the district made an agreement with the state Department of Water Resources, which effectively ended the issue of Delta quality as far as San Felipe exports were concerned.[7][†]

In 1976, the Carter administration took office. Again, enemies of the San Felipe Division expected it to be countermanded and its construction blocked. But the new administration's review ended in a favorable verdict, and the project became one the administration adopted and began recommending for funding by Congress each year.

An argument advanced repeatedly in opposition to San Felipe was that it was being imposed by stealth and did not meet a real need; that only greedy land speculators supported the project; that "the people" if asked would reject such a scheme. It was therefore demanded of the district that it hold an advisory election. At that time (later cured by special legislative act) the use of public funds for

a plebiscite without other than persuasive effect was illegal. The district refused. State Senator Alfred Alquist conducted a straw vote in most of the district, which produced a four to one favorable response, but this was thought inconclusive. The district pointed out that to accept San Felipe water, it would have to go to voters to issue bonds, and that this vote would indicate the public's position. But opponents also rejected this, stating that this was asking the public to vote on a matter already decided, because by election time the district would have bound itself to buy the water.

As it happened, the district's revenue bond election held on May 31, 1977 was successful, and the contract with the Bureau was signed the following month. There was a further result of the success of the revenue bond election. The district's governing act had contained a specific dollar limit on the amount it could impose per acre-foot as a groundwater extraction charge.[8] To sell revenue bonds based on such a charge, the district could not, as a practical matter, be limited in its ability to set the rate. The legislature amended the act with a provision that there would be no dollar limit if revenue bonds were authorized by the voters and issued by the district. These events have now taken place.

Several legal challenges were mounted against San Felipe. Each failed entirely. The area of attack was, in one case, the Environmental Impact Statement required by federal law.[9] The federal judge found it in order. In another case, it was alleged that the project was exceeding the congressionally imposed limit and must be enjoined. The action was dismissed for failure to prosecute. In a third case, the plaintiffs sought without success to invalidate the groundwater charge.■

SOURCES, CHAPTER 7:

1. Public Law 72, Aug. 27, 1967 in the 90th Congress.

2. Public Law 356, Oct. 14, 1949 in the 81st Congress.

3. Stats 1955, c. 1289.

4. Public Law 488, June 3, 1980 in the 86th Congress.

5. Repealed by Stats. 1968, c. 45.

6. State Water Resources Control Board. *Water Quality Control Plan (Interim), San Francisco Bay, Basin 2*, June 1971.

7. Exchange of Letters: Robert T. Sapp, Chairman, SCVWD Board of Directors, to Ronald B. Robie, Director, Department of Water Resources, Sept. 2, 1975, and response, Robie to Sapp of even date.

8. Stats 1951, c. 1941, Sections 26.7.

9. National Environmental Policy Act.

[†] **Second Edition Note.** As it turned out, this was only the beginning of Delta water quality issues and their impact on CVP exports. See Chapter 13.

CHAPTER 8

Financing the 1980s

By Lynn Longa

For the first time in its

50-year history, the

district was authorized

to issue revenue bonds.

Of all the various aspects of water management, none is more challenging than providing financing. From its very beginning the district has gone to the people it serves and sought financial support for its programs. To meet the water needs of the community in the 1980s and beyond, the district has planned a major expansion of its distribution, treatment and recharge facilities. In May of 1977, the district went to voters, seeking approval of a $56 million revenue bond issue to fund initial project construction.

The district was fortunate that a motivated group of private citizens took the initiative to campaign, since the district itself could not participate. The committee had as its campaign manager one of the leading citizens of San José, former Santa Clara County Executive Howard Campen. In addition to the many hours of time he personally spent on the campaign, he organized a large campaign staff consisting almost entirely of volunteers. Known as the Measure H Committee, the group mounted an all-out effort, using brochures, mailings, posters and telephoning, as well as extensive publicity and advertising in newspapers, radio and television.

Election day came on May 31, and the measure passed with 53 percent of the vote. For the first time in its 50-year history, the district could issue revenue bonds.

Revenue bonds had been chosen instead of general obligation bonds for a variety of reasons. In the past, revenue bonds tended to have a higher interest rate. However, by the mid-1970s, the difference had narrowed. Revenue bonds are paid for by those who use or benefit from the project/s the bonds have financed; in the case of the Water District, such bonds are repaid through the sale of water supplied by the project/s. Ad valorem (general obligation) bonds are paid for through property taxes.

A second factor in the district's choice of revenue bonds is that they required only a majority vote, as opposed to the two-thirds approval needed to authorize general obligation bonds. The bonds secured a 53 percent yes vote, proving this factor to be important.

The Series A Issue of $2 million (the first increment of the total authorization of $56 million), was sold June 20, 1978. The Series B bonds, for $21 million, were sold April 1, 1980.■

EPILOGUE (FIRST EDITION)

Water for an Ever-Growing Community

By Norman Y. Mineta, Member of Congress

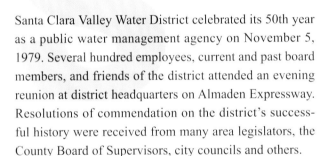

Santa Clara Valley Water District celebrated its 50th year as a public water management agency on November 5, 1979. Several hundred employees, current and past board members, and friends of the district attended an evening reunion at district headquarters on Almaden Expressway. Resolutions of commendation on the district's successful history were received from many area legislators, the County Board of Supervisors, city councils and others.

One of the overriding discussions in the evening was about the San Felipe project and how disagreements, doubts, hostility and legal challenges have all been overcome. With the Pacheco Tunnel nearly completed at the time of this book's publication, the San Felipe Water Project neared reality.

During 50 years of service to the citizens of Santa Clara County, the district has met with and overcome many obstacles in providing water for an ever-growing and changing community. According to *The Global 2000 Report* commissioned by President Jimmy Carter, for the remainder of the twentieth century, water is going to be one of mankind's most sought after natural resources ev-

erywhere in the world. We need it for direct human consumption in our cities, for irrigation on our farms, and, increasingly, even for the production of energy. The Santa Clara Valley Water District has been notable for its commitment to long-range planning. Here in California, we have to depend on the storage and transportation of water rather than on an ever-flowing supply from the skies and rivers. This agency has been in the forefront of efforts to develop a total system which can serve over a million people, now and into the twenty-first century.■

~ San José, October 22, 1980

It took two years to fill San Luis Reservoir, the largest offstream reservoir in the world. The day would come when the Santa Clara Valley would tap this federal facility.

CHAPTER 9

The Dream is Built

By Donna Krey

In 1976, when the American Society of Civil Engineers designated the entire system of the Santa Clara Valley Water District as a California Historical Engineering Landmark, it was because it stood as a unique and ingenious water supply system. It merged nature's provision—a large, natural groundwater basin—with the clever use of local reservoirs and percolation ponds to efficiently maintain groundwater levels. This landmark system was attracting interest from all over the globe, and employees at the Water District would continue to host many visiting groups of interested engineers and foreign delegations.

With this kind of recognition, district officials possessed a heady optimism as the 1970s came to a close. The goal of early water planners—to replenish the groundwater basin and control land subsidence—had been achieved.

A United Nations delegation toured the valley's water system, photographed here at Stevens Creek Reservoir, circa 1947.

The agency stood strong with the blending of expert staff in both water supply and flood management from the 1968 merger. Construction of the San Felipe Division of the federal Central Valley Project (CVP) was also underway; this would represent the county's third imported water source.[†] Along with San Felipe came designs for a new high-capacity water treatment plant and an expanded In-County Distribution System (the extensive network of major pipelines that carry water to and from storage and treatment facilities and to turnouts used by the water retailers). The dream of an integrated, multi-source system for delivering water to the

---

[†] To recap: The county's local water supply was first augmented in 1952 when the cities of Palo Alto, Milpitas, Sunnyvale and Mountain View initiated contracts with the city of San Francisco's Hetch Hetchy system. The second imported water source was the State Water Project (SWP); this contract was initiated in 1965 by officials of the Santa Clara County Flood Control and Water Conservation District (a predecessor of SCVWD). The San Felipe Water Project (CVP), became the third source of imported water; it came online in 1987.

growing valley was being built, and the Santa Clara Valley Water District was rising in stature among the state's water management agencies. With San Felipe, the Water District would become the only urban agency in the state contracting with the CVP as well as the State Water Project (SWP), standing as a major water user with both urban and agricultural interests.

The outlook for flood protection efforts was greatly improved as well. Although the 1978 passage of Proposition 13 had been a blow to property tax revenues for local governments, a new state law empowered the Water District to launch a Flood Control Benefit Assessment Program in 1981. With subsequent voter approval in 1982, this new local revenue enabled the Water District to leverage state and federal funding for the construction of several major flood protection projects.

Formidable and unsuspected challenges lay ahead. But in 1980, the entire Santa Clara Valley was riding high with its growing prowess in high technology, and for the moment, the Water District could bask in the accomplishment of devising and expanding a water system that could support the valley's growth.

San Felipe:
Our Tap to San Luis Reservoir

The first muffled blast came on April 18, 1979. It sounded from deep within the belly of a mountain east of Gilroy; exploding dynamite that gouged a hole in solid rock, clearing the path for a new water source for the Santa Clara Valley. That was the start of the Pacheco Tunnel, the linchpin in the much-anticipated San Felipe Water Project. As more fully described in Chapter 7, this newest branch of the CVP would move water from the Delta-supplied San Luis Reservoir across the Gabilan Mountain Range and into both Santa Clara and San Benito counties. Once completed, the underground pipeline system was expected to add 152,500 acre-feet of water each year to the Santa Clara Valley's supply—less than the 216,000 acre-feet originally anticipated in the draft stages of the project (Chapter 7), but still considered enough to meet about 25 percent of the valley's annual water demand through 2020.

The importance of securing San Felipe water was confirmed in the Water District's 1975 Master Plan. In that plan, analysts predicted that by 1980 the population of Santa Clara County would surge to nearly 1.3 million, and annual water demand would rise to 406,180 acre-feet (given the rate of consumption at that time). These figures were projected to soar for the next four decades until, in 2020, the anticipated population would be nearly 1.9 million and demand would reach 545,900 acre-feet.[††] Because local water combined with SWP and Hetch Hetchy sources could supply only about 70 percent of that amount, it was clear the valley needed to find another source. And the best source, according to the Master Plan, would be the San Felipe project.[1]

The Master Plan's near-term projections for population growth proved accurate: In 1980, the county had close to 1.3 million residents. But annual demand for water in 1980, at 350,000 acre-feet, was about 56,000 acre feet less than anticipated—largely because the 1976-77 drought affected water consumption habits.[2] Nevertheless, the additional water would be needed. Events that would soon be encountered, such as the lengthy 1987-1992 drought

Table C.
Components of the
San Felipe Water Project

Component	Cost To Date*
	(in millions)
Pacheco Tunnel	$ 83.3
Pacheco Pumping Plant	33.6
Pacheco Conduit	32.6
Pacheco Substation and other operating facilities	.5
Santa Clara Tunnel	9.3
Santa Clara Conduit	71.1
Coyote Pumping Plant	20.0
Hollister Canal and Conduit	27.6
San Justo Dam and Reservoir	39.9
Interest during construction	35.8
Total:	$344.6

* Capitalized costs as of 2002; repayment of the project is scheduled through 2036.

[††] Population and demand projections were updated in subsequent years; demand projections were lowered as water consumption habits changed—a result of the 1987-1992 drought. See Chapter 14 for projections as of 2004.

and restrictions on the pumping of Delta water (a "regulatory drought"), would make every drop of CVP supplies, along with other imported water, essential to the South Bay's survival.

It took eight years to build the San Felipe—a fraction of the project's lengthy history. Before it delivered its first gallon of CVP water on June 10, 1987, the San Felipe Water Project had existed "39 years as a dream, 23 years as a defined concept, 20 years as an authorized project."[3] It survived budget cuts during the Vietnam War, environmental challenges, major design changes, political skirmishes and a host of other obstacles. But with the 5.3-mile Pacheco Tunnel underway in 1979, the San Felipe had finally become a reality. Director Sig Sanchez made this comment about the project's importance: "San Felipe was the key to the development of Silicon Valley. The supply is hidden from view as it flows into our county through tunneled mountains and under the valley floor, but its impact is visible in our cities that have been able to grow according to their general plans—without depleting the groundwater basin."[4]

At the time of its construction, the San Felipe Water Project—with a price tag exceeding $300 million—represented the largest public works project in the history of Santa Clara County.[5] The federal portion of the project was financed by the Bureau of Reclamation; responsibility for the local portion was under the jurisdiction of the Santa Clara Valley and San Benito Water Districts. Repayment of the project was scheduled through 2036; Table C shows the costs of the project components as of 2002.[6]

The San Felipe Water Project consisted of a dozen separate construction projects, with the Pacheco Tunnel featuring as one of the more spectacular components. From the time that first dynamite charge was detonated in April 1979, it captured the public's interest. Building the tunnel involved some staggering logistics: Mining crews worked around the clock, five days a week, blasting their way through 150,000 cubic yards of prehistoric rock and earth. Explosions came from both ends of the mountain, as miners dug their way toward a middle meeting ground.[7]

No wonder people wanted a peek inside that mountain. And, surprisingly, they were given the opportunity. Throughout construction of the tunnel, the Bureau of Reclamation allowed public tours of the site. Those going on a tunnel-tour were given hard hats, rain slickers, boots and gas masks. Frank Sweeney, a reporter for the *San Jose Mercury News*, closely followed the tunnel's construction, going underground several times to check on its progress. After one of his subterranean adventures, Sweeney wrote this description, published on February 2, 1981:

No wonder people wanted a peek inside that mountain . . .

Participants on a tour prepare to enter the Pacheco Tunnel, January 1981.

Dinosaur Point—It's a 15-minute train ride into the earth, two miles from the light at the end of the tunnel. A small engine tows a steel mesh-encased "man car" that carries 16 people, none comfortably. It carries the men who are building the keystone of a project to bring Central Valley water into Santa Clara County.

The train rumbles through the darkness, illuminated at intervals by dim lights. Noise reverberates off the steel-shored walls as the engineer sounds long blasts of the horn to warn those ahead that the express is rolling through. There's not much room to get out of the way quickly in a tunnel only 12 feet wide.

The rock perspires deep underground . . . 1,200 feet below the surface where construction miners labor 24 hours a day in the eerie glow of work lights. It is hot and muggy. The humidity is enough to steam your glasses or camera lens. Water drips down your neck, and gray mud clings to equipment, to clothes, to anything that it touches.

Mud and moisture may have plagued the crews working on the Pacheco Tunnel, but they felt nothing when an earthquake registering 5.5 on the Richter scale jolted the area in January 1980. About six months later, miners did get a scare when they encountered small pockets of highly flammable—and deadly—methane gas. Tunneling from the west was temporarily delayed as a dozen new safety measures were implemented. In the two years it took to carve out the tunnel, no deaths occurred and there were no serious injuries.[8]

On May 28, 1981, at 5:36 a.m., miners tunneling from the east side of the Gabilan Mountain Range met the crew digging from the west side. "They were more than 13,000 feet from daylight in either direction," said Sweeney. At that historic moment, 10 months ahead of schedule, the Pacheco Tunnel's two holes merged. They were within a fraction of an inch of perfect alignment.

Later that day, officials were on hand to commemorate the occasion, including William Hart, the Bureau of Reclamation's engineer in charge of the project, and Dennis McCarry, project manager for the contractor, the Guy F. Atkinson Company of South San Francisco. These two men filled buckets with San Luis Reservoir water and poured the liquid into other buckets held by James Lenihan, Santa Clara Valley Water District Board Chairman, and Ralph Gabriel, from the San Benito County Water Conservation and Flood Control District. This was "the first water through the Pacheco Tunnel." The "holing through," dramatic as it was, did not complete the tunnel; it would be another 20 months before that was accomplished, after the tube had been lined with a concrete sleeve and finishing work was done.[9]

While the joining of the Pacheco Tunnel's twin bores grabbed most of the public's attention, other components of the San Felipe Water Project—pipelines, pumping plants and smaller tunnels—were equally important, and several were constructed simultaneously.

As workers were finishing the Pacheco Tunnel in 1982, the smaller Santa Clara Tunnel already had been excavated eight miles to the west. This tunnel would carry water from the Pacheco Conduit under the end of the Gabilan Mountains and into Santa Clara County. Rather than being blasted with dynamite, the one-mile Santa Clara Tunnel was created with a giant boring machine, nicknamed the "Mole." On the front of its cylindrical body, the Mole carried a huge, rotating cutting wheel that shaved rock from the face of the tunnel as it moved forward, leaving in its wake a perfectly round 13-foot hole. Sweeney, the *Mercury News* reporter, was waiting to see the Mole on the day it was due to punch out of the far side of the mountain

"The Holing Through"
of the
Pacheco Tunnel

Left. *After two years of digging, crews tunneling from both sides of the mountain finally met each other at 5:36 a.m. on May 28, 1981.*

Top. *Later that day, Ralph Gabriel, board chairman from the San Benito Water District, pours the "first water" through the Pacheco Tunnel into a bucket held by James Lenihan, board chairman for the Santa Clara Valley Water District.*

97

eral water coming from the south; Hetch Hetchy water running east to west. We had groundwater to draw on if needed, and water in local reservoirs for groundwater recharge. We had the ability to transfer water from one facility to another if a plant went down. It was a system with a tremendous amount of flexibility."[17]

San Felipe celebrated. On June 10, 1987, the first CVP water poured into Calero Reservoir. Using five of the Pacheco plant's 12 pumps, the project sent 180 cubic feet of water per second through the network and into the Water District's Cross Valley Pipeline—and at 10:10 a.m., a small crowd of Water District officials, staff and journalists waiting at Calero watched it gush out of the pipe and into the reservoir.[18]

Two months later, on August 8, 1987, the Water District hosted a dedication ceremony to mark the San Felipe's historic debut in Santa Clara County. The celebration featured about 800 guests who filled a 9,000-square-foot tent that was erected next to the Pacheco Pumping Plant at San Luis Reservoir. Guests included representatives from the San Benito County Water Conservation and Flood Control District and members of the private sector (both groups helped fund the dedication event). Speakers at the podium included the Water District's General Manager John O'Halloran, along with U.S. Bureau of Reclamation Commissioner C. Dale Duvall, and former *San Jose Mercury News* reporter, Harry Farrell, who detailed the story of this monumental project in his 1987 book entitled, *The San Felipe Story*.

Also attending the event were David Porteur, chairman of the San Benito district board, and James Lenihan, chairman of the Santa Clara Valley district board. These two men joined Duvall in what was then termed, "The Great Turn-On." Together, they grasped a large water valve wheel and gave it a turn, signaling to the pump plant operators to switch on three 2,000-horsepower pumps. With a

loud hiss, the pumps sprang into action, and the audience roared and clapped its approval. Television cameras and newspaper reports captured the moment.

Bill Hart of the Bureau then presented the "key" to the San Felipe Water Project to Water District board directors James Lenihan, Patrick Ferraro, Robert Gross and Sig Sanchez. The gesture symbolized the terms of a contract signed the year before, on September 8, 1986, between the Bureau and the Water Districts of Santa Clara and San Benito counties. The agreement gave the Santa Clara Valley Water District full responsibility for operating and maintaining those parts of the federal project that served both counties—such as the Pacheco and Coyote pumping plants, Pacheco Tunnel and Pipeline, and the bifurcation facility.

The long-awaited CVP water could not have come at a better time. While water officials were flipping the San Felipe's on-switch, California was entering a six-year drought—a devastating scourge that dried up local water sources and made the imported water a critical factor in the valley's survival (Chapter 11).

1983 Master Plan Revisions: New Plant, New Pipelines, New Remote Control

With the San Felipe project underway, in 1983 officials at the Water District took another look at the 1975 Master Plan and recognized a need to revise the recommended strategies. Much had evolved since 1975, from engineering techniques to new, sprouting communities that needed water. In the revised 1983 Master Plan, the board of directors approved the addition of 13 major construction projects, estimated to cost $155.3 million. The goal was to complete all projects by 1990, thereby enabling full utilization of the valley's local and imported water sources.[19]

To help fund the construction, in November 1984, 72 percent of the voters approved an election measure that allowed the Water District to issue revenue bonds as needed for improvements in the agency's Water Utility Enterprise. This meant the Water District could sell revenue bonds "for beneficial use within the district" without returning to the electorate for approval of each issue.[20] The agency used this authority, along with cash reserves and current revenue, to help finance the Santa Teresa Treatment Plant and other facilities. (Later, the Water District would again use the 1984 authority to issue refunding bonds in 1986 and 1994 and new revenue bonds in December 2000).

The largest of the 1983 Master Plan proposals was the $59 million Santa Teresa Water Treatment Plant, which would treat raw San Felipe water as well as water from other sources. The plant would have the capacity to treat 100 million gallons per day (mgd) of water, compared to the 40 mgd capacity of the Water District's Penitencia plant in east San José and the 80 mgd capacity of the Rinconada plant in Los Gatos.

The new project took root in the early 1980s when the Water District began looking for an appropriate site. The search led to the former Graystone Quarry, a 48-acre site in the Santa Teresa Hills that once yielded "the most perfect building stone in the world."[21] The strategic location off Graystone Lane would allow the new plant to serve the growing residential areas in Blossom and Almaden valleys as well as in the Edenvale and Evergreen areas. By early 1982, the process of acquiring the land was underway and design work was scheduled to begin by the year's end.

Nearby homeowners, however, were leery of how this facility—and its construction—would affect their neighborhood. They quickly organized and presented their concerns to the Water District. The agency responded by conducting a series of public meetings to discuss resident objections. Public involvement in the project thus started early and was present throughout each stage of development. The Water District worked with residents to address major concerns,

and when the groundbreaking ceremonies were held in June 1986—more than two years after initial plans were introduced—public opposition to the treatment plant had given way to community acceptance. Residents believed their voices had been heard, their apprehensions eased.

Gary Kawaoka, a 30-year Water District employee, was the community liaison during the treatment plant's development. He recalled some of the compromises made by the Water District: "We spent about a quarter of a million dollars to keep the noise down with special enclosures and other measures. We graded the top of the property, so the plant couldn't be seen from below. We made sure the lighting reflected downward."[22] The Water District also agreed not to fence off the entire acreage, but only the treatment

Santa Teresa Water Treatment Plant, 1989.

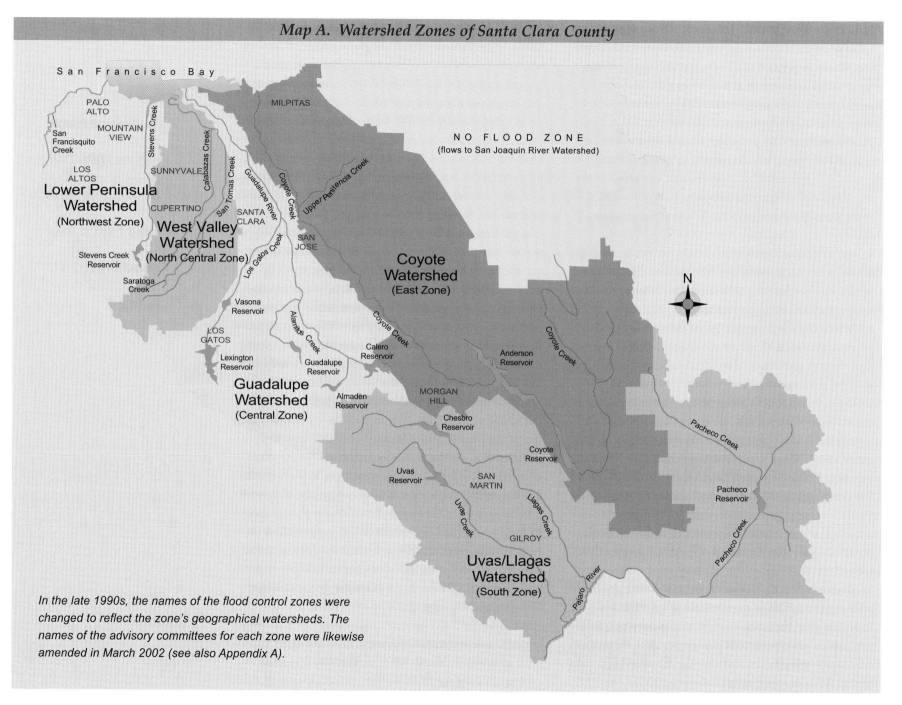

Map A. Watershed Zones of Santa Clara County

San Francisco Bay

PALO ALTO

MOUNTAIN VIEW

San Francisquito Creek

LOS ALTOS

SUNNYVALE

CUPERTINO

SANTA CLARA

SAN JOSE

MILPITAS

Stevens Creek

Calabazas Creek

San Tomas Creek

Guadalupe River

Coyote Creek

Upper Penitencia Creek

NO FLOOD ZONE
(flows to San Joaquin River Watershed)

Lower Peninsula Watershed
(Northwest Zone)

West Valley Watershed
(North Central Zone)

Coyote Watershed
(East Zone)

Stevens Creek Reservoir

Saratoga Creek

Los Gatos Creek

Vasona Reservoir

LOS GATOS

Lexington Reservoir

Alamitos Creek

Guadalupe Reservoir

Guadalupe Watershed
(Central Zone)

Calero Reservoir

Coyote Creek

Anderson Reservoir

Coyote Creek

Almaden Reservoir

MORGAN HILL

Chesbro Reservoir

Coyote Reservoir

Pacheco Creek

Uvas Reservoir

SAN MARTIN

Llagas Creek

Pacheco Reservoir

Uvas Creek

GILROY

Pacheco Creek

Uvas/Llagas Watershed
(South Zone)

Pajaro River

N

In the late 1990s, the names of the flood control zones were changed to reflect the zone's geographical watersheds. The names of the advisory committees for each zone were likewise amended in March 2002 (see also Appendix A).

knew we couldn't survive. Our income was only $75,000 annually. State and federal regulations were increasing as were the expenses related to meeting those requirements. We would not be able to afford the consultants required to do the work."[30]

According to Sturla, prior to the merger, Gavilan customers were paying about $7 per acre-foot for agricultural water and $10 per acre-foot for municipal and industrial (M&I) water. As shown in Appendix B, under the rate structure of the Santa Clara Valley Water District, the agricultural rate was slightly lowered in South County to $5.50, while the M&I rate bore a more substantial increase to $22 per acre-foot.

The merger became official in December 1987. Full integration of all the county's reservoirs and groundwater facilities could now proceed.

Progress on Flood Protection

Having made progress on its mission of providing the valley with an adequate water supply, the Water District was anxious to progress with its second mission: flood protection. Despite a semi-arid climate and periodic droughts, the valley's 800-plus miles of creeks and rivers carry the risk of flooding during seasons of heavy storms. During the twentieth century, severe flooding occured somewhere within Santa Clara County every five years on average.[31] (Note: Surveys conducted in the early 2000s with improved technology resulted in an update to the previously published number of 700 miles of waterways under district jurisdiction; the updated number in 2004 was 827 miles.) Efforts to manage flooding began in the early 1950s. As discussed in Chapter 4, the original Santa Clara County Flood Control and Water Conservation District was created at that time, as were the five flood control zones (see Map

A). Each zone was a separate fiscal entity with taxing authority, and voters decided on bond measures for funding flood protection work within their respective zones.[32]

A good start on flood protection was made between the 1950s and early 1980s, with enough improvements made to enable roughly 300 miles of the county's streams to handle flood flows.[33] Robert Smith, flood control manager during the 1980s, noted that by 1986, the Water District (including predecessor agencies) had spent nearly "$200 million in flood control projects in the past 30 years, and this work vastly reduced the amount of damages we would have had in recent floods."[34]

But the bulk of flood protection work still lay ahead. In booming Silicon Valley, the continuing conversion of agriculture lands to urban uses was making the stakes much higher, the potential for significant property damage greater. As explained by Director Sig Sanchez, whose service on the Water District board began in 1980, "There wasn't much pressure to build flood protection projects when the valley was mostly farms and orchards. But with the high tech boom and population growth, we desperately needed projects to protect properties in the lowlands that had grown to values totaling in the billions."[35]

Setting project priorities. The Water District's zone-by-zone approach greatly shaped the present-day flood protection system in Santa Clara County. As discussed in Chapter 6, five advisory committees assisted the Water District board in its oversight of the work in each zone. Committee membership came from the city jurisdictions and citizenry within the respective zones. Libby Lucas, an active community member who began serving on the Coyote Flood Control and Watershed Advisory Committee in 1994, shared her perspective on the relationship: "The advisory committees helped the Water District to connect with the communities it was serving and to tap the firsthand knowledge some members had of the creek systems."[36]

During the twentieth century, severe flooding occured somewhere within Santa Clara County every five years on average.

105

High tech was rapidly

transforming the region

into a multi-billion dollar

economy; lack of a

flood control project

wasn't going to stop it.

With the potential for flood damage in so many areas of the county, a method was needed to determine which projects to build first. The Water District board sought input from the advisory committees to determine the priority of projects. During the 1970s, the committees ranked projects according to weighted criteria, such as the greatest potential for property damage, or improvements that reduced maintenance costs. By the early 1980s, a computer program—the Waterways Management Model—was employed as a tool to help with this analysis. To reflect changes in public values and environmental requirements, the Water District added new criteria, including preference for projects with the least environmental impact and those which included recreational benefits.[37] Scores in these assessments became the basis for establishing priority-ranked lists of projects in the five flood control zones.

To qualify for federal and state funding assistance, the criterion of most importance was the benefit-cost ratio, a figure that would determine the support of the U.S. Army Corps of Engineers (Corps), the federal agency charged with building the nation's larger flood protection projects. The ratio showed the value of prevented damages for every dollar spent. For example, a 2:1 ratio would mean that a benefit of $2.00 of avoided property damages would be achieved for every $1.00 spent. The Corps would only support projects if the benefit of avoided damages was at least equal to the cost of the project—a minimum 1:1 ratio.[38]

From the viewpoint of the Santa Clara Valley Water District, the benefit-cost analysis was not the only determinant in whether a project should move foward. Preventing human loss and the loss of pets or livestock; shielding people from the emotional trauma associated with catastrophic events; preventing disruption of work and school . . . these equally important factors led the Water District board to conduct its own programs for reducing flooding problems countywide. Stated Director Sig Sanchez,

"Flood protection offers benefits going well beyond the financial value of property. The cost evaluations simply help us determine which projects should get done first."[39]

Having arrived at a list of priority projects, the next step was to fund the work. Large flood protection projects typically involve land acquisition, utility relocations, bridge and box culvert construction, channel improvements and—from the 1970s onward—environmental mitigation. These components add up to a hefty price tag, usually more than local governments can afford. While state and federal programs exist to assist with financing flood protection work, a local contribution is essential to qualify for such assistance—a local revenue source is needed. For years, the Water District's Flood Control Program relied on property tax revenue. Then Proposition 13 passed.

Infamous Proposition 13 curbs funding. On June 6, 1978, the voters of California passed the People's Initiative to Limit Property Taxation, better known as Proposition 13 or simply "Prop. 13." As an amendment to the state constitution, the proposition limited the real estate tax on a parcel of property, residential and commercial alike, to "one percent of its purchase price until the property is resold."[40] (Prior to 1978, the property tax rate in much of California had climbed to about 3 percent of property value.) After the initiative passed, the Water District, along with public agencies statewide, grappled with deeply reduced property tax revenue. In 1979, revenue for the district's Flood Control Program dropped a stunning 57 percent.[41] "We had several projects on the drawing board, but project design quickly became less of a concern than how to develop new funding," recalled Stan Wolfe, formerly a special program administrator at the Water District.[42]

It should be noted that in the mid- to late-1990s, real estate valuations in the Bay Area skyrocketed such that property tax revenues dramatically increased despite the one percent cap. Between 1979 and 2004, the Water District received a total of $558 million in property tax revenue, with the later years weighing heavily to produce an average annual increase of eight percent.[43] The caveat to this phenomenon, however, was that the monetary value of potential property damages from a flood also skyrocketed.

But back in the late '70s, the immediate effect of Prop. 13 was to cause a shortfall in funding. By 1980, some of the flood control zones had exhausted all their reserves.[44]

Not only were new projects slowed or halted, so were maintenance and repairs to existing facilities—activities that were important to maintaining the floodflow capacity of streams. For those who were responsible for providing the valley with flood protection, the specter of catastrophic flooding loomed. This was intensified as new industrial and residential developments mushroomed in the valley, increasing the numbers of properties at risk. Cities in the

Courtesy San Jose Redevelopment Agency

The Innovation Triangle (formerly referred to as the Golden Triangle) became the most concentrated space of high tech businesses in the nation. The low-lying area was also easily flooded by Coyote Creek, the Guadalupe River and high tides. The triangle is bounded by the Bay on its northern side, with Highway 101 (angling past the airport), and Interstate 880 (angling toward the Bay's east shore) creating the other two sides. Photo circa 1988.

South Bay were allowing such development to occur based on projected installation of flood management projects, realizing that in the interim, developments in flood hazard areas were left vulnerable.[45]

Some might question the wisdom of this, but as Chief Executive Officer Stan Williams later pointed out, "High tech was rapidly transforming the region into a multi-billion dollar economy; lack of a flood control project wasn't going to stop it."[46] Williams recalled that in the 1980s, Silicon Valley developers were very interested in building in the lowlands of Santa Clara County; the 4,600-acre "Innovation Triangle" area of northern San José was a prime example. Formerly referred to as the Golden Triangle, or Rincon de Los Esteros, land in this Industrial Redevelopment Project Area of the city of San José remained relatively inexpensive compared to the Peninsula. Destined to become one of the country's most successful industrial parks, Innovation Triangle provided space for the greatest concentration of high-tech companies in the nation, with offices for 2,400 businesses (Cisco Systems, Sony America, Hyundai Electronics and Sun Microsystems, to name a few). Economic powerhouse that it was, the Guadalupe River, Coyote Creek or tidal flooding along the South Bay shoreline could easily inundate this area. The San Jose Redevelopment Agency took note and built a $2.55 million stormwater pump station as part of the triangle's infrastructure, but it was large-scale flood protection measures that were needed.[47]

"Revolutionary" funding tool—benefit assessments.
Silicon Valley wasn't the only high growth area in the floodprone parts of California. The loss of tax revenue for flood protection in the state could not be long tolerated. In quick response to the passage of Prop. 13, Assemblyman Robert Frazee of Carlsbad authored AB549, the Benefit Assessment Act, which passed in 1979. The new law authorized local agencies to seek voter approval for "benefit assessments" for flood control and other public improvements. The law also carefully distinguished these assessments from ad valorem property taxes. Although they appeared on property tax bills, benefit assessments paid for actions that increased property values (such as removing flood hazards) whereas general taxes paid for government services. And unlike Prop. 13, which prevented imposing special taxes without a two-thirds voter approval, AB549 allowed benefit assessments to be approved with a simple majority vote. (This would change, however, in 1996, when Proposition 218 passed and enacted new procedures for benefit assessments, including a two-thirds vote requirement.[48])

Benefit assessment advocates considered the new mechanism to be a revolutionary approach to equitably funding flood protection. Rather than assessing only those parcels that flooded, assessments would apply to parcels that generated runoff—the source of the flooding problem. Whether or not the parcel was in a floodprone area, the owner contributed to flood program revenue—because most everyone either traveled, worked or did business in floodprone areas, as well as depended on communication and power lines or sewage and water supply systems in those areas. Parcels with higher runoff—larger parcels and parcels with impervious surfaces, such as buildings and paved areas—would be charged a higher rate.[49]

In 1981, the Water District initiated a countywide "Flood Control Benefit Assessment Program." The average homeowner was assessed $12 per year, a rate that would raise about $6.5 million annually for both capital projects and routine maintenance work.[50] The plan required voter approval to continue beyond one year, and the Water District prepared for a June 1982 ballot measure. Just as the "dream water system" was being built, the benefit assessment program held promise for building a much-needed network of flood protection projects—the subject of Chapter 12. ■

SOURCES, CHAPTER 9:

[1] *Master Plan: Expansion of In-County Water Distribution System*, SCVWD, 1975, p. I-23.

[2] *Urban Water Management Plan*, SCVWD, April 2001, Figure 4-10, p. 28.

[3] Farrell, Harry. *The San Felipe Story*, SCVWD, 1987, p. 13.

[4] Sanchez, Sig. Interviewed by Cheryl Wessling, April 1, 2004.

[5] *Review/Outlook 1982-83*, SCVWD, p. 5; also, U.S. Board of Reclamation Web site: www.usbr.gov

[6] CVP costs provided by Lynn Hurley, SCVWD staff, e-mails to Cheryl Wessling, May 3, 2004; also, *Project Financial Statement for the Period Ending September 30, 2002, Central Valley Project, California – Consolidated, Schedule No. 1*, U.S. Bureau of Reclamation, 2002.

[7] Sweeney, Frank. "A rocky job under Pacheco Pass," *San Jose Mercury News*, March 31, 1980, p. 1B.

[8] *Review/Outlook 1982-83*, SCVWD, p. 3.

[9] Farrell, Harry. *The San Felipe Story*, SCVWD, 1987, p. 63.

[10] Sweeney, Frank. "San Felipe crew sees light at end of tunnel for water," *San Jose Mercury News*, April 30, 1982, p. 1B.

[11] *Review/Outlook 1982-83*, SCVWD, p. 5.

[12] *Review/Outlook 1984-85*, SCVWD, p. 15.

[13] Hart, William. Interviewed by Donna Krey, July 18, 2003.

[14] *USA Counties 1998*, U.S. Department of Commerce, Economics and Statistics, Bureau of the Census, 1998.

[15] Dean, Tom. Interviewed by Donna Krey, March 13, 2003.

[16] *Review/Outlook 1981-82*, SCVWD, p. 3; also, *Water Supply and Distribution Facilities*, brochure, SCVWD, pp. 4-6.

[17] Esau, Ronald R. Interviewed by Cheryl Wessling, March 1, 2004.

[18] *Review/Outlook 1986-87*, SCVWD, p. 15.

[19] *Review/Outlook 1982-83*, SCVWD, p. 5; also, SCVWD News Release (no title), March 14, 1983.

[20] District Act: Section 25.2, "Revenue bonds; water and electric power facilities; special election," SCVWD.

[21] *Review/Outlook 1988-89*, SCVWD, p. 4.

[22] Kawaoka, Gary. Interviewed by Donna Krey, April 8, 2003.

[23] *Review/Outlook 1983-84*, SCVWD, p. 3.

[24] *Review/Outlook 1988-89*, SCVWD, p. 4.

[25] Butler, Debra. "More than a Pipe Dream: Milpitas Pipeline Becomes a Reality," *Aquafacts*, SCVWD, Fall 1993, pp. 10-14.

[26] *Review/Outlook 1989-90*, SCVWD, p. 20.

[27] *Water Supply and Distribution Facilities*, brochure, SCVWD, July 1997, pp. 1-2.

[28] *Review/Outlook 1985-86*, SCVWD, pp. 10-11; also, *Review/Outlook 1986-87*, SCVWD, p. 16.

[29] Foley, Jack. "Gilroy vote tallies change but outcome of election doesn't," *San Jose Mercury News*, Nov. 9, 1987, page 1B.

[30] Sturla, Jack. Interviewed by Donna Krey, Nov. 26, 2003.

[31] Creek mileage from Nguyen, Ngoc (SCVWD staff). E-mail to Cheryl Wessling, April 7, 2004; also, flooding average from SCVWD News Release (no title), Nov. 8, 1985.

[32] *Flood Control in the Santa Clara Valley: An Overview*, SCVWD, circa 1992, pp. 15-16.

[33] *Review/Outlook '81-'82*, SCVWD, p. 4.

[34] Smith, Bob. As quoted in SCVWD News Release (no title), Nov. 20, 1986.

[35] Sanchez, Sig. Interviewed by Cheryl Wessling, April 1, 2004.

[36] Lucas, Libby. Interviewed by Kathleen McNamara, May 2, 2003.

[37] Hoeft, Bill (retired SCVWD staff). Interviewed by Cheryl Wessling, March 31, 2004.

[38] Wessling, Cheryl. "Local flood control construction activity hits peak level," *Aquafacts*, Summer/Fall 1994, SCVWD, p. 6.

[39] Sanchez, Sig. Interviewed by Cheryl Wessling, April 1, 2004.

[40] Excerpt of Proposition 13 obtained at: http: en.wikipedia.org/wiki/California_Proposition_ 13 _ (1978)

[41] Ibid; also, *Annual Report 1979*, SCVWD, p. 2; also, property tax revenue figures provided by Hoeft, Bill. Interviewed by Kathleen McNamara, Sept. 9, 2003.

[42] Wolfe, Stan. Interviewed by Kathleen McNamara, May 20, 2003.

[43] Hoeft, Bill (SCVWD staff). Interviewed by Kathleen McNamara, Sept. 9, 2003.

[44] *Annual Report 1980*, SCVWD, p. 2.

[45] *Review/Outlook 1981-1982*, SCVWD, p. 4.

[46] Williams, Stan. Interviewed by Cheryl Wessling, Aug. 11, 2003.

[47] San Jose Redevelopment Agency Web site, Rincon de Los Esteros section: www.sjrcdevelopment.org/indust.html.

[48] Bennetti, Anthony (SCVWD General Counsel). Interviewed by Kathleen McNamara, Aug. 13, 2003.

[49] Wolfe, Stan (SCVWD staff). Interviewed by Kathleen McNamara, May 20, 2003. Also, Hoeft, Bill. "Benefit assessment program puts flood control dollars to work where they count," *Aquafacts*, Summer/Fall 1994, SCVWD, pp. 9-11.

[50] *Review/Outlook 1981-82*, SCVWD, p. 4; also, record of benefit assessment revenue from Grasso, Norma (SCVWD staff), e-mail to Cheryl Wessling, April 7, 2004.

A badly corroded fuel tank is excavated at a local trucking facility in 1992. Thousands of leaking tanks—with the potential to contaminate groundwater— have been discovered in the valley since the 1980s.

CHAPTER 10

The Dream Imperiled

By Cheryl Wessling

Yes, the Santa Clara Valley had built an outstanding water supply system with a diversified portfolio of water sources that well served the needs of its residents. But along with this variety—imported water, groundwater and local surface water—came complex and sometimes alarming water quality problems. In the early 1980s, a string of incidents would imperil Water District operations: First, in 1981, the discovery of underground toxic spills raised frightening public health issues and the possible loss of valuable aquifers. Second, in the same year, source water conveyed through the Sacramento-San Joaquin Delta was causing serious problems at district treatment plants, affecting the district's ability to meet drinking water standards and again raising public health concerns. A solution to the Delta water quality problem—one that the Water District battled for—was the proposed Peripheral Canal; its defeat in 1982 represented another predicament as it left the Water District—along with most of California—to endure ongoing water treatment challenges.

The Water District's Flood Control Program also faced challenges. In 1982 and 1983, severe flooding caused tragedy and enormous property damage, and depleted the funds of the young benefit assessment program—the new funding strategy described at the end of Chapter 9.

Urgent action was needed on all fronts of water management, and the pace of work quickened at the Water District.

Underground Toxic Spills
Imperil Groundwater

Throughout its early history and through the mid-1900s, the Santa Clara Valley enjoyed excellent quality groundwater, and thousands of wells in the county were pumped for both drinking water and irrigation. The concern in managing groundwater was primarily an issue of quantity, not quality. Managers were focused on replenishing the

Hazardous materials workers at the same trucking facility, opposite page.

One year after CERCLA

was signed, the ticking

time bomb in Santa

Clara County went off.

groundwater source and on preventing land subsidence and saltwater intrusion that could result from overdrafting. (The problem of intruding seawater was not so much a water quality problem as it was a problem associated with depleted aquifers—a quantity issue.) But in the 1970s, water quality concerns took center stage.

Superfund era begins. During the 1970s, numerous toxic spills and catastrophes had taken place across the nation, pointing to the desperate need for bringing the dumping and careless storage of toxic and hazardous waste under control. Some of the more severe and publicized events included:

- In 1977, a chemical fire in Bridgeport, New Jersey exploded and took six lives due to the careless storage of benzene, toluene and PCBs.

- In 1978, nearly one million gallons of wastewater containing DDT, chloroform and other toxins spilled into Glen Avon, a small town in Riverside County. The spill resulted from heavy rains that flooded the Stringfellow Acid Pits, a 17-acre site where the toxic wastes were stored.

- Also in 1978 was the infamous case of the Love Canal, where a small, blue-collar community in Niagara Falls, New York experienced illnesses, birth defects, miscarriages and cancer from exposures to a "sealed" canal, which had been used by Hooker Chemical Company for dumping about 20,000 tons of pesticides, solvents, dioxin and more.[1]

By 1979, the EPA estimated that "thousands of inactive and uncontrolled hazardous waste sites in the United States could pose a serious risk to public health." Officials recognized that in addition to these "ticking time bombs," spills of hazardous substances were equally a problem. Under the leadership of Senator Robert Stafford of Vermont, congressional leaders agreed that legislation was needed to address the release or threat of release of toxic substances; liability for contamination; and the right of the public to sue for harm. This became the Comprehensive Environmental

Response, Compensation, and Liability Act (CERCLA), signed into law on December 11, 1980 by President Jimmy Carter. The act was dubbed "Superfund" for the $1.6 billion Superfund Trust Fund that was set up to provide financing for the cleanup of toxic sites (the amount of the fund would later increase and decrease with changing presidential administrations). The financing came from a tax paid by manufacturers of chemicals, and from portions of court judgments made against polluters.[2]

One year after CERCLA was signed, the ticking time bomb in Santa Clara County went off.

In late 1981, officials at Fairchild Instrument and Camera Corp., which operated a semiconductor fabrication plant in south San José, placed a phone call to the Santa Clara Valley Water District. According to Dan Kriege, then-manager of the Operations and Maintenance Department, Fairchild called to report that, "a substantial amount of chemicals appeared to be missing from their tank, and they were worried about a leak." Kriege cited the phone call as a pivotal incident that "changed the world of the Water District."[3]

Fairchild's fiberglass underground tank was used to store waste solvents, primarily 1,1,1-trichloroethane (TCA). Periodically, a vendor was to pump the waste for reprocessing. When Fairchild realized that the tank was not filling on schedule, the company suspected it was leaking and called the San Francisco Bay Regional Water Quality Control Board (Regional Board) and the Santa Clara Valley Water District for assistance. (The State Water Resources Control Board and nine associated regional boards have regulatory authority to control and protect surface and groundwater quality in California.) In December 1981, the tank was excavated in the presence of regulators and Water District staff, and the leakage was verified. The tank had released about 60,000 gallons of a mixture of water and TCA.[4]

The Regional Board took immediate action to test the nearest drinking water well. Well #13, owned by the Great Oaks Water Co., revealed a shocking level of TCA—about 6,000 parts per billion (ppb)—and was removed from service.[5] The Fairchild leak and its impact on Well #13 naturally raised the frightening question of whether such leaks were a widespread problem. Although it was not the first solvent spill in Santa Clara County, it was among the largest and it garnered much media attention.[6]

The Regional Board launched a two-prong investigation with assistance from the Water District and the state Department of Health Services; one effort checked the safety of the county's water supply wells, the other searched for additional leaking storage tanks. Water from 120 water supply wells across the county was tested. In July 1982, the investigating agencies were relieved to pronounce that, with the exception of the Well #13, the county's water supply wells—for the time being—were free of contamination.[7] But the news regarding leaking storage tanks wasn't nearly as good.

Leaking chemical storage tanks turned up around the county like a spreading rash. By the end of 1982, 24 sites contaminated from either fuel or solvent storage tanks had been identified. Tanks leaking solvents were distinguished from those leaking fuel as they posed a greater threat to groundwater, being highly soluble, mobile and long-lasting. Left unchecked, solvents could seep into deep aquifers, possibly causing the loss of this water source.[8]

Local ordinance becomes state model. The problem of leaking tanks sent up a red flag that code requirements for chemical storage tanks were not adequate. "We were caught off guard by the leaking tanks," recalled former Water District board member Patrick Ferraro. "Somehow the industries of high technology and defense overlooked the fact that solvents dissolve things—including the tanks that are supposed to contain them."[9]

In late 1982, Water District staff worked with the Santa Clara County Fire Chiefs Association, the City Managers Association and environmental groups to write and promote a countywide Hazardous Materials Storage Permit Ordinance. A model ordinance was drafted and approved by the Santa Clara County Intergovernmental Council, which set tough new standards for the storage and handling of hazardous chemicals, and spelled out the responsibilities of storage tank owners, including their fiscal responsibility for clean-up should an unauthorized release of chemicals occur.[10]

The Hazardous Materials Storage Permit Ordinance was the first in the nation to take specific aim at preventing contamination from underground storage tanks, and state and federal laws would eventually follow this local example. In 1983, Assemblyman Byron Sher of Palo Alto sponsored a statewide UST Law that authorized cities and other local agencies to develop programs for regulating the design and construction of underground storage tanks and to require monitoring and leak reporting; the Water District's program would be the first in the state.[11] But while the ink for these new laws was drying on the codebooks, more chemical leaks and spills were discovered. After a survey in 1982, the Regional Board had identified 100 additional leak sites, mostly along Highway 101 in the cities of Santa Clara and Sunnyvale.[12]

Water District staff rapidly went to work on developing guidelines for the construction of monitoring wells to be built by the Water District, water retailers or private companies. The goal was to keep tabs on the quality of the water beneath booming Silicon Valley. District staff maintained a database of both monitoring wells and the location of leaking underground storage tanks, and notified the cities—which now had regulatory authority—of any leaking tanks in their jurisdiction.[13]

The Water District wasn't alone in its efforts to protect

Leaking chemical storage tanks turned up around the county like a spreading rash.

groundwater. Public outcry over apparent corporate negligence for the environment, water supplies and public health led to the formation of action groups around the country, including in Santa Clara County. In 1982, San José resident Ted Smith formed the Silicon Valley Toxics Coalition (SVTC). The coalition became highly effective at publicizing the environmental and public health problems caused by practices of high-tech industries.[14] From the Water District's point of view, SVTC was helpful in creating a groundswell of public attention that would bring about solutions. "Ted Smith was, and continues to be, a leader in bringing the issues of water quality to public consciousness and in demanding corporate responsibility," said Director Sig Sanchez.[15]

Superfund spotlight on Santa Clara County. By 1986 (four years after the Fairchild leak discovery), the assessment of the county's drinking water wells had changed; the good news had turned to bad. Thirty-nine public and 56 private drinking water wells had been closed due to leaks and spills of solvents, fuel or other similar chemicals. Although the impact to the valley's overall water supply was small, the threat to groundwater—the largest local water source—was unacceptable. Concerned that contamination would worsen while the regulatory agencies discussed responsibility and funding issues, the Water District offered to take on the administrative oversight costs for the cleanup of leaking fuel tank sites; there were about 1,000 of these sites in the county by mid-1989 (see also Table D).[16] "The Water District board recognized the need to act, and approved the formation of a program to investigate and provide oversight on the cleanup of leaking tanks," said Jim Crowley, an engineer who eventually became manager of the Water District's Leaking Underground Storage Tank Oversight Program.[17] The program began as a pilot effort in 1986 with the San Francisco Regional Water Quality Control Board. Gubernatorial approval was required to formalize the program because it essentially assigned a state regulatory task to a local agency. Approval came from Governor George Deukmejian in 1987, and by 1989, Water District staff had overseen cleanup of 135 of the worst fuel leak sites.[18]

Not all sites became Superfund sites—only those of a magnitude that seriously threatened the environment and public health, and that required assistance from the federal Environmental Protection Agency (EPA) with cleanup and funding. By 1985, 28 sites were proposed for the Superfund National Priorities list; 23 sites eventually were listed, giving Santa Clara County the unfortunate distinction of

Table D. Chemical Leaks and Spills in Santa Clara County

(as of March 2005)

	Number of sites identified	Number of sites closed (% closed)	Number of sites still open
SLIC and Superfund sites*	729	217 (30%)	501
LUST sites**	2453	1969 (80%)	484

* SLIC (Spills, Leaks, Investigation and Cleanup) sites typically involve solvent leaks and require groundwater cleanup. Included in the SLIC statistics are 23 Superfund sites. Regulatory staff commonly believe that hundreds of additional SLIC cases still remain unidentified.

** LUST (Leaking Underground Storage Tank) sites are fuel tank leaks. Of the 484 open LUST sites, 338 are contaminated with MTBE. Most of these MTBE cases are no longer considered a high threat and are in a monitoring-only mode, as MTBE concentrations have decreased to below 200 ppb at virtually all sites.

Source: SCVWD staff provided updated numbers from a composite of sources including online databases maintained by the Regional Water Quality Control Boards (www.waterboards.ca.gov).

having the greatest concentration of Superfund sites in the country.[19] The reputation of high tech as a "clean industry" did an about-face. Director Joe Judge, who was appointed to the Water District board in 1986 by county supervisors because of his specific interest in marshalling resources to address the leaking storage tank issues, recalled the general shock being felt throughout the county. "Prior to the Well #13 incident, valley leaders really had no inkling of the potential for this industry to release toxins into the environment," said Judge. "Everyone assumed we had built an economy on a clean industry—cleaning up is what this industry now had to do."[20]

Cleaning up. For the companies whose operations resulted in leaks or spills, the cleanup process was usually a long and expensive one. By 1986, IBM had spent $45 million and Fairchild had spent $28 million on cleanup and the reconstruction of chemical storage facilities on their respective sites in south San José. In 1986 alone, these companies together pumped more than 17,000 acre-feet of groundwater as they attempted to flush the basin. (They pumped groundwater from the affected area, treated it, reused some and disposed of the remainder in nearby creeks.) Kriege noted that this represented "a significant and unacceptable waste of water, but even less acceptable was allowing degradation of the groundwater source."[21]

The bottom line in cleanup efforts was the question, "How clean is clean?" The Regional Board largely settled the issue in 1989, when it decided to rule on a case-by-case basis, setting cleanup standards based on the site, the chemical involved and the exposure pathway.[22]

Abandoned wells: seek and destroy. Water District managers and hydrologists had long subscribed to the prevailing view that the thick layers of clay near the surface of the valley floor would protect groundwater, acting as an "aquitard" to keep contaminants from reaching the deeper aquifers. But unused wells, some of which stretched down-

Everyone assumed we had built an economy on a clean industry—

cleaning up is what this industry now had to do.

In this 1984 photograph, an abandoned well near Highway 237 and Great America Parkway is being destroyed by Maggiora Bros. Drilling, Inc., with administration and inspection by the Water District. Local media became interested in the work. The deep well was considered to be a potential conduit for aquifer contamination. After removing the turbine pump columns from the well, it was pressure-sealed with concrete slurry.

Unwilling to be caught

offguard again, the

Water District became

hawk-like, scouring the

landscape for potential

conduits to the basin.

ward for several hundred feet, could easily convey any substance to deep aquifers. Originally drilled for irrigating farmland, thousands of wells were abandoned as the land converted to industrial or residential uses—often unseen and buried beneath development.[23] Now recognizing this, on the heels of the hazardous materials ordinance and the requirement for monitoring wells, in late 1983 the Water District implemented a third effort to protect groundwater: In coordination with the Regional Board, the county and South Bay cities, the Water District drafted new guidelines for the destruction of these old, abandoned wells.[24]

With the guidelines in place, Water District staff began the well sealing program. From 1984 to 1985, they identified about 1,100 abandoned wells, focusing on areas where plumes of contaminated groundwater were known to exist. During that year, the Water District sealed 150 of these, 600 more were sealed by others. For the next few years, the Water District would budget $800,000 annually for the well-sealing program.[25] As discussed in Chapter 9, in 1986 the Water District had launched an extensive well registration program in South County to implement a pumping extraction charge—the abandoned well program would tie in with this effort.

By the early 1990s, most wells in the high-priority areas (where contamination existed) had been sealed, and the program's budget was reduced. However, beginning in 1994, with wetter winter seasons and a district policy to maximize recharge of the subbasin, pressure in the subbasin caused artesian conditions to spring around the valley—pointing the way to previously hidden wells. "Water was seeping under freeways and homes," recalled Mike Duffy, wells and water production unit manager at the Water District. "People thought they had leaking pipes and would call a plumber. But the problem often turned out to be a buried well that—because of high pressure in the aquifer—was causing water to migrate upward."[26]

The Water District was called for assistance with these problematic artesian wells, occurring at a rate of about 30 to 40 a year. Duffy estimated that thousands of abandoned wells might remain unidentified, reflecting the prolific efforts of early valley farmers and residents to tap the underground water supply.

Throughout the 1980s and into the '90s, the work of the Water District would now include oversight of fuel cases; review of solvent leak cases and liaison with regulatory agencies; identifying and sealing wells; training sessions on new clean-up practices; and new policies regarding the construction, destruction and siting of wells.[27]

To handle the burgeoning load associated with water quality issues, in 1986, then-General Manager John O'Halloran established the agency's water quality division. The district had the good fortune of hiring Roger James, a former executive director of the San Francisco Bay Regional Water Quality Control Board, as the division's first manager. "With his expertise in water quality regulations and trends, James helped our agency step up its performance on water quality issues," recalled Director Sig Sanchez. "We began participating in technical groups and engaging in policy development in Sacramento and Washington, D.C."[28] So began a drive in the district's culture to take leadership in the state on pressing water quality problems.

Unwilling to be caught offguard again, the Water District became hawk-like, scouring the landscape for potential conduits to the basin. District staff worked with the EPA, the Regional Board and the public works departments of local cities to develop a program for permitting and registering new and existing stormwater infiltration devices such as dry wells, drainage ponds and detention ponds. The Water District board adopted that program in 1993, and city and county inspectors immediately began receiving training on how to locate and identify these infiltration devices.[29]

In April 1995, the Water District reorganized its workload associated with leaking tanks under a separate unit, the Leaking Underground Storage Tank Oversight Program. The staff in this unit coordinated local efforts with those of the state. Commented Art Baggett, Jr., chair of the State Water Resources Control Board in 2003:

The Santa Clara Valley Water District has been an integral part of the state's UST Local Oversight Program for nearly 15 years, and has been a leader in developing new strategies to expedite

cleanups in a cost effective manner. The district's work over the years has influenced the direction of the state's UST Cleanup Program and has inspired many in the program to stay on the cutting edge of issues and technology.[30]

There was no respite for those involved in water quality issues during the latter twentieth century. While one group of district staff focused on groundwater threats, folks at the water treatment plants were dealing with a different water quality problem, one rooted in the Delta area 70

Installation of new double-walled underground storage tanks at a site in San José, 2002. The improved design followed new storage tank requirements that resulted from the discovery of many leaking tanks.

miles north of the valley and one that could shut down the treatment plants if not solved.

Trihalomethanes Threaten Public Health and Imperil Operations

With the 1974 passage of the federal Safe Drinking Water Act (SDWA), the Water District's laboratory, like those belonging to water agencies across the country, was confronted with a host of required tests and the challenge of ensuring that the contents of the water met numerical standards. "For the first time in history, water utilities were accountable to a federal agency and responsible for ensuring that the chemical content of water was regularly monitored, measured and reported, and that specified parameters did not exceed allowable levels," explained Jim Scott, a long-time lab supervisor at the Water District.[31]

The Water District, with its lab already in operation for several years, had no problems complying with the early requirements of the SDWA; through the 1970s, water treatment was relatively simple and easily met the regulatory standards.[33] A Water District publication explained the treatment procedure used at that time:

> First, the water is disinfected [with chlorine] to kill bacteria. Then alum is added, which forces large dirt particles to clump together and settle. Clear water is skimmed off the surface and passed through a charcoal and sand filter to remove smaller dirt particles. At this point, more chlorine is added to keep bacteria from forming

> after the water leaves the treatment plant. The water is now ready to drink, and is piped to water retailers.[34]

But by 1980, the poor quality of the imported raw water was proving this simple treatment approach to be inadequate. The Sierra river water that traveled through the Delta was increasingly subject to heavy amounts of agricultural pesticides and peat as well as saltwater intrusion from the San Francisco Bay.[35] The decrease in the quality of this water was matched by an increase in the chemicals required to treat it: The amount of chemicals need to treat a million gallons of Delta water more than doubled between 1973 and 1981.[†]

Furthermore, with the valley's rapid growth and associated increase in water demand, the quantity of chemicals needed to treat the water escalated. In 1973, the district treated about 15 billion gallons of water; in 1981, 24 billion gallons, a 63 percent increase in eight years.[36] With the nation experiencing high inflation in the late 1970s, the Water District's treatment costs soared. These costs ultimately were reflected in the wholesale water rates (see Appendix B). Not just in Santa Clara County, but also throughout the state, the era of spending more for treatment of water as well as investing in more sophisticated treatment methods had commenced.

THMs—the main treatment challenge. While the treatment process remained effective in removing peat and other substances from Delta water, it could not overcome a certain chemical reaction: When chlorine came in contact with the organics common to Delta water, they reacted

The era of spending more for treatment of water as well as investing in more sophisticated treatment methods had commenced.

[†] In the early 1970s, to treat a million gallons of water imported through the Delta required 110 pounds of alum, 90 pounds caustic soda, 36 pounds of chlorine and 9 pounds of polymers. Within a decade, these amounts doubled. With high inflation, the cost of these chemicals also more than doubled: In 1973, a ton of alum cost $40.50; by 1981 it had risen to $95.49. Caustic soda increased from $89.75 per ton to $204.40, and chlorine was up from $115 per ton to $215.90.

together to form treatment byproducts. One of these, trihalomethanes, or THMs, was particularly alarming. The EPA warned that the tasteless, odorless THMs had been found to be cancer-causing. (Although in 2003, researchers still had no definitive findings on the health risks of low exposure to THMs, throughout the 1980s and 1990s, they were regarded as carcinogenic.)[37]

During the hot, dry summer of 1981, the water moving slowly through the Delta contained more organic compounds than usual. The Rinconada treatment plant, which processed this water, was unable to meet the standard for THMs for three months in a row. The EPA standard was a limit of 100 ppb; Rinconada's treated water tested at 106 ppb that summer. By the time it was served to most customers, however, it had been mixed with groundwater, so that the water at the tap did meet the EPA standard.[38]

"THMs were a thorn in our side when it came to water quality," said Pat Ferraro, a Water District board director from 1973 to 1995. "The real disappointment was that had the Peripheral Canal proposal passed, it would have largely solved the problem for all of the state's recipients of Delta water, as it would have routed the relatively clean Sierra river water around the Delta instead of through it."[39]

The Water District began investigating alternative methods of disinfection, and by 1983, it implemented a modified treatment process at Rinconada. Instead of using straight chlorine to disinfect the water, the process applied chloramines—a mixture of chlorine and ammonia. This relatively simple process change was already in use in cities such as Denver, Dallas and Philadelphia, and in California, was being pursued in Alameda, Contra Costa and San Diego counties.[40] The new process reduced the development of THMs by about a third, according to Jim Scott, the laboratory supervisor.[41]

In 1986, the Water District—with its lab data and analyses of THM levels—began working with the federal

Lab technician, 2002.

Control room at Rinconada Water Treatment Plant, 1967.

The Laboratory's History and Role

The valley's first water treatment plant was the Rinconada plant, built in Los Gatos in 1967 to process raw water imported from the State Water Project. The facility included a laboratory for testing water quality. Initially, the lab monitored only Rinconada's water, but it would later also monitor water at the Penitencia and Santa Teresa water treatment plants, built in 1974 and 1989, respectively, as well as perform some tests for the water retailers.

Seven years after its construction, the activities of the laboratory expanded: In 1974, President Gerald Ford signed the Safe Drinking Water Act (SDWA), a law aimed at monitoring and improving the quality of the nation's drinking water. The Act authorized the federal Environmental Protection Agency to establish numerical standards for various constituents in drinking water and to require compliance from all owners or operators of public water systems. All states had to adopt and enforce every federal standard, but could also add to or strengthen them. California passed its own SDWA in 1996 with requirements specific to the state. Monitoring for compliance with these federal and state standards became the focus of the Water District's laboratory.[32]

EPA on the new Integrated Environmental Management Program (IEMP). This federal effort aimed to identify public health risks from both water and air pollution, and to develop strategies for prevention and cleanup. In 1987, an IEMP report concluded that consumption of water with THMs might cause one to three additional cancer cases countywide per year, based on a lifetime of exposure. The EPA pointed out that, ultimately, air pollution posed a far more significant public health risk in Santa Clara County than imported surface water. Nevertheless, the standard for THM—100 ppb—was deemed appropriate, and all sizeable water utilities were mandated to abide by it.[42]

While the 1981 incident of above-level THMs was never repeated, keeping water under the 100 ppb limit would remain a challenge. And THMs were not the only substance of concern. In 1986, the SDWA was amended to require water utilities to address 80 additional contaminants beginning in 1989, with at least another 25 contaminants to be monitored beginning in 1991. With the task of monitoring 105 or more new substances coming down the pike, water utilities statewide began to reach for new treatment technologies. That story is covered in Chapter 14.

While water utilities worked to keep THMs to a minimum through the treatment process, policy makers also took action. Delta water quality issues became one of California's most important and controversial issues from the 1970s forward, and the Santa Clara Valley Water District became strongly vocal on the need for improving Delta water quality.

1982: Peripheral Canal Squelched

By choosing in 1965 to import water through the State Water Project (SWP) and then in the 1980s from the federal Central Valley Project (CVP), the Santa Clara Valley became tied to the complex water management decisions that centered on the Sacramento-San Joaquin Delta, one of the largest and most unique deltas in the world and the hub of both the SWP and CVP operations. As mentioned in Chapter 7, the Water District committed to support the water management interests of the Delta as a condition of contracting for CVP supplies. Determining the "water management interests" of the Delta and how to meet competing demands was highly controversial, however, and one of the most turbulent debates was over the proposed Peripheral Canal.

Canal as the hope for water quality. In the early half of 1980, the state legislature passed SB200, a $6 billion water facilities package that included the proposal to build the Peripheral Canal, a facility originally conceived as part of the SWP. Edmund G. (Pat) Brown, California's governor from 1959 to 1967 and the SWP visionary, saw this facility as essential to solving some of the Delta's environmental problems. Going around the periphery of the Delta, the 43-mile earthen channel would transport a portion of Sacramento River water directly to pumping stations near Tracy, where the cleaner river water—having avoided transport through the Delta—could be pumped to SWP and CVP users residing south of the Delta. This would be similar to San Francisco's Hetch Hetchy Aqueduct and the Mokelumne Aqueduct of the East Bay Municipal Utility District, which both function as "peripheral canals." These systems bring Sierra river water to their customers by going around the Delta instead of through it, intentionally avoiding the Delta's salty tidal waters.

Of importance to the environment, the Peripheral Canal would bypass important fishery spawning areas, and would include outlets that would provide water releases for fisheries and waterfowl habitat. The design also promised to manage flows in a more efficient manner, helping to conserve water.[43] The Santa Clara Valley Water District fully supported the proposal, recognizing that it would "bring cleaner, less salty water to Santa Clara

County," and would help to ensure the delivery of the district's annual imported water entitlements (see also Table F, Chapter 11).[44]

Because SB200 contained changes to the state constitution, it required voter approval. The proposal appeared as Proposition 8 on the November 1980 ballot, and California voters approved it by a 54 to 46 percent margin. Opponents to the project, however, didn't give up. Effectively selling the idea that the canal project was a costly boondoggle (its price was estimated at $600 million—a cost that translated to about $3.00 per family per year in Santa Clara County), they gathered enough signatures to put a referendum on the June 1982 ballot. Voters were asked to reconsider the value of the Peripheral Canal under Proposition 9. One of the state's most vehement battles for voter opinion thus commenced with the combined pro- and anti-campaigns for Prop. 9 spending more than $6 million (1982 dollars).[45]

Ironically, while it had been former Governor Pat Brown's vision to unify Californians with a water project that would meet statewide needs, the Peripheral Canal debate intensified regional hostilities. Northern Californians became possessive, fighting to keep southlanders from "stealing our water."[46] The statewide anti-canal campaign was led by then-Contra Costa County Supervisor Sunne McPeak, who argued that the proposal would hurt the environment and allow southern Californians to be wasteful with northerners' supply. (Interestingly, in later years, McPeak would support looking at some form of a canal on the Delta's periphery.)

In Santa Clara County, officials at the Water District joined with local leaders to form a citizens' committee that, working against the odds, promoted the canal. The committee emphasized the canal's importance to providing high quality water, and how it would reduce treatment costs that were increasing because of salinity and organics in Delta water. "The cost of chemicals required for treatment of our imported water is rising dramatically," pointed out General Manager John O'Halloran in 1980. "Without the Peripheral Canal, we'll have to introduce more and more chemicals into the treatment process to meet drinking water quality standards."[47]

According to former Director Patrick Ferraro, the committee was successful in convincing the editorial board of the *San Jose Mercury News* of the soundness of the Peripheral Canal. Said Ferraro, "After supporting the District so strongly all during the battle to build San Felipe, they [the editorial board] needed to stand behind us in the effort to protect the quality of that imported water." The *Mercury News* wound up being the only paper in Northern California to endorse the Peripheral Canal.[48]

State Senator Alfred Alquist, representing Santa Clara County, also touted the canal in the pre-referendum days. In a speech made in San José, Alquist, after emphasizing the canal's virtues, warned his audience: "Without adequate water and energy development, we will have no choice but to lower our standard of living and learn to accept less. SB200 is our best chance, and certainly our last chance for many years to come, to make California's water future brighter and more secure."[49]

Nevertheless, on June 8, 1982, Californians soundly defeated Proposition 9, entitled, "Water Facilities Including a Peripheral Canal." The statewide vote stood 63 percent against; 37 percent in favor. But in the Bay Area, 90 percent of voters had come out against the measure. Leaders at the Water District expressed their disappointment: "Having voted against the bill, voters denied what the district believes is a vital link to bringing our full entitlement of clean water from state reservoirs."[50] The water quality problems of the Delta would escalate in the coming years, and valley water officials would find themselves continuing their involvement in resolving them (see Chapter 13).

Having voted against the bill, voters denied what the district believed was a vital link to obtaining the full entitlement of clean water from state reservoirs.

Though mourning Proposition 9, not all was a loss. Water officials had something to celebrate—on the same June 8th ballot, voters in Santa Clara County overwhelmingly approved Measure A, the Flood Control Benefit Assessment Program, to help finance flood management projects. It was money that was going to be needed—more urgently than expected.

1982-1986: Severe Flooding Imperils Property and Public Safety

When Water District officials first launched benefit assessments to help fund flood protection efforts (Chapter 9), they knew voter approval was needed within one year, and they prepared a measure for the June 1982 ballot. In the months preceding the vote, nature delivered what the most brilliant campaign strategist could not: Severe flooding occurred throughout the valley.

Early in January of 1982, an El Niño-driven storm centered itself over much of the Bay Area. In the Santa Clara Valley, during the first week of the year, high flows occurred along San Francisquito Creek in Palo Alto, undermining roads and destroying fences, retaining walls and bridges. Meanwhile, in South County, Uvas and Llagas creeks and associated tributaries swelled and escaped their embankments, flooding the cities of Morgan Hill and Gilroy. Some of the damage included:

On Walnut Lane and Forest Street in Gilroy, water seeped into ten homes to a level of one to three feet. A public health hazard developed as flows overtopped and eroded the Llagas Creek levee near the evaporation ponds of the Gilroy Sewage Treatment Plant. Near the county's southernmost boundary, flood-water pooled up to nine feet deep over 200 acres of agricultural land. In response to the disaster, Governor Jerry Brown issued a State of Emergency Declaration and President Ronald Reagan declared the county a federal disaster area. Reports showed that a total of 136 homes and 14 businesses had flooded, sustaining damages costing $4.6 million.[51]

Three months later, starting on March 31 and lasting through April 13, fresh storms hit the already-saturated county again. On March 31 and April 1, the lower reaches of Coyote Creek, Upper and Lower Penitencia creeks and the Guadalupe River gushed into nearby neighborhoods. The Guadalupe muddied the Willow Glen area and flooded about 20 homes and five businesses. Coyote Creek, roaring with water spilling out of Coyote and Anderson reservoirs, overtopped banks between Highway 237 and Montague Expressway. The water surged across 800 acres of land. About 1,600 people voluntarily evacuated from Mobile Parks West near Zanker Road and North First Street, and about 400 more people evacuated from Alviso. All told, about 480 homes and 75 businesses were flooded. Damage estimates on public and private property exceeded $10 million.[52]

The following June, valley residents went to the polls and readily stamped their approval on the benefit assessment measure by a 3-to-1 margin. Assessments would continue until 1991 with the proviso that any increases could not exceed 2 percent annually.[53] Unfortunately, the voters' enthusiasm to get flood protection projects moving could not help, in time, to prevent the floods that loomed in the near future. As noted in a 1983 district report:

The probability of floods occurring before implementation of flood prevention measures is quite high. A 50-year flood has an 18 percent chance of occurring during a ten-year period; a 100-year flood has about a ten percent chance of occurring during this same period. There is strong potential, therefore, that a damaging flood will occur before the problem can be resolved.[54]

Two times in the very next winter—in January and March of 1983—the potential became a reality. Flooding was severe enough to again force evacuations in Alviso, leaving that community with standing water in many homes for several days. In the March event, Alviso experienced the double whammy of high tides in the south San Francisco Bay combining with heavy rains and floodwater, inundating some areas up to ten feet. The sludge ponds of the nearby sewage treatment plant flooded, creating a public health hazard. Newscasts throughout the country showed rescuers helping residents into boats as they were being evacuated from the murky floodwaters. Weeks later, Congressman Norman Mineta arranged for members of the House Public Works Committee to fly to San José and take a bus tour of the disaster area. Patrick Ferraro, a board member at the time, and Richard Santos, who was a victim of the Alviso flood and would later become a board member, both recalled that the high ranking tourists, led by a police escort, were not greeted warmly by disaster victims, who resented the late attention to their situation.[55] However, as Chief Executive Officer Stan Williams later pointed out, the catastrophe generated enough political heat to finally result in financial support by Congress of the water district's proposed flood control projects on both the Guadalupe River and Coyote Creek (see Chapter 12 for discussion of these projects).[56]

Voters agree to increased rates (1986). The 1982 and 1983 floods generated costly damages to private and public property, including district facilities, proving the funding level of the benefit assessment program to be inadequate. The Water District board realized an increase to the base rate of assessments was necessary to cover flood damage costs as well as to accelerate project construction, but this action required voter approval.

Concurrently, a second factor pointed to amending the benefit assessment program. District officials were learning about a funding tool that could help expedite project construction. By issuing Certificates of Participation (COPs), an agency could finance construction costs in a manner similar to a home mortgage—the project could be built now and paid for in installments over a period of years.[57] Benefit assessment revenue could provide the debt security, but that, too, required voter approval.

There was a third reason to change the benefit assessment program, and that was inflation. In the mid-1980s, inflation was about 4 percent, exceeding the 2 percent annual increase cap approved by voters in June of 1982.[††] Changing the cap would require voter approval.[58]

With these significant incentives to seek voter action, the Water District placed Measure F on the November 1986 ballot. The measure enfolded three proposed changes—a higher base rate; the use of COPs; and matching the annual increases to the rate of inflation (based on the San Francisco-Oakland-San Jose Consumer Price Index for all Urban Consumers). The baseline rate would increase to $25 annually for the average property owner in the Central and East flood control zones and to $40 in the Northwest and South zones (no action was proposed for the North Central Zone, which at the time was not seeking to increase its assessments). Assessments would also continue beyond the original 1991 sunset date and instead end in 2000.

Stormy weather again ensured a positive outcome; severe flooding occurred in the early spring of 1986 in many parts of the county. In November, voters in the Central,

The probability of floods occurring before implementation of flood prevention measures is quite high.

[††] The statewide rate of inflation in California varied greatly between 1980 and the early 2000s. The rate was very high in the early 1980s—10.9 percent in 1981—but hovered between 3 and 5 percent in the mid-1980s. In 2002, the rate was 2.0 percent.

Floods of the 1980s

January-April 1982

A tropical storm caused serious flooding and erosion from January 3 to 5. In South County, flooding on Llagas Creek was a one percent event. Flood-water swept into both Morgan Hill and Gilroy, and flows overtopped the levees around the sludge ponds of the Gilroy Sewage Treatment Plant, causing a potential health hazard. That month, Santa Clara County Emergency Services reported 136 homes and 14 businesses had flooded, with damages estimated at $4.6 million, including $830,000 in damages to facilities of the Water District.

A lengthy storm arrived again in the spring, from March 31 to April 13, and caused serious flooding in Alviso, Milpitas and northern San José. Flood-water poured out from Coyote Creek, covering 800 acres between Agnews State Hospital and the Leslie salt pond levees, including the sludge ponds of the San Jose/Santa Clara sewage treatment facility. About 1,600 people were evacuated from Mobile Parks West; residents in parts of Alviso also volun-tarily evacuated the area. The county's Emergency Services reported that the spring flooding affected 480 homes and 75 businesses; total public and pri-vate damages were estimated at $10 million.[61]

A driver fords across Old Piedmont Road, which was flooded by Berryessa Creek, January 22, 1983.

Area flooded by Lower Penitencia Creek, near Highway 17 and Marilynn Drive, March 1, 1983.

January-April 1983

In San José, rain started falling in August, and by November the city had received 6.07 inches of rainfall; at this time of year, 1.77 inches was normal. Storms continued and in January, the saturated valley began to flood, affect-ing areas in Gilroy, Morgan Hill, San José, Cupertino, Sunnyvale, Milpitas and Palo Alto.

In February and March, high tides, record rainfall and swollen runoff conspired to overtop and erode levees along Coyote Creek, flooding north-ern San José, Milpitas and Alviso. Water levels of up to eight feet deep led to the evacuation of Alviso for more than one month. Mobile Parks West was also evacuated. Highways 237, 17 and Montague Expressway were closed by flooding, restricting thousands of area commuters for several days.

'83 - continued

Spring storms were no less gentle. Downpours in April caused large floods on the Guadalupe River and on Coyote and Penitencia creeks. Toyon Elementary School near Upper Penitencia Creek had to be evacuated. Flooding from Coyote Creek forced residents in Mobile Parks West and Alviso to evacuate again.

All told, more than 1,900 persons were evacuated. The floods damaged 466 homes; two homes were destroyed. More than 165 businesses were damaged. Total damage was estimated at $20.8 million.

The rain continued until May. The 1982-83 rainfall season set new records around the South Bay. In San José, 30.25 inches of rain hit the ground, just .06 of an inch short of beating the record set in 1889. Some areas of the county received almost 100 inches of rain.[62]

Calabazas Creek poured onto Miller Avenue in the city of Cupertino, February 1986.

February 1986

Flooding hit several areas of the county, with particular force in South County, where a flood approximating the one percent level occurred on Uvas Creek. Damage countywide was estimated at $7.3 million. In Gilroy, about $3 million in damage occurred as more than 200 homes near Uvas Creek were flooded—some with as much as four feet of water. Several farms were also inundated.

Both Calabazas and Upper Penitencia creeks (in Cupertino and east San José, respectively) also flooded, affecting a number of businesses and homes. The Guadalupe River filled to its banks but flooded only a very small area in downtown San José. During the floods, the Water District spent more than $44,000 fighting floodwaters, and handed out nearly 50,000 sandbags.[63]

The grounds of Majestic School in San José are left with a muddy aftermath from flooding on Berryessa Creek, January 16, 1983.

East, Northwest and South zones passed Measure F; in 1990, voters in the North Central Zone approved a similar measure.[59] It wasn't only flood victims who were interested in passing the measure. Anyone living in a designated flood hazard area was paying mandatory flood insurance premiums; with flood protection in place and approved by the Federal Emergency Management Agency, the insurance requirement could be either reduced or eliminated (see Chapter 12 for discussion of the flood insurance program).

Measure F would prove to be a significant boost to flood protection in the valley. According to Stan Wolfe, a former special programs administrator who helped implement the benefit assessment program, the increased base rate, inflation adjustments and COPs together enabled the completion of projects from five to 20 years sooner than the original 1982 plan would have allowed.[60] The COP revenue also helped fund maintenance costs on the many conduits, channels, waterways, levees and dams that constituted the county's flood management system.[†††]

~

The 1980s were tough years, presenting many challenges with regard to local and imported water quality issues as well as severe flooding, and these spurred the Water District to become proactive. The agency would continue to develop innovative mechanisms to protect local water sources and advocate for conditions that would improve the imported supply (chapters 13 and 14). District leaders would also push hard to fund and construct major flood protection projects (Chapter 12). But while making inroads on these issues, the valley would contend with yet another imperilment to its operations: the longest drought of the century—a story that requires its own chapter.■

[†††] In 1987, the Water District established a public facilities financing corporation to sell the certificates, and the first issue was sold in 1988 for $21.5 million. A second issue sold in 1990 for $18.5 million; in 1994, a third issue sold for $92 million; and in 2000, a fourth issue sold for $83.1 million. As the benefit assessment program expired in 2000, this latter issue was the last time the Water District would exercise the voter-approved authority to enter debt for the Flood Control Program. It should be noted that while the cost of interest is the notable disadvantage of debt-financing, the savings from avoiding future inflation in land acquisitions and construction costs may significantly offset this cost.

The Problem of Flooding in Alviso

Alviso, named for explorer Ignacio Alviso of the late 1700s, is a breezy place at the southernmost end of the San Francisco Bay. It is also a place that has been subjected to frequent flooding.

Three main influences account for Alviso's flooding problems:

First is simply the community's location between the Guadalupe River and Coyote Creek—two waterways with long histories of flooding during heavy storms. High tides and wind-driven waves along Alviso's shoreline can also combine with storm flows to create flooding conditions.

The second adverse influence are the salt ponds in the southern Bay. Created in the mid-1850s, these ponds have affected the normal sediment deposition processes of both Coyote Creek and the Guadalupe River. The sediment load of these streams used to disperse across a broad stretch of coastline, but the ponds caused sediment to back up, leading to the need for regular dredging to keep channels navigable, and reducing the capacity of these channels to carry floodwaters into the Bay.

Land subsidence is the third influence on Alviso's hydrology. As discussed in Chapter 1, subsidence became a problem in the valley in the early twentieth century, as farmers pumped groundwater without any replenishment. By the mid-1900s, Alviso had subsided approximately 12 feet, placing it below sea level (see also chapters 4 and 6). Construction of a levee system was required to keep seawater from inundating the area. The city of San José—which annexed Alviso in 1968—built a ring levee to protect the area. (The levee would later prove to be a menace itself, when it was found to contain signficant amounts of asbestos. Actually declared a Superfund site, the city was required to replace the levee). The city also installed several pumps to assist in draining the area, but these proved inadequate.

When Alviso flooded in 1982 and 1983, it was largely because of Coyote Creek. In the larger March 1983 flood, the fast-flowing creek broke through its own antiquated levees, inundating Alviso. While pursuing a

Alviso Post Office during the March 1983 flood.

largc-scalc flood protection project on Coyote Creek, the Water District took interim measures in the summer of 1983, lessening the constriction on Coyote and building barriers to prevent overflow.

Much of the flooding potential associated with the Guadalupe River ended when the Water District completed levee improvements in 1985, with further protection afforded by the progress and eventual completion of the Guadalupe River Park and Flood Protection Project. The flood protection project on Coyote Creek was completed in 1996.

There remains a threat of flooding from high tides. As discussed in Chapter 15, the South Bay Salt Pond Restoration Project's goal to remove the salt ponds and restore the tidal flats of the Bay could be a significant opportunity toward helping to protect Alviso from tidal flooding.[64]■

SOURCES, CHAPTER 10:

[1] Environmental Protection Agency Web site: http://www.epa.gov/superfund/action/20years/ch2pg1.htm; also, University of Alabama at Birmingham, Failure Case Studies Web site: http://www.eng.uab.edu/cee/faculty/ndelatte/case_studies_project/environmental.htm

[2] Ibid.

[3] Kriege, Dan. Interviewed by Cheryl Wessling, Feb. 26, 2004.

[4] *Investigation and Cleanup of Soil and Groundwater at South Bay Superfund Sites*, State Water Resources Control Board and U.S. Environmental Protection Agency, 1993, p. 3; also, Kriege, Daniel and Ferraro, Patrick. "Water Quality Issues: The Local Agency Perspective," *Proceedings: 13th Biennial Conference on Groundwater, 1985*, p. 17.

[5] Ibid; also, Iwamura, Tom (retired SCVWD staff). Comments to draft book.

[6] Judge, Joe. Interviewed by Cheryl Wessling, March 13, 2004.

[7] *Review/Outlook 1981-82*, SCVWD, p. 9.

[8] *A Challenge for the '90s: Protecting Santa Clara County's Water*, brochure, SCVWD, 1992, p. 15.

[9] Ferraro, Patrick. Interviewed by Elizabeth Emmett, April 21, 2003.

[10] Verification of involved groups provided by Ferraro, Patrick. Comments to draft book, March 27, 2004.

[11] *Investigation and Cleanup of Soil and Groundwater at South Bay Superfund Sites*, State Water Resources Control Board and U.S. Environmental Protection Agency, 1993, p. 19; also, *Leaking Underground Storage Tank Oversight Program, A Guide to Satisfying Regulatory Requirements and Protecting Groundwater*, SCVWD, p. 2; also, Goldie, Beau (SCVWD staff). Comments to draft book, June 28, 2004.

[12] *Review/Outlook 1983-84*, SCVWD, Introduction.

[13] Iwamura, Tom (retired SCVWD staff). Comments to draft book, March 16, 2004.

[14] Silicon Valley Toxics Coalition Web site: www.svtc.org

[15] Sanchez, Sig. Interviewed by Cheryl Wessling, April 1, 2004.

[16] *A Comprehensive Groundwater Protection Evaluation for South San Francisco Bay Basins*, State Water Resources Control Board, May 2003, p. 28.

[17] Crowley, Jim. Interviewed by Elizabeth Emmett, Aug. 18, 2003.

[18] *Review/Outlook 1988-89*, SCVWD, p. 24.

[19] *Investigation and Cleanup of Soil and Groundwater at South Bay Superfund Sites*, State Water Resources Control Board and U.S. Environmental Protection Agency, 1993, p. 3.

[20] Judge, Joe. Interviewed by Cheryl Wessling, March 13, 2004.

[21] Kriege, Daniel and Ferraro, Patrick. "Water Quality Issues: The Local Agency Perspective," *Proceedings: 13th Biennial Conference on Groundwater, 1985*, p. 20.

[22] *Investigation and Cleanup of Soil and Groundwater at South Bay Superfund Sites*, State Water Resources Control Board and U.S. Environmental Protection Agency, 1993, p. 11.

[23] Duffy, Mike. Phone interview with Cheryl Wessling, Nov. 15, 2004; also, Kriege, Daniel and Ferraro, Patrick. "Water Quality Issues: The Local Agency Perspective," *Proceedings: 13th Biennial Conference on Groundwater, 1985*, p. 20.

[24] SCVWD News Release (no title), Oct. 25, 1984.

[25] *Review/Outlook 1985-86*, SCVWD, p. 3.

[26] Duffy, Mike. Phone interview with Cheryl Wessling, Nov. 15, 2004.

[27] Crowley, Jim. Interviewed by Elizabeth Emmett, Aug. 18, 2003.

[28] Sanchez, Sig. Interviewed by Cheryl Wessling, April 1, 2004.

[29] *Review/Outlook 1993-94*, SCVWD, p. 13.

[30] Baggett, Jr., Arthur. E-mail to Elizabeth Emmett, Jan. 23, 2004.

[31] Scott, Jim. Interviewed by Elizabeth Emmett, Jan. 21, 2004.

[32] *Water Supply and Distribution Facilities*, brochure, SCVWD, July 1997, p. 9; also, description of distribution system in SCVWD News Release (no title), March 24, 1980; also, Environmental Protection Agency Web site: www.epa.gov/safewater/sdwa/sdwa.html

[33] Scott, Jim. Interviewed by Elizabeth Emmett, Jan. 21, 2004.

[34] *A Challenge for the '90s: Protecting Santa Clara County's Water*, brochure, SCVWD, 1992, p. 5.

[35] *Review/Outlook 1981-82*, SCVWD, p. 8.

[36] Table E data, ibid.

[37] American Water Works Association Web site: www.awwa.org

[38] *Review/Outlook 1981-82*, SCVWD, p. 8; also, SCVWD News Release (no title), Jan. 12, 1982.

[39] Ferraro, Patrick. Interviewed by Elizabeth Emmett, April 21, 2003.

[40] Thurm, Scott. "Officials Drink in New Ideas to Treat Water Safely," *San Jose Mercury News*, Sept. 9, 1990; also, SCVWD News Release (no title), Feb. 27, 1984.

[41] Scott, Jim. Interviewed by Elizabeth Emmett, Jan. 21, 2004.

[42] *Review/Outlook 1986-87*, SCVWD, p. 21.

[43] Description of environmental features of proposed canal provided by Cotton, Frank (SCVWD staff). Comments to draft book, April 22, 2004.

[44] *Review/Outlook 1981-82*, SCVWD, p. 8; also, SCVWD News Release, "The Peripheral Canal: The Third of its Kind," Oct. 28, 1980; also, SCVWD News Release, "Canal Delays Mean Increased Costs," Oct. 28, 1980.

[45] SCVWD News Release, "Canal Delays Mean Increased Costs," Oct. 28, 1980.

[46] Ferraro, Patrick. E-mails to Cheryl Wessling, September 2003, also: Esau, Ronald. Interviewed by Cheryl Wessling, March 1, 2004.

[47] O'Halloran, John as quoted in SCVWD News Release, "Peripheral Canal Means Good Water for Santa Clara County," Oct. 28, 1980.

[48] Ferraro, Patrick. E-mails to Cheryl Wessling, September 2003.

[49] Alquist, Alfred, as quoted in *Water and Power in California*, Feb. 20, 1981, Remarks to California Water Resources Association, attached to SCVWD News Release, Feb. 20, 1981.

[50] *Review/Outlook 1981-82*, SCVWD, p. 1.

[51] *Report on Flooding and Flood Related Damages, Santa Clara County, January 1 to April 30, 1982*, SCVWD, p. 1; also, El Niño data from *Heads Up*, internal flyer, SCVWD, Sept. 9, 1997, and from Dept. of Atmospheric Sciences, University of Illinois Web site at: http://ww2010.atmos. uiuc.edu/(GI)/guides/mtr/eln/def.rxml

[52] Ibid.

[53] Hoeft, Bill. "Benefit assessment program puts flood control dollars to work where they count," *Aquafacts*, Summer/Fall 1994, SCVWD, p. 9; also, SCVWD News Release (no title), June 24, 1981.

[54] *Status Report of Corps of Engineers in Santa Clara County*, SCVWD, October 1983, p. 1.

[55] Santos, Richard. Interviewed by Cheryl Wessling, Sept. 25, 2003; also, Ferraro, Patrick. Comments to draft book, March 29, 2004.

[56] *Face to Face: Alviso Flooding*, video, SCVWD, 1983.

[57] Hoeft, Bill (SCVWD staff). Interviewed by Kathleen McNamara, Sept. 9, 2003; also, *1995/96 Budget Overview*, SCVWD, June 21, 1995, p. 2, footnote.

[58] "Comparison of Inflation Rates," California column, found at: www.sdchamber.org/Consumer_Price_ Index.html

[59] Hoeft, Bill. "Benefit assessment program puts flood control dollars to work where they count," *Aquafacts*, Summer/Fall 1994, SCVWD, p. 9; also, Ty Yong Kim, "Fee hike for flood control improvements goes to ballot," *San Jose Mercury News*, July 30, 1986; also, SCVWD News Release, "Flood Control Vote Sought," Aug. 1, 1986.

[60] Ibid; also, Wolfe, Stan. Interviewed by Kathleen McNamara, May 20, 2003.

[61] *Report on Flooding and Flood-Related Damages, Santa Clara County, January 1 to April 30, 1982*, SCVWD, Aug. 24, 1982, pp. 1-12; also, *Review/Outlook 1982-83*, SCVWD pp. 1-3.

[62] *Review/Outlook 1982-83*, SCVWD pp. 1-3.

[63] *Review/Outlook 1985-86*, SCVWD, p. 15.

[64] Influences on Alviso's flooding described by Williams, Stan (SCVWD chief executive officer). Interviewed by Cheryl Wessling, Aug. 11, 2003.

Anderson Reservoir

CHAPTER 11

1987-1992: Drought Strikes Long and Hard

By Donna Krey

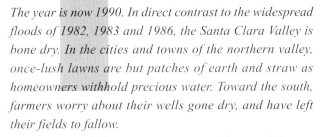

The year is now 1990. In direct contrast to the widespread floods of 1982, 1983 and 1986, the Santa Clara Valley is bone dry. In the cities and towns of the northern valley, once-lush lawns are but patches of earth and straw as homeowners withhold precious water. Toward the south, farmers worry about their wells gone dry, and have left their fields to fallow.

Local firefighters, too, are uneasy: The wooded areas are like tinderboxes, filled with dead trees and brittle undergrowth. Most unnerving—to those paying attention to hydrologic conditions—are the county's depleted reservoirs, several exposing their floors of dry, cracked mud.

~

Scenes similar to this were found throughout California in the summer of 1990. The state was locked in the fourth year of what would be a historic six-year drought. This dry siege began in 1987, and was especially notable because of its duration: It was the longest drought since California

began recording such events in 1850. It was also significant because it permanently changed the strategies of water management agencies throughout the state, as well as the water consumption habits of citizens.

The Drought Settles In

July 1, 1986 to June 30, 1987 was the "rainfall year" that jumpstarted the drought. In San José, only 7.9 inches—compared to the average 14.1 inches—of rain had fallen on the valley floor. The Water District's 10 reservoirs carried 14 to 40 percent of their capacity, and groundwater levels were low. Rainfall in the previous year, 1985-86, had been average—even including flooding in February, as described in Chapter 10—but it fell short of saturating the valley's aquifers.[1] With nearly half of the county's water supply coming from groundwater, it has always been less than ideal to begin a year with an undercharged basin.

In April 1988, for the second time in the valley's history, citizens were asked to voluntarily conserve water.

The year 1986-87 was, in fact, remarkably dry—recorded in California as the ninth driest of the century. The state's most important barometer of water conditions, the Sacramento River Index, stood at 9.2 million acre feet (MAF) in February 1987, about half of the annual average of 18.9 MAF. Officials at the state Department of Water Resources gave hydrologic conditions their most severe designation: "critically dry."[2]

Rainfall in the next year, 1987-88, was again scarce and California endured a second critically dry season. The thought of an extended statewide drought became a distinct possibility. Water District officials looked at 25 wells scattered throughout the county, noting that groundwater was dropping to a worrisome level; it was the Water District's policy to maintain groundwater levels so as to prevent land subsidence and saltwater intrusion (see Appendix D).

Conservation requested. In April 1988, with local reservoirs virtually empty and no spare water for replenishing aquifers, the Water District board turned to valley residents for help: The board asked residents to voluntarily use 15 percent less water than they had used in 1987. This would be the second time in the valley's history that residents were asked to voluntarily conserve; the first instance was the 1976-1977 drought (Chapter 6). Joe Pandit, board chairman in 1988, said the Water District asked residents to use water efficiently and "to do small things, like fix leaks and stop hosing off driveways."[3]

Elsewhere in the Bay Area, water agencies were taking far more stringent and financially punitive actions. The East Bay Municipal Utility District implemented a water-rationing plan whereby residents in Alameda and Contra Costa counties were allowed to buy 200 gallons a day at the current rate; the next 200 gallons they used would cost about 50 percent more.[4] Similarly, the San Francisco Water Department, which controls the Sierra-fed Hetch Hetchy system, initiated a mandatory rationing program with a

goal to reduce consumption by 25 percent. This affected not only the people of San Francisco, but also the municipal contractors that bought Hetch Hetchy water to serve 1.6 million residents in Santa Clara, Alameda and San Mateo counties. The plan included stiff penalties for excessive water use during the summer of 1988. If some Hetch Hetchy water users didn't take the rationing program seriously at first, they were quickly converted when they saw their water bills that summer. In San Francisco, individual fines climbed as high as $10,000. Some contracting entities, including the city of Milpitas and five other Bay Area water retailers or districts, were fined with sums nearing $100,000 for exceeding their July allotments. The tiny Purissima Hills Water District, which serves fewer than 2,000 customers in Los Altos Hills, faced more than $140,000 in penalties.[5]

"In the first two years, the drought's impact was more intense among water systems that had limited supply options," explained Director Sig Sanchez, whose third term of service coincided with the drought. "In the Santa Clara Valley, we had imported water in addition to our local supplies—we had more options."[6]

However, a few months after requesting voluntary conservation, Water District officials became concerned that people were largely oblivious to the message. The privately-held water retailers in the area (Appendix B) earned their revenue from the volume of water sold, and were reluctant to ask customers to conserve until there was more evidence of long-term drought. Furthermore, the news media wasn't giving much coverage to the problem. Consequently, in July 1988, the Water District spent $70,000 on a public awareness campaign that featured conservation messages on local radio, television and theater screens. The agency also distributed 50,000 conservation kits to residents and 5,000 conservation "table tents" (placards placed on dining tables) to local restaurants.

▶ *How much water is one million acre-feet?*

Think of one acre-foot as a one-foot deep pool of water that covers a football field (about one acre). If you could stack one million of these, it would make a column of water rising 189 miles into the sky.

Roller Coaster Ride to Mandatory Conservation

By the fall of 1988, it was clear that the water use reduction goals in the valley were falling short of their mark. Water District managers looked with growing anxiety at lackluster conservation numbers, at reservoirs with their lowest-ever carryover storage, and at declining groundwater levels, which in one particular area had dropped from 78 feet below ground in April 1988 to 110 feet below ground by October. With one eye on the cloudless sky, they began formulating a plan for possible mandatory rationing. The Water District met with its retailers to coordinate a countywide rationing effort, in case of a third year of below-average rainfall. They selected April 1, 1989—after the peak rainfall and runoff period—as the target date to announce a large-scale water use reduction plan. As the winter wore on, the season remained dry. The network of reservoirs held only 5.2 percent of their capacity. It was all too clear that the state of California was entering a third year of drought.[7]

Cuts to imported water loom. With local water sources strained, the Water District was counting on its imported supplies to ease shortages. But in February 1989, the U.S. Bureau of Reclamation "dropped the other shoe." The agency announced that it would be reducing the Water District's annual contract allocation of 152,500 acre-feet from the federal Central Valley Project (CVP) by 50 percent. The state Department of Water Resources (DWR) also had bad news: There was a possibility of a 15 percent cut to the Water District's allocation of 88,000 acre-feet from the State Water Project (SWP).[†] To compensate for this loss, the Water District would need to further deplete groundwater supplies, and valley water users would need to cut their consumption by a whopping 45 percent.[8]

Fortunately, such extreme measures were not required. Heavy rains fell in California during March, and although the storms largely bypassed Santa Clara County, they did boost water levels in statewide storage facilities. This enabled the delivery of 100 percent of the Water District's SWP allocation and a less severe 22 percent cut to the CVP allocation. For added insurance, the water district successfully negotiated a $4 million water transfer agreement with Yuba County for 90,000 acre-feet of surplus water to be conveyed, as needed, through the SWP. (In 1989, the Water District took delivery of 17,000 acre-feet of the Yuba water; 25,600 acre-feet arrived in 1990, and 29,400 acre-feet was available during 1991.[††])[9]

"It was a roller coaster ride in 1989," said Director Joe Judge, who chaired the Water District board that year. "We rapidly moved from the worst-case scenario—half our imported water allotments—to the happier scenario of receiving almost our full allotments, and then some."[10] Fortunately, with the CVP and SWP allotments and supplemental water from Yuba County totaling 259,000 acre-feet, the imported water component of the valley's water operations was ample in 1989. Local water sources, however, re-

In March 1989, for the first time in the valley's history, citizens were mandated to conserve water. Specifically, residents and businesses were to use 25 percent less water than they did in 1987.

[†] From 1968 to 1988, the Water District's SWP allocation was 88,000 acre-feet. As part of the original contract agreement, the amount would gradually increase by 2,000 acre-feet per year, until it reached 100,000 acre-feet starting in 1994. See Table F.

[††] In 1989, the Water District took delivery of 17,000 acre-feet of the Yuba water; 25,600 acre-feet arrived in 1990, and 29,400 acre-feet was available during 1991. The balance of 18,000 acre-feet was lost in conveyance. Such "carriage water losses" are common and occur when transfer water purchased north of the Delta is conveyed to pumps in the southern Delta, and reflect various Bay-Delta regulatory standards that are controlling pumping operations at the time of the transfer. Losses may be as high as 30 percent of a transfer.

mained dismally inadequate. The total demand in Santa Clara County of almost 400,000 acre-feet still required significant groundwater extraction. Action would be needed to avoid overdrafting the aquifers.

Conservation mandated. On March 21, 1989, the Water District board voted in favor of recommending a mandatory 25 percent countywide reduction in water use. Specifically, residents and businesses were to use 25 percent less water than they did in 1987; that year, the county used a record-high 393,000 acre-feet of water. The Water Commission (see Appendix A) adopted the board's recommendation two days later. As the district board had no police authority and could not enforce the mandatory requirement, it needed the cities and county to adopt enforceable ordinances for conservation.[11]

Within a few months, all the cities and the county adopted ordinances restricting water use (Table E). Added support came from the three major water companies in the area—San Jose Water Company, California Water Service Company and Great Oaks Water Company. Governed by the state Public Utilities Commission, these companies adopted similar water use restrictions and were given approval to charge penalties for excessive water use. The mandatory rationing plan became effective April 1, 1989 and was expected to stay in place indefinitely.

With the local water retailers and jurisdictions in the county now involved in a unified conservation program—and with sanctions looming for those who didn't reduce their consumption—media interest quickened. Television, newspapers and radio outlets requested daily updates on the drought's status. To coordinate district-wide operations, a drought task force, composed of members from all district departments, regularly met. Clearly, dealing with the drought was now the top priority of the Water District.

Spreading the message. In February 1989, shortly before conservation was mandated, the Water District launched an intensive public awareness campaign that trumpeted the conservation message through radio and television spots, print ads, posters, movie theater advertising, road signs, billboards and a school educational program. The campaign cost about $500,000.[12] Teddy Morse, public information officer for the Water District during the drought years and through 2003, said that while the price tag for the campaign seemed high at the time, "the district board unanimously approved this crucial expenditure. People needed to cut back on their water usage, and that was the focus of the campaign. Most of the budget went toward media buys—those were costly, but also effective in reaching a lot of people at once."[13]

The success of the enforceable ordinances, rate structures and public awareness campaign was established

Table E. Water Use Restrictions

In the spring of 1989, the 13 South Bay cities, the county and local water companies all issued a fairly uniform set of water use restrictions. Some jurisdictions adopted customized rules, but there were 10 general restrictions—listed below—that went into effect countywide; violators of these restrictions were subject to a charge of misdemeanor.

- Watering landscaping during daylight hours.
- Serving water in restaurants unless requested.*
- Washing vehicles with a hose lacking an automatic shutoff valve.*
- Wasting water through flooding or runoff on sidewalks, streets and gutters.*
- Wasting water because of broken or defective plumbing, sprinklers or watering systems.*
- Using water to clean patios or other hard, paved surfaces.
- Operating decorative fountains.
- Using potable water in construction.
- Flushing hydrants, except when required for public health or safety.
- Using a single-pass cooling process in new construction.*

* After mandatory conservation ended, the Water District board asked the municipalities to maintain these five practices as code violations in their ordinances, thus curbing water-wasters in post-drought times. As of June 2005, some or all of these restrictions are still in effect among most of the cities, including Cupertino, Gilroy, Milpitas, Morgan Hill, Mountain View, Palo Alto, San José, Santa Clara, Saratoga and Sunnyvale.

when, at the end of 1989, numbers on the valley's water usage came in at 19 percent below the 1987 level.[14] As water conservation became a matter of habit, this reduction level would grow. The public was generally heeding the Water District's message: Our most precious resource must not be wasted.

Residents, Businesses and Industry Help Battle the Drought

The public's willingness to conserve was the key to the valley's surviving six years of water shortages. From individuals to major companies, everyone got into the act.

Leading by example, directors cut their own consumption. Director Patrick Ferraro shared with the *San Jose Mercury News* in a March 1990 article that at his San José home, his four-person family used only 150 gallons of water per day in July 1989, and in later months, reduced usage to a meager 100 gallons a day. "Our biggest savings is achieved by flushing toilets with bath water. We don't use the garbage disposal; instead, we use a compost bucket. We have no outdoor irrigation at all." Director Joe Judge reported in the same article how he exceeded the 25 percent reduction goal. By November 1989, he had saved 7,480 gallons of water beyond what was required. Judge adopted "two- to three-minute military showers," as one way of reducing his usage.[15]

Director Judge also publicly advocated using restraint in watering lawns, letting them die if necessary to conserve water. Representatives of the landscaping industry quickly confronted him on this point. "At one particular board meeting, we had landscapers overflowing the board room, lobby and parking lot in their attempt to testify to the fact that with water conservation methods and drought-tolerant plants, lawns and other landscaping could be maintained during a drought," recalled Judge.[16]

As a result of the outcry, Director Judge recommended and the board approved the formation of a Water District Landscape Advisory Committee. One of the committee's original founding members, Jeff Sheehan, a landscaping business owner, spoke about the '"symbiotic relationship" that evolved between the Water District and landscape industry. "Water District officials kept us apprised of water conservation goals and available supply, and we kept them apprised of what the industry could do to help meet those goals," said Sheehan. "It was critical to the survival of the industry that we supported the goals of conservation. With irrigation for landscaping consuming roughly half of the municipal and industrial component of the valley's water supply, it was essential that we worked together."[17]

On a statewide level, the landscape industry promoted solutions that reduced water consumption but still maintained landscaping. By the early 1990s, drip irrigation, automatic timers, drought tolerant plants and educational literature were regular inventory in shops that sold landscape and garden supplies.

With landscape irrigation consuming roughly half of the M & I component of the valley's water supply, it was essential that we worked together.

This particular drought ushered in a new, statewide emphasis on water-efficient irrigation. As a result, drip irrigation and drought-tolerant plants became a normal approach to gardening and landscaping. At left: A drip irrigation emitter.

135

Table F. Imported Water Deliveries to Santa Clara County, 1986 - 2004

This chart shows Santa Clara County's annual total water usage and the county's reliance on imported water sources, particularly during the drought years (highlighted). After the drought, imported water continued to be affected by a "regulatory drought," meaning reduced supplies due to environmental regulations and operational rules (see Chapter 13, p. 196). Note that the greatest use of water occurred in 1987. Conservation measures implemented during the drought resulted in long-lasting reductions in water use; despite significant population growth, as of 2004, the county's total water use remains below 1987 level.

ⓐ *in acre-feet (rounded)*

ⓑ Year	Total Water Used in SCC	from State Water Project *contracted / delivered*		from Central Valley Project *contracted / delivered*		**ⓒ** from Transfers/Other	from **ⓓ** Hetch Hetchy
1986	337,000	88,000	88,000	0	0	3,000	68,000
1987	393,000	88,000	88,000	152,500	37,000	7,000	76,000
1988	310,000	88,000	88,000	152,500	80,000	0	63,000
1989	317,000	90,000	90,000	152,500	119,000	17,000	59,000
1990	325,000	92,000	92,000	152,500	76,000	29,000	59,000
1991	291,000	94,000	28,000	152,500	48,000	59,000	47,000
1992	314,000	96,000	43,000	152,500	80,000	0	52,500
1993	326,000	98,000	62,000	152,500	74,000	0	54,000
1994	340,000	100,000	50,000	152,500	89,000	19,000	56,000
1995	346,500	100,000	29,000	152,500	109,000	0	59,500
1996	365,500	100,000	44,000	152,500	101,000	1,000	61,000
1997	387,000	100,000	61,000	152,500	91,000	0	63,000
1998	349,000	100,000	39,000	152,500	79,000	1,000	58,500
1999	373,000	100,000	53,000	152,500	117,000	0	61,500
2000	383,000	100,000	60,000	152,500	91,000	18,000	63,000
2001	386,000	100,000	36,000	152,500	112,000	51,000	63,000
2002	382,000	100,000	55,000	152,500	123,000	17,000	61,000
2003	367,000	100,000	57,000	152,500	92,000	33,000	N/A
2004	387,000	100,000	53,000	152,500	102,000	32,000	N/A

DROUGHT (years 1987–1992)

San Luis Reservoir stores imported water supplies.

Explanations

a An acre-foot equals 326,700 gallons of water. In 2004, an acre-foot represented a year's supply of water for two families of five.

b The year 1986 reflects usage in the northern county only. South County did not factor into Water District figures until after the 1987 merger with the Gavilan Water District (see Chapter 9).

c "Transfers/Other" is largely the direct purchase of water from other agencies and the state Emergency Drought Water Bank. It also includes smaller amounts involved in project surplus water, carryover and rescheduled water.

d As of 2005, eight entities in the northern county contract directly with the city of San Francisco for Hetch Hetchy water. Hetch Hetchy is an important part of Santa Clara County's total water usage, but is not managed by the Santa Clara Valley Water District. The contracted amount is not shown as there are no entitlements on this system. Rather, deliveries depend upon a gross quantity for all the suburban contractors to share, according to a formula.

In addition to conservation in homes and in landscaping, the Water District took aim at water efficiency in industry. District staff worked specifically with IBM and Fairchild—two of the area's largest corporate water users—to reduce the amount of water pumped from the ground at the companies' south San José sites. Both businesses were extracting groundwater to clean up sites contaminated by leaking chemical storage tanks (see Chapter 10). The Water District initiated a program in 1989 to reduce extractions and to reuse the water for transportation projects. This resulted in almost the entire 3,000 to 5,000 acre-feet of annually pumped water being treated and reused at construction sites.[18]

Other local governments pursued similar conservation measures. Both Santa Clara County and the city of San José issued an edict to contractors who used potable water from fire hydrants to control dust at construction sites; such contractors would not, stated the agencies, be considered as bidders when it came time to award multi-million dollar contracts for road-building projects. Instead, contractors were directed to get their water from the San Jose-Santa Clara Water Pollution Control Plant, which offered a nearly limitless supply of reclaimed water. The message worked: In July 1989, the *San Jose Mercury News* reported that contractors working on county transportation projects in June trucked more than 6.5 million gallons of recycled water to construction sites throughout the valley—compared to the 950,000 gallons just one month earlier. This saved enough drinking water to supply the daily needs of nearly 4,500 families.[19]

Such efforts enabled the valley to fend off the more severe effects of the drought during the 1989-90 rainfall season. But statewide, the drought was not relenting. Although the Sacramento River Index had crept up to 14.8 MAF, 1989 was still classified as a dry year (as discussed earlier, a flow of 18.9 MAF was normal). More than 10 mil-

Conservation messages

were everywhere—in

the media, malls,

schools, restaurants,

workplaces and even

plastered on the sides

of 300 county buses.

lion Californians, one-third of the state's population, were now subject to mandatory water conservation or rationing.[20]

In February of 1990, the Water District was again informed of impending cuts to imported water deliveries: 50 percent from the CVP allocation of 152,000 acre-feet; 15 percent from the SWP allocation of 92,000 acre-feet. Cities with Hetch Hetchy contracts would see a 25 percent cut (see Table F for annual cuts to imported water deliveries through the drought years as well as subsequent years). The combination of these announcements spelled a loss of 100,000 acre-feet for the Water District.[21] And this time around—unlike in 1989—spring rains offered no reprieve. The valley would have to make do with less water.

Mandatory conservation, which the district board had lifted during the winter months of 1989-90, was reinstated beginning on April 1, 1990. The board approved a four-prong strategy: 1) Impose a 20 percent rationing program (25 percent in South County) with rate incentives; 2)

continue water use restrictions with an enforcement program; 3) expand the use of reclaimed water; and 4) continue the water use reduction public information campaign. The board was looking for a slightly higher reduction of water use in South County because of the greater reliance on groundwater there and associated concern for overdrafting. As it happened, on May 8, six cities in the northern county also became subject to a 25 percent water use reduction; the San Francisco Public Utilities Commission imposed that percentage for areas receiving Hetch Hetchy water supplies.[22]

When the 1989-90 rainfall season ended in June, rainfall was 71 percent of normal. The valley braced for a fifth consecutive year of drought—and Water District board members pulled out the stops on conservation. They injected an additional $100,000 into the district's public awareness campaign. Conservation messages were everywhere—in the media, malls, schools, restaurants, work places and

In 1990, the Water District included the Smothers Brothers' humor in their effort to reach county residents with the message to conserve water.

even plastered on the sides of 300 county buses. "People couldn't go anywhere without hearing about the drought," said Morse.[23]

Smothers Brothers' humor helps. Working with an outside public relations firm, district officials agreed to incorporate some humor in the campaign, as a way to make the conservation message more appealing to residents. The Smothers Brothers, a comedy team with local roots, were enlisted as the campaign spokesmen. They appeared in television commercials, their voices aired over local radio waves and their faces on king-sized bus boards reminded passing motorists that saving water was "The New California Lifestyle." The campaign proved successful: In 1991, Santa Clara County residents and businesses reduced their water consumption by 28 percent, the highest annual reduction rate in the county since water rationing began.[24]

The campaign not only told people to save water, but also how to do it. It was not uncommon to see a neighbor watering outdoors from a pot of cooled water that had boiled pasta or eggs. Others let the landscaping go, and brown lawns became symbolic of the dry times. Signs that read "Victim of the Drought" sprouted in dead gardens and city parks. Throughout the valley, people were making a conscious effort to turn the faucet off when they brushed their teeth, to take shorter showers, to keep water from spilling over onto concrete areas—*"No matter how much you water the cement, it won't grow,"* stated one Water District ad. Residents looked for leaks in faucets, water heaters and toilets. They drove dirty cars. And during the summer of 1990, few kids played in the sprinklers.

While the drought maintained its chokehold on the state, it was also teaching people valuable lessons about water conservation and community action. It also confronted them with a financial paradox brought on by several years of water shortages—they were paying more for using less water.

Drought Exacts a Dear Price

In order to meet demand during the drought, many water management agencies had no choice but to purchase higher-priced water from the state's Emergency Drought Water Bank. They also had to deal with new fixed costs associated with implementing water-recycling systems and other technologies. The financial consequence of all this was higher water rates.

Rate increases. In 1988, the Santa Clara Valley Water District sold an acre-foot of municipal and industrial water (M&I) at wholesale for $100. In 1989, the price rose to $135. In 1990, the same quantity sold for $175. And in May 1991, the Water District board of directors approved a rate hike to $262 per acre-foot, almost a 50 percent increase over the previous year (see Appendix B for a water rates history chart).[25] Explained former Director Patrick Ferraro, "The additional water purchases necessitated by the drought almost depleted our cash reserves. We deferred capital improvements in the Water Utility and instituted a hiring freeze, but there was no avoiding rate increases to cover the costs of drought-related measures."[26]

Retail suppliers passed the rate increases onto consumers. San Jose Water Company, the largest retailer in Santa Clara County, hit its 203,000 customers with eight rate increases during the drought, building to a 61 percent increase from 1988. Company spokespersons explained the increases as necessary to keeping pace with the higher cost of doing business during the drought. In Alameda and Contra Costa counties, customers were paying about 48 percent more than they did in 1988. In San Francisco, rates rose about 55 percent in three years. To the south, 1991 water rates in Los Angeles reflected a 46 percent in three years.[27] (Note: Rate increases proposed by privately-owned water retailers are subject to approval by the state Public Utilities Commission.)

The largest water retailer in Santa Clara County hit its 203,000 customers with eight rate increases during the drought.

As these figures indicate, water rates throughout the state varied greatly and largely depended on who was supplying the water and where the source originated. A number of factors could affect the final price paid by the customer, including the distance the water traveled and the level of treatment it required to be usable. Some water companies used rates to fully recover the cost of acquiring and delivering supplies; others used a combination of water rates and property taxes to cover costs. The varying approach among water companies meant that customers in one city could very well pay more for their water than customers in a neighboring town.

Drought's Price

» People paid more for less water.

» Hydroelectric power generation was cut in half.

» In state forests, more than 10 million trees were dead.

» More fish species became endangered.

» About 580,000 acres of farmland had to be fallowed.

» Fires incinerated tinder-dry areas, causing loss of property and life.

Several large forest fires occurred during the drought, such as this one in Calaveras County in 1992.

Courtesy California Department of Water Resources

Other costs and tragedy. Besides escalating the cost of water, the drought had severe consequences for the economy, jobs and the environment, and, sadly, fatal consequences for wildlife and some people.

The connection between a stable water supply and a healthy economy was never so plain: A 1990 report by Spectrum Economics of San Francisco, prepared for the California Urban Water Agencies, showed that a single-year shortage of 30 percent in water supplies could, hypothetically, cost the state as much as $8 billion in lost production and precipitate the direct loss of 56,000 jobs.[28]

It was more than a hypothesis in the farming sector. Economists from the state Department of Water Resources estimated that farm income in 1990 alone suffered reductions of $455 million. That same year, about 194,000 acres were fallowed statewide because of the lack of water. By the end of 1991, that acreage had tripled. The horticulture industry—flower growers, the leading component of Santa Clara County's agricultural sector—was also hit hard. Officials estimated unemployment in that sector was at 20 percent because of the drought.[29]

The drought also took a serious toll on energy generation, cutting in half the state's hydroelectric power production. California's environmental resources were likewise scathed, with dramatic reductions occurring in wildlife and fishery populations. Three fish species that spawned in the Bay-Delta Estuary were added to the federal registry of endangered species by the drought's end. And by early 1991, more than 10 million trees stood dead in state forests.[30]

But the most merciless consequence of the drought was fire: In October 1991, in the tinder-dry Oakland and Berkeley hills, nearly 2,000 acres of land were incinerated by a raging firestorm that claimed more than 20 human lives and thousands of homes. In terms of structural damage, it was the second worst fire in U.S. history, eclipsed only by the October 2003 fires in southern California.[31] Fall-season fires in 1991 also scorched thousands of acres in Sonoma County and in the Los Padres National Forest; locally, in Santa Clara County, the Loma Prieta fire damaged more than 15,000 acres in watershed areas.

The drought thus attacked nearly every aspect of life in California, literally drying up, if not burning up, its resources.

Statewide Response to Drought Crisis

In the fall of 1990, the Water District's board of directors decided to continue mandatory conservation through the winter. The reason was the uncertainty of imported water deliveries. It was a wise move. Winter came, but with very little precipitation.

Water bank forms. In response to the growing crisis, newly-elected Governor Pete Wilson signed an executive order in February 1991, creating a Drought Action Team. Among other things, the team recommended establishing an Emergency Drought Water Bank, whereby the state would purchase water for $125 per acre-foot and resell it for $175 per acre-foot to those with critical urban and agricultural needs. Within 100 days, the water bank had entered into 351 short-term contracts for the sale of 821,045 acre-feet. The banked water came primarily from farmers who chose either to sell some or all of their contracted water supplies for that year because they could instead turn to groundwater or leave their fields to lie fallow.[32]

The state Department of Water Resources operated the water bank and established priorities to guide the sale of water. Although its price for water was high, water-strapped utilities would turn to the bank often during the next two years, and the Santa Clara Valley Water District was among its customers. Such purchases were part of the Water District's basic strategy in the battle against the

drought: Maximize the imported water supply and minimize groundwater pumping. Director Joe Judge was emphatic about the importance of this approach: "I strongly advocated that we buy all the supplemental water available to us and reserve our groundwater as an emergency supply, because no one knew when the drought would end."[33]

By early spring of 1991, the status of deliveries on imported water contracts for the valley was like a recurring nightmare. Again, only a fraction of the contract amounts were promised for delivery: 25 percent of the CVP contract, 20 percent of the SWP contract and 50 percent of the Hetch Hetchy contract. This devastating scenario would have resulted in a delivery of a mere 116,000 acre-feet to Santa Clara County—as opposed to the total contracted supply of 348,000 acre-feet.[34] The valley could not survive on these minimal deliveries. Overdrafting the groundwater basin would be the next, inevitable step. While the board of directors prepared to ask for a conservation level of 45 percent, district staff scrambled to secure other supplies. They pursued water purchases from other agencies; they tapped the Emergency Drought Water Bank; and they filed hardship appeals to SWP and CVP operators, asking—if futilely—for full deliveries to Silicon Valley, the nation's high-tech engine. Then, the following month, good news finally came from where it was least expected—right out of the blue.

Miracle March. March 1991 roared in, bringing a record rainfall that was quickly dubbed "the Miracle March rains." Seasonal rainfall averages rose to between 76 and 98 percent of normal, and local reservoir storage at the end of the month was 37 percent of capacity. Equally important, Miracle March greatly improved the statewide water picture.

The Department of Water Resources delivered 30 percent instead of the predicted 20 percent of the district's allotment; the Bureau of Reclamation granted 10,000 acre-

The district's strategy: Buy all the supplemental water available and reserve groundwater as an emergency supply— because no one knew when the drought would end.

feet of "hardship water"; and Hetch Hetchy deliveries were cut only 25 percent instead of the expected 50 percent. The efforts to secure supplies from other agencies paid off, with 10,000 acre-feet from Placer County conveyed to the district through SWP facilities. Another 20,000 acre-feet was purchased from the Emergency Drought Water Bank. Altogether, the Water District was able to supplement its imported water supply by a total of 64,000 acre-feet.[35]

With these additional supplies, along with more water in local reservoirs, the valley escaped the imposition of a 45 percent conservation level during the summer of 1991 (the 25 percent conservation level remained in place). But the Miracle March rains, though ample, did not end the drought. While both precipitation and the Sierra snowpack climbed to 75 percent of average, and water storage in the state's 155 major reservoirs gained 4 million acre-feet to reach 60 percent of average, conditions were still shy of normal. A dry April soaked up some of the bounty, and state hydrologists predicted runoff in the Sacramento River basin would be scant enough to earn 1991 the distinction of being the driest of years in the five-year-old drought—the eighth driest year of the century in California.

Also straining local and state water supplies was a ballooning population. U.S. Bureau of Census figures show that between 1980 and 1990, California added six million people—a 26 percent increase. By 1990, the growth rate in the state was three times the rate of the rest of the nation. In Santa Clara County, population growth was slower than the state's overall rate, but it was significant nevertheless. Between 1980 and 1990, the county grew by 202,506 people—an increase of about 16 percent.[36] And, by all forecasts, the growth was expected to continue. Water District officials forged ahead with the construction necessary to support a growing population; as discussed in Chapter 9, the Water District expanded its In-County Distribution System during the drought years.

Though Miracle March was a saving grace, and key facilities had come online, the root problem was still at hand: The drought wore on. By this time, three-fourths of California's population was subject to mandatory rationing. The 1990-91 water year ended with statewide precipitation at only 76 percent of normal. Worse, water runoff was 43 percent of normal, as California's parched soil absorbed much of the water that would otherwise have flowed into the state's reservoirs. Concern about imported water supplies again dogged the Water District, and the board extended its mandatory 25 percent conservation goal to 1991-92, the sixth consecutive year of drought.

Historic MOU launches conservation programs. Most California water agencies were more than ready for statewide action against the drought. On December 11, 1991, in a dramatic show of unity, a Memorandum of Understanding Regarding Urban Water Conservation (MOU) was drafted and signed by representatives of more than 120 water agencies and public interest groups. Attendees of the event, with Director Patrick Ferraro representing the Water District, gathered on the steps of the State Capitol. A low-flush toilet was placed at the center of the stage, and agency representatives ceremoniously pledged to conserve water by adopting 16 Best Management Practices (BMPs) for implementation over the period from 1991 to 2002. The practices included Ultra Low-Flush Toilet (ULFT) replacement programs, public information programs, low-flow showerhead distribution plans and enactment of water-efficient landscape ordinances. Governor Pete Wilson made the 16 BMPs a condition of permit approvals from the State Water Resources Control Board in 1992.[37] Water suppliers who signed the charter represented 80 percent of the state's population, ensuring that the majority of the people in the state were now involved in a program that could save an estimated one million acre-feet of water per year—roughly the amount of water used every year by nearly 10 million Californians.

With the adoption of statewide water conservation BMPs in 1991, ultra-low flush toilets became mandatory in new construction.

As a result of the MOU, the Water District began rolling out several water conservation programs. The metaphor "leaving no stone unturned" could be aptly replaced with "no sponge unsqueezed" in regard to the district's approach: The Water District not only targeted water use in residences, businesses, industry and agriculture, but engaged in public education and professional training efforts to change the collective mindset of water use.

Residential plumbing fixtures—toilets, showerheads and washing machines—were among the first to be targeted. In September of 1991, slightly ahead of the MOU, the board had already approved a ULFT rebate program. County residents who installed an approved ultra low-flush toilet would receive a $75 rebate. In 1992, the program's first year, the Water District issued more than 14,000 rebates in conjunction with 11 participating water retailers.[38] "We sponsored the ULFT rebates because toilets were the major water waster inside the house. Replacing toilets that consumed up to 7 gallons per flush with the new 1.6 gallon-per-flush toilets was an important step," recalled former Director Joe Pandit.[39]

In 1995, the district board expanded the rebate program to include toilet replacements in commercial facilities. By the late 1990s, more than 45,000 rebates in total had been issued. The impact of this substantial effort to replace water-guzzling toilets was an annual reduction in countywide water demand of 14,500 acre-feet (2002 estimate). Following on the heels of the ULFT program was a low-flow showerhead distribution plan. During the first year, 1992, the Water District provided 20,000 kits to county residents, and a similar distribution target was set for subsequent years.

To reduce the water used by washing machines, the Water District was one of three entities in the service area of PG&E to partner with the energy company in offering rebates of $150 to $225 to residents who installed approved tumble-action clothes washers. (The other entities were the East Bay Municipal Utility District and the city of Davis.) This program helped save both water and energy.[40]

Turning outdoors, landscape irrigation was the Water District's first target of concern. The Water District and its newly formed Landscape Advisory Committee worked together on a Model Water Efficient Landscape Ordinance, as required by AB325, the state Water Conservation in Landscaping Act. The ordinance spelled out water-efficient irrigation measures and a water budget for all new commercial, industrial and institutional construction projects. The Water District adopted the ordinance in June 1992; water conservation staff then assisted the county and local cities in adopting their own AB325 ordinances. As a result of

Displays, such as this one at a home improvement show in 1996, were a large part of the Water District's efforts to educate the public on the importance of water-efficiency in the garden.

putting these landscape ordinances in place, the Water District estimated a savings of 4,000 acre-feet of water annually, countywide.[41]

The next target was water used in commerce and agriculture. The Water District began offering water-use audits to businesses that engaged in heavy water use processes and encouraged process changes and/or equipment upgrades that conserved water. Out in the fields, three programs aimed to help farmers reduce agricultural water use: 1) a free test to determine the overall efficiency of irrigation pumps; 2) a mobile lab that provided field-by-field analysis of irrigation practices followed by possible recommendations for cost-effective modifications; and 3) low-interest loans up to $50,000 to assist with the purchase of approved irrigation equipment.[42] (These efforts to reduce agricultural water use also qualified as EWMPs, or Efficient Water Management Practices, and they helped the Water District to satisfy a federal mandate under the 1992 Central Valley Project Improvement Act—see also chapters 12 and 14.)

The Water District also substantially increased its focus and resources on public education, with the goal of developing public awareness and action in conserving water. One example of many public outreach efforts was the Water District's award-winning Drought Resource Center, a display featured at the Santa Clara County Fair during the hot summers of the early 1990s. Conservation ideas, from plumbing improvements to drought-tolerant gardening, were offered to many of the 650,000 fair goers.[43] From the 1990s forward, the Water District sponsored many public workshops on drought-tolerant gardening, and offered professional workshops for landscapers and industrial water users. While these workshops focused on specific techniques, the inherent message was always the same: Water was a precious resource to be conserved and used wisely.

1991 and 1992 Storms
Drench the Drought

In the same month that the historic Memorandum of Understanding regarding water conservation BMPs was signed, three storms showered the valley and lifted rainfall averages to about 74 percent of normal. This boost, along with residents conserving nearly 30 percent over 1987 usage levels, helped improve the local water supply situation. But state and federal suppliers remained unable to deliver full entitlements to the Water District. On January 28, 1992, the Water District board adopted a contingency plan that addressed potential shortages of up to 50 percent in supply, and included mandatory rationing levels as high as 35 percent.[44]

Then, in March 1992, a near-normal amount of rain fell throughout the state. Reservoirs collected the runoff and rose to near-normal levels for the time of year. The improved supply picture led the board of directors to ease the mandatory conservation goal from 25 percent—where it had stood since 1989—to 15 percent throughout the county. The lowered reduction level—was adopted with applause to valley residents who had so impressively cut back on their water use.

The Water District's efforts were also recognized: In November 1991, the U.S. Bureau of Reclamation recognized the agency for its water conservation programs—including the model ordinances and the formation of the Landscape Advisory Committee—and for its highly effective public information campaigns. By the time the summer of 1992 came around, saving water had become a habit for many county residents, and the board's 15 percent conservation goal was easily exceeded. Countywide, water use was down about 24 percent (compared to 1987 usage) through September 1992. The public's efforts to conserve resulted in a savings of about 360,000 acre-feet of water from 1987 to 1992—about one year's worth of water for the entire county.[45]

Despite the public's good performance, water supply conditions remained dire. As of October 1992, SWP reservoirs still held less than 50 percent of their capacity, and the federal CVP reservoirs stood at about 25 percent. Projected allocations from each of those sources were, again, half of the contract amounts.[46]

While the Water District braced for a possible seventh dry season, December 1992 arrived with a generous gift: the wettest winter since 1986. The rain that fell that month was enough to effectively wash away six long years of drought. By the end of the winter, the valley's creeks were running freely. Saturated watershed areas were steadily draining into the county's reservoirs, causing many to spill over. The groundwater basin was well on its way to becoming replenished to its pre-drought levels. Residents drank in the wonder of the rain. At Lexington Reservoir—seen from Highway 17 as a dried-up mud-hole just months ago—people crowded along the banks to gaze at the water rushing down the spillway into Los Gatos Creek.

Up and down California, the burden of the drought was dissolving. SWP and CVP deliveries climbed to levels not seen since 1985. In February, the water content of the Sierra snowpack was recorded at 175 percent of the historical average for that month. State reservoir levels rose to 80 percent of normal or more, a remarkable improvement considering that many had been practically empty for the past few years. On February 24, 1993, Governor Pete Wilson made it official: He declared an end to the drought, saying, "Thanks to God for ending the drought and thanks to the people of California for enduring it."[47]

The Water District, now flush with local and imported supplies, replaced its mandatory conservation plan with a voluntary one. The idea was to keep promoting efficient use of water, and the board reinforced this by recommend-

ing that restrictions continue throughout the county on specific wasteful water uses (see Table E). The board also gave its water retailers something to cheer about besides the plentiful rainfall: In an unprecedented action, the board approved reducing the price of wholesale water by $22 in the northern county (from $262 to $240 per acre-foot) and by $9 in South County (from $117 to $108 per acre-foot).[48]

Silver Linings

The economic and environmental side effects of California's prolonged dry spell would remain with the state for years, but the drought also offered a few silver linings. Some would say it provided a much-needed wake-up call for water planners throughout the state. Many water utilities were forced to re-evaluate their supply and delivery systems and made improvements and innovations that proved critical in helping California cope; these included changes in project operations, land fallowing, water transfers, water banking, water recycling and purchases of supplemental supplies.

Some of these methods have remained in effect. Water transfers, for example, have thrived, proving that this concept has lasting benefits for the people of California. In 2001, enough water to supply three million people for a year was exchanged outside of the usual operations of the state's major water projects. Farmers in the Sacramento Valley are selling water to farmers in the San Joaquin Valley; cities have formed partnerships with farm districts near Bakersfield to capture winter flood water, percolate the supply and then withdraw it during dry years; some irrigation districts are selling water directly to the state to help endangered fish.[49]

Perhaps the most compelling side effect of the drought was the lesson Californians learned about the

The public effort to conserve resulted in a savings of about 360,000 acre-feet of water from 1987 to 1992.

vulnerability of their water supply. "The drought instilled an appreciation for this life-giving commodity," stated Director Sig Sanchez.[50] Many of the water-saving practices that began during the dry years have become habitual. A report released by the Bay Area Water Agencies Coalition in April 2003 showed that residents in the San Francisco Bay Area's five most populous counties were using less water in the early 2000s than they did in 1986. Despite the fact that the region had grown by 17 percent between 1986 and 2000, water use in the East Bay, Silicon Valley and the Peninsula had grown by only three percent. The coalition's report estimated that with this pattern, the five counties were attaining roughly 150,000-acre feet per year of conservation-related savings (see also discussion of regional efforts in Chapter 14).[51]

One silver lining that the Santa Clara Valley Water District, with its dual missions, could not help but appreciate was the opportunity to advance flood protection—indicated by the title of one district publication which pronounced: "Who Worries About Flood Protection During a Drought? We do!"[52] The dry years did afford the chance to advance projects and perform stream maintenance, as there was little water in the streambeds to slow progress. Yet the dry creeks would be a double-edged sword for flood protection: Construction was easier, but the lack of water exacerbated the problem of endangered species, making construction projects subject to more stringent environmental reviews. As told in Chapter 12, most district flood protection and maintenance work would become mired in environmental concerns. ∎

The drought instilled an appreciation for

this life-giving commodity.

SOURCES, CHAPTER 11:

[1] *Review/Outlook 1986-87*, SCVWD, p. 16.

[2] *California's Continuing Water Crisis: Lessons from Recurring Drought*, 1991 Update, Association of California Water Agencies, June 1991, p. 8.

[3] Pandit, Joe. E-mails to Cheryl Wessling, March 2004.

[4] Spalding, John. "EBMUD OKs Water Use Plan," *San Jose Mercury News*, April 27, 1988, p. 3B.

[5] Spalding, John. "Milpitas Fined for Water Use; Five Others Are Also Penalized," *San Jose Mercury News*, Aug. 17, 1988, p. 1B.

[6] Sanchez, Sig. Interviewed by Cheryl Wessling, April 1, 2004.

[7] *Drought Status Report*, SCVWD, November 1989.

[8] Ibid.

[9] *Response to 1989 and 1990 Drought*, SCVWD, May 1990; also, contract cost provided by Ferraro, Patrick. Comments to draft book, March 22, 2004; also, Yuba County transfer data provided by Maher, Joan (SCVWD staff). E-mail to Cheryl Wessling, April 29, 2005.

[10] Judge, Joe. Interviewed by Cheryl Wessling, March 13, 2004.

[11] *Review/Outlook 1989-90*, SCVWD, p. 18; also, *Review/Outlook 1990-91*, SCVWD, p. 4.

[12] *1989 Drought Plan*, prepared by The Drought Committee, SCVWD, March 1, 1989, p. 13.

[13] Morse, Teddy. Interviewed by Donna Krey, March 19, 2003.

[14] *Review/Outlook 1989-90*, SCVWD, pp. 17-18; also, Calvert, Cathie. "Water Customers Appear to Like the District's New Act," *San Jose Mercury News*, July 17, 1990, p. 2B.

[15] Kutzman, David. "Not all water board members think dry," *San Jose Mercury News*, March 11, 1990, p. 1B.

[16] Judge, Joe. Interviewed by Cheryl Wessling, March 13, 2004.

[17] Sheehan, Jeff. Phone interview with Cheryl Wessling, March 15, 2004.

[18] *1989 Drought Plan*, prepared by The Drought Committee, SCVWD, March 1, 1989, p. 13.

[19] *San Jose Mercury News*, "Contractors Soaking up Used Water," July 12, 1989

[20] *California's Continuing Water Crisis: Lessons from Recurring Drought*, 1991 Update, Association of California Water Agencies, June 1991, p. 8.

[21] *Drought Status Report*, SCVWD, November 1990.

[22] Ibid.

[23] Morse, Teddy. Interviewed by Donna Krey, March 19, 2003.

[24] *Drought Status Report*, SCVWD, December 1991.

[25] *California's Continuing Water Crisis: Lessons from Recurring Drought*, 1991 Update, Association of California Water Agencies, June 1991, p. 8.

[26] Ferraro, Patrick. E-mails to Cheryl Wessling, September and October 2003.

[27] Thurm, Scott. "San Jose Water Rates Up Again; 61% in 4 Years," *San Jose Mercury News*, Dec. 9, 1991, p. 1B.

[28] Wade, William. *Impacts on the Industrial Sector and the Need for Urban Reliability Standards*, Spectrum Economics, Inc., Aug. 27, 1990.

[29] *California's Continuing Water Crisis: Lessons from Recurring Drought*, 1991 Update, Association of California Water Agencies, June 1991, p. 18-23; also, horticulture component of Santa Clara County agriculture found at California Farm Bureau Federation Web site: www.cfbf.com/counties/co-43.htm

[30] Ibid; also, Ferraro, Patrick. Comments to draft book, March 22, 2004.

[31] *California's Narrow Escape: Water Year 1991 in Review*, Association of California Water Agencies, November 1991, p. 1.

[32] *Preparing for California's Next Drought; Changes Since 1987-92*, State Department of Water Resources, July 2000; also, Zlotnick, Greg. Comments to draft book, May 18, 2004.

[33] Judge, Joe. Interviewed by Cheryl Wessling, March 13, 2004.

[34] *Drought Status Report*, SCVWD, December 1991, Executive Summary.

[35] Ibid.

[36] *Historical Population Estimates for Santa Clara County, 1970-1999*, Santa Clara County Planning Office; also, CensusScope, University of Michigan, Social Science Data Analysis Network Web site: www.censusscope.org.

[37] *Integrated Water Resources Plan, Final Report*, SCVWD, January 1997, p. 7-1.

[38] Ibid, p. J-1.

[39] Pandit, Joe. E-mail to Cheryl Wessling, Oct. 30, 2003.

[40] *Integrated Water Resources Plan, Final Report, Appendices*, SCVWD, January 1997, pp. J-1 - J-3.

[41] Ibid.

[42] Ibid.

[43] *Annual Report 1991-1992*, SCVWD, p. 13.

[44] Ibid, p. 12.

[45] Davis, Ron. "Emergency Drought Water Bank is extended," *Aquafacts*, SCVWD, Winter 1993, p. 15.

[46] Ahrens, Elizabeth. "Drought Ends with a Splash!" *Aquafacts*, SCVWD, Spring 1993, pp. 4-7.; also, *Annual Report 1992-93*, SCVWD, p. 3.

[47] Murphy, Dean. "Drought is Over, Wilson Declares," *Los Angeles Times*, Feb. 25, 1993, p. 1.

[48] *Annual Report 1992-1993*, SCVWD, p. 4.

[49] Vogel, Nancy. "Water Exchanges Help State Through Dry Years," *Los Angeles Times*, April 4, 2002, p. B1.

[50] Sanchez, Sig. Interviewed by Cheryl Wessling, April 1, 2004.

[51] *Advancements in Water Conservation*, Bay Area Water Agencies Coalition, April 2003, pp. 1-8.

[52] *Aquafacts*, Summer/Fall 1994, cover title, SCVWD.

"They show that we did something right."

~ Tom McEnery, former mayor of San José, speaking of wildlife
that continues to inhabit the Guadalupe River watershed.

A heron and egret on the Guadalupe River, 2002.

CHAPTER 12

Fish, Frogs and Flood Protection

By Kathleen McNamara and Cheryl Wessling

Chinook salmon on the Guadalupe River, 1998.

Ironically, the first year of the twentieth century's longest drought, 1987, was the same year that design work began on one of the valley's most needed flood protection projects: The Guadalupe River Park and Flood Protection Project, running through downtown San José. During the drought, this river's "dusty bottom baked in the seemingly endless days of sunshine,"[1] but there were thousands of flood victims (from 1982, 1983 and 1986 flood events) who had stark memories of the Guadalupe's wetter days.

The story of the Guadalupe project is long and complex, like that of all major flood protection projects in the valley. Several issues complicated these capital-intensive public works that centered on rivers and creeks. A key challenge was securing federal funding from congressional budgets that fluctuated in size and for which there was nationwide competition. With the passage of environmental laws in the late 1960s and early '70s, addressing the needs of fish, frogs and other wildlife became the norm. Funding needs increased to provide for environmental mitigation, while project schedules lengthened to accommodate regulatory reviews. Obtaining permits from regulators responsible for implementing the Endangered Species Act could involve delays, as the process reflected the often-conflicting goals of flood protection and wildlife management. Yet another layer of complexity came from the need to achieve a common vision with involved neighborhoods, cities and—where federal money was involved—the U.S. Army Corps of Engineers (Corps).

Intent as the Water District was on building them, most flood protection projects were spread across decades of effort. "It's a wonder any major flood protection project ever got built," commented Director Sig Sanchez, who had

TERMS

» *The 100-year or one percent flood*

The Water District designs its flood protection projects with a capacity to provide for a 100-year flood, also called a one percent flood. The volume of a 100-year flood is different on every stream and is based on a stream's historical flow data; on any stream, the flow of a 100-year flood is so large that it has only a one percent chance of occurring in any given year.

In a floodplain, the chance of experiencing a one percent flood increases with time: During the life of a 30-year home mortgage, a one percent flood has about a 30 percent chance of occurring.[5]

helped shepherd several such projects in his fifty-plus years of public service.[2] In the interim, homes and businesses in the valley's floodplain continued to experience occasional flooding, frustrating property owners who suffered damages and/or were tired of paying flood insurance premiums. Such premiums had become mandatory: With flooding being the nation's most common disaster (nearly nine of every 10 presidential disaster declarations include flooding as a major component), Congress passed the National Flood Insurance Act of 1968 and the Flood Disaster Protection Act of 1973.[3] Together, these acts required identification of all the nation's flood hazard areas and made flood insurance mandatory in such areas.

The flood insurance mandate. The chore of mapping the nation's flood hazard areas fell to FEMA, the Federal Emergency Management Agency. By 2003, flood hazard areas were mapped in more than 20,000 communities, including such areas in Santa Clara County. Communities with mapped floodplains participate in the National Flood Insurance Program, which sets forth corrective and preventive measures for reducing flood damage. Communities may also enhance the flood-carrying capacity of local streams. In floodplains where measures provide protection from a 100-year flood event, FEMA will eliminate or reduce the insurance requirement (as of 2004, flood insurance typically cost $300 to $500 per year, but could also be higher in some locations).[4]

While the slow progress of projects frustrated both floodplain residents and Water District officials who were charged with the mission of providing flood protection, it can be argued that it played to the valley's benefit to have its projects protracted so as to be constructed in an era where public values placed a greater emphasis on preserving riparian habitat. Had the projects been built in the earlier part of the century, the valley's waterways could have wound up looking like those of Los Angeles—a network of

wide, concrete channels incapable of supporting a significant level of aquatic life. As it was, a number of earlier projects built by the Water District were constructed as concrete channels, predominantly in the northern county.

In addition to project construction delays, lengthy delays in stream maintenance activities also became common. These activities focused on the regular removal of creek debris and sediment in order to preserve a channel's flood-carrying capacity. In the early 1990s, this type of work was being subjected to an annual permit process that required more environmental analysis of impacts. Regulators increasingly found reasons—primarily a rising number of threatened and endangered species—to delay permits, resulting in an escalating backlog of maintenance work.[6] Such a backlog was potentially disastrous: Unattended channels would steadily fill with sediment and vegetative growth, making flooding all the more likely.

To accelerate progress on both project construction and maintenance, the Water District, in the latter twentieth century, would have to evolve from an agency that had worked relatively autonomously to an agency seeking collaboration. It would have to relinquish least-cost designs for environmentally-sensitive approaches that would readily earn permits from regulators. It would have to effectively lobby in Sacramento and Washington D.C., where funding decisions were made. In the area of flood protection, the Water District would, simply put, have to change its attitude and approach while developing its financial savvy (see also Chapter 15 for discussion of policy changes led by the district board of directors).

The evolution of the Water District's approach can be seen in the four vignettes presented here, including three large federally-assisted projects and one smaller local project. It can also be seen in the Water District's Stream Maintenance Program that, in 2001, achieved and modeled a new standard of permit compliance for the nation.

Vignette: The Guadalupe River Park and Flood Protection Project

Few public works projects in Santa Clara County have been as drawn-out as the Guadalupe River Park and Flood Protection Project. The three-phase project, extending a total of 14 miles through downtown San José, endured a long 50-year journey through the "political labyrinth" before construction commenced in 1992.[7]

The Guadalupe River, or Rio Guadalupe as named in 1776 by explorer Juan Bautista de Anza, has a long history of flooding. Early newspaper articles describe large floods occurring in 1862, 1895, 1911 and 1917. The flood of 1955 was the river's worst in recorded history. That year, the Guadalupe inundated 8,300 acres, left 809 families homeless and caused more than $1.3 million in damages.[8] The Guadalupe significantly flooded again in 1963, 1969, 1982, 1983, 1986 and twice in 1995.

Despite the number of times the Guadalupe demonstrated its power for destruction, obtaining federal assistance for a flood protection project was difficult. The Corps first began to study flooding problems on the Guadalupe in 1941. When the Korean War broke out in 1950, the study came to a halt. Another study started in the 1960s, but was dropped when the federal administration could not justify investing in the project. Bonnie Bamburg, member of the Guadalupe Flood Control and Watershed Advisory Committee since 1976, explained:

In the 1950s and '60s, the Guadalupe floodplain held mostly old buildings and a lot of asphalt, and not much else. The Corps initially felt the project was too expensive when compared to the projected savings in flood damage. But in the 1970s, the architectural value of old, historic buildings was gaining both local and national

interest. The historical quotient began to weigh more heavily, improving the benefit-cost ratio to favor the project.[9]

In 1972, the Corps resumed the Guadalupe flood management study, but with changing federal administrations, the priority of the project continued to ebb and flow. As discussed in Chapter 10, unusually wet winters in 1982 and 1983 created severe flooding along both the Guadalupe River and Coyote Creek, and for a moment, the national spotlight was on San José as hundreds of people were evacuated from their homes. The silver lining was that the Corps was prompted to complete its study, and in 1985, the Corps released its final flood control report, now including

Guadalupe River flooding along Santa Clara Street, downtown San José, 1995.

Summary:
Guadalupe River Park and Flood Protection Project

Location: I-880 to I-280

Total cost: $253 million (as of December 2004)

Description: The project aims to protect downtown San José and areas downstream from a one percent flood, which could affect more than 4,300 structures and cause $576 million in damages (2002 estimate).

Status: Phases One and Two were completed in 1994 and 1996, respectively. Phase Three, which addressed fishery issues, was completed in December 2004. Additional projects are planned on the river's upper and lower reaches.

We wanted a people-

friendly, artistic plan—

a green parkway that

would enrich the

downtown area.

The 19.7-mile long Guadalupe River threads through downtown San José. The flood project's design integrated with a park, including the purple Children's Discovery Museum (2004).

environmental documentation. The report "established a financially feasible project that justified federal funding."[10]

City's vision of a park. While Water District officials were pursuing the Corps and federal funding, the downtown San José area that flanked the Guadalupe was undergoing a transformation. Under the leadership of Mayor Tom McEnery and Director Frank Taylor of the San Jose Redevelopment Agency, millions of dollars were being poured into downtown improvements, and they saw the riparian greenery of the Guadalupe as an aesthetic component of their plan. Starting in the 1970s, San José officials began articulating a vision of an urban river park along the Guadalupe. "We did not want to replicate the Santa Cruz dikes or the concrete channels in Los Angeles. We wanted a people-friendly, artistic plan—a green parkway that would enrich the downtown area," recalled McEnery in 2003.[11] The river park that San José leaders hoped for would include bike trails, parks and open space—all along the Guadalupe's potentially troublesome banks. In the 1980s, San José city officials and the city-sponsored Guadalupe Gardens Task Force (a group that provided oversight of riverside development in the downtown core) began meeting with the Water District, the Corps and other key groups to promote their vision.

But Corps officials and city representatives could not agree on the project design. Even in the late 1980s, the Corps still held steadfast to traditional construction methods—concrete embankments, riprap and safety fencing. The key criterion of the Corps was, at the time, to build a project as economically as possible. City leaders, on the other hand, objected that these traditional methods were unaesthetic, and conflicted with the goal to draw people to the park and to provide recreational access along the river. In fact, city officials went to Washington D.C. to testify against the Guadalupe project; they had no desire to see it built according to the Corps' plan.[12]

Dismayed by this turn of events, Water District officials, intent on their mission to provide flood protection, quickly went to work as arbitrator between the city and the Corps. By 1990, the three agencies came to agree on a new design that would include the river park. Unfortunately, the good will behind their effort would be thwarted: When the compromise design was sent for approval to the assistant secretary of the Army for Civil Works (the federal administration's overseer of Corps activities), project sponsors were told that the design varied too much from the original submission, and worse, the inclusion of the river park would have to be fully financed by the local sponsors, rather than the proposed 50-50 split between federal and local entities. The city and Water District argued against a 100 percent local funding arrangement, but the result was that in March 1991, federal funding for the Guadalupe River Park and Flood Protection Project was officially suspended.[13]

Throughout the remainder of 1991, two champions of the project—congressmen Norm Mineta and Don Edwards—intensified their work on Capitol Hill to reignite the project's flickering status. They managed to include the Guadalupe project in an Energy and Water Resources Development Appropriations Bill. As the bill gathered support in congressional hearings, the Corps proposed a compromise that the federal administration might find palatable: If the local sponsors would fund the design changes in the less developed sections (downstream of Julian Street), then federal funding would be provided on the downtown section of the project (upstream of Julian Street). Concurrent with this offer, the federal administration was again changing with incoming President Bill Clinton. Congressman Mineta arranged a meeting among all parties and a new assistant secretary of the Army for Civil Works, who agreed to support the revised plan.[14]

In March 1992, local sponsors were able to seal the federal administration's approval and financial commit-

With changing federal administrations, the priority of the project continued to ebb and flow.

ment. And finally, on August 25, 1992, 51 years after the first Guadalupe River study, construction commenced.[15]

In the end, the Water District, Corps and city of San José designed a project that would reap many kudos. In 1992, the American Society of Landscape Architects honored the city's landscape design consultant, Hargreaves Associates, for the design of the river park.[16] The Corps would point to the project as a model of integrating flood protection with recreational amenities and environmental mitigation. And in 2003, this project would be publicly noted in the *San Jose Mercury News* for how it "gracefully" restored the Guadalupe River.[17] But before that accolade was published, the mitigation component of the project would need greater attention.

Fish stop Phase Three. Construction of Phase One and Phase Two of the downtown section of the Guadalupe project proceeded smoothly; the phases were completed in 1994 and 1996, respectively. Phase Three (which ran from Interstate 280 to Coleman Avenue, a distance of 1.8 miles) was halted before construction could commence. This phase would hang in limbo as potential litigation and an intense political process unfolded over the Water District's responsiblities to address aquatic habitat on the river.

In February 1992, the Water District received its permit from the State Water Resources Control Board to proceed with construction on Phase Three (a "Conditional Certification under the Clean Water Act Section 401"). But in mid-1994, the State Board—largely due to "prompting from the local environmental community"—directed that construction be halted upstream of Coleman Avenue until the permit conditions—specifically, environmental mitigation—were met. Staff from the U.S. Fish and Wildlife Service also "noted problems with the project," stating concern that while environmental mitigation on the Guadalupe project had been projected for Phase Three, there was little evidence that this mitigation would take place.[18]

The group that was most vocal about the Guadalupe project's environmental impacts was the Guadalupe-Coyote Resource Conservation District (RCD). While the Corps proceeded to review its mitigation approach, the Water District invited the Guadalupe-Coyote RCD to "take its concerns" to the earlier-mentioned Guadalupe Gardens Task Force. Although members of the RCD began to meet monthly with the task force, they were in no conciliatory mood. For a period of years, the RCD board had been trying to signal the Water District that they were dissatisfied with the Guadalupe project, arguing that both the project and district-owned dams failed to comply with water laws that protected wildlife and aquatic resources. In particular, the RCD pointed to Section 5937 of the Fish and Game Code:

> *The owner of any dam shall allow sufficient water at all times to pass through a fishway, or in the absence of a fishway, allow sufficient water to pass over, around or through the dam to keep in good condition any fish that may be planted or exist below the dam.*
> ~ *Fish and Game Code, Section 5937*

In August 1994, a portion of the Guadalupe River had dried up during the conduct of district maintenance work; a Guadalupe-Coyote RCD member observed the "dryback" and reported it to the state Department of Fish and Game. Department staff verified the dryback, and then confronted the Water District on how this conflicted with existing laws. Department staff then sought enforcement from the Santa Clara County District Attorney's Office. Citing Section 5937, the district attorney filed a civil suit against the Water District's operations manager for a misdemeanor violation (state law allowed for civil complaints against employees who decided the operations of water utilties).

On August 25, 1992,

51 years after the first

Guadalupe River study,

construction commenced.

But challenges to the

project were far from over.

Similarly, in August 1995, the district attorney's office filed a civil complaint against the Water District and its new general manager, Stan Williams, for unlawfully obstructing the flow of water in the Guadalupe River (People of the State of California vs. Santa Clara Valley Water District and Stanley M. Williams). In this case, the Water District was required to pay $12,500 in fines to the Department of Fish and Game and $12,500 to the Santa Clara County Fish and Wildlife Propagation Fund. The Water District was also served an injunction requiring that through December 1999, the district was to "maintain a live stream from the confluence of Alamitos and Guadalupe creeks downstream to Gauging Station 23B by maintaining a flow of at least one cubic foot per second of water at all times."[19]

While Water District officials considered how to respond to these legal challenges, the environmental groups continued to press their case. In July 1996, the Guadalupe-Coyote RCD, Western Water Canoe Club and two fishery groups, Trout Unlimited and the Pacific Coast Federation of Fishermen's Associations, working with legal representation from the Natural Heritage Institute, notified the Water District of their intent to sue both the Water District and the Corps in a federal court, claiming that the Guadalupe project violated the Clean Water Act on more than a dozen counts.[20] As discussed in Chapter 15, the pro-fish groups would also file a complaint before the State Water Resources Control Board, seeking to amend the water rights and reservoir operations of the Water District on the basis that such operations were not providing adequate flows for fish and other wildlife in three specific streams: Coyote Creek, Stevens Creek and the Guadalupe River. Of particular concern were steelhead trout and Chinook salmon that, if sparsely, populated these streams. At the time, both of these fish species were headed for the federal register of threatened and endangered species (see also Appendix E).

MONDAY, JULY 15, 1996

☆ San Francisco Chronicle

'We tried to work it out. But they just kept going ahead with their plan'
— NANCY BERNARDI, CONSERVATION DISTRICT BOARD MEMBER

Flood Project Threatens Fish, Foes Say

Suit planned over habitat changes on Guadalupe River

By Maria Alicia Gaura
Chronicle South Bay Bureau

Despite 50 years of study and a $139 million budget, a massive flood-control project on San Jose's Guadalupe River may be forced to halt because the project's designers have neglected the fish.

The U.S. Army Corps of Engineers, in partnership with the Santa Clara Valley Water District, has already com about half of the Guad

Flood Control Project — an ambitious attempt to prevent flooding and create a rambling riverside park through San Jose's crowded urban core.

But biologists monitoring the project say its widened streambeds and concrete-lined channels could prove lethal to the Guadalupe's dwindling salmon and steelhead runs and must be substantially redesigned.

With amazing persistence, an unknown number of steelhead trout and Chinook and Coho salmon still make the annual trek from the Pacific Ocean through San Francisco Bay and into the Guadalupe River. Dumbfounded

see three- and four-foot fish wriggling past construction sites and mounds of urban detritus to breed in the river's upper reaches.

The Guadalupe-Coyote Resource Conservation District, a small state-sponsored watchdog agency, has announced plans to sue the Army Corps and the water district in federal court, demanding a more fish-friendly design for the flood control project. The suit will probably be filed July 22, following a mandatory 60-day advance notice.

The same group will file a complaint before the State Wa-

unlawfully harming wildlife by altering and draining streams and blocking the passage of spawning fish.

"We tried to work it out. We talked and talked," said Nancy Bernardi, a conservation district board member. "But they just kept going ahead with their plan.

"When they drew up this plan 10 or 15 years ago they didn't really know much about the fish," Bernardi said. "And now the plan is so politically ingrained that nobody really wants to change anything."

Water district officials admit the flood control project was de-

Page A16 Col. 1

Breaking ground on the Guadalupe project, August 25, 1992. Left to right are General Manager Ronald Esau, Congressman Norman Mineta, Colonel Laurence Sadhoff from the Army Corps of Engineers and Chairman Patrick Ferraro of the Water District board. Within two years, this long-awaited project would again be delayed, this time by the need to address fishery issues.

Guadalupe Collaborative Stakeholders

- Guadalupe-Coyote Resource Conservation District
- Trout Unlimited
- Western Water Canoe Club
- Pacific Coast Federation of Fishermen's Associations
- Natural Heritage Institute
- Santa Clara Valley Water District
- U.S. Army Corps of Engineers
- State Water Resources Control Board
- Regional Water Quality Control Board
- State Department of Fish and Game
- U.S. Fish and Wildlife Service
- National Marine Fisheries Service
- City of San José
- Guadalupe Gardens Task Force

All sides agreed that not much was known about the historical runs of salmon and steelhead on the Guadalupe when the design of the flood control project was first taking place in the 1980s. However, the Guadalupe-Coyote RCD contended that there was certainty of the existence of the fish; that critical studies were warranted; and that the Water District and Corps simply did not want to make design changes to accommodate the fish. Noted Nancy Bernardi, an RCD board member, the threat of lawsuits was needed because "the plan is so politically ingrained that nobody really wants to change anything."[21]

Some of the newer Water District board members were having similar thoughts. Rosemary Kamei, who joined the board as a director in 1993, offered this recollection:

Shortly after joining the board, I realized that the agency had several projects mired in environmental difficulties, and potential litigation was starting to mount. The environmental component of our projects was reactive, barely meeting the minimum requirements and existing more as an afterthought. This approach was not helping us achieve our flood protection goals—we needed a proactive integration of environmental compliance in our work. The fishery issues on the Guadalupe were a clear example.[22]

In early 1997, members of the Guadalupe Gardens Task Force—now a nonprofit group called the Guadalupe River Park and Gardens Corporation (and renamed to Friends of the Guadalupe River Park & Gardens in 2002)—tried to facilitate a solution. Jerry Estruth, a former San José city councilmember and a member of the group, recalled how they suggested that the Water District use a collaborative process to engage all sides in a mitigation plan that would lead to complying with the State Board's

conditions. Stated Estruth, "During our meetings with the conservation folks, we saw that they were presenting a solid case. We needed to negotiate a solution or this entire flood protection project could be shut down."[23]

The collaborative approach was a new concept to the Water District. The board of directors agreed to have General Manager Stan Williams explore the idea. After meeting with consultants and floating the idea with the Corps and city of San José, Williams proposed a two-track approach, one collaborative effort to develop an acceptable mitigation plan that would keep Phase Three of the Guadalupe project alive, and one longer-term effort to address fishery issues on other streams as well as the Guadalupe.

By the end of 1997, the first facilitated meeting of the Guadaupe Collaborative was held. All involved parties, including the complainants and regulators (see inset), were invited to develop a new mitigation plan. The originally proposed concrete channel for Phase Three was changed to a 3,000-foot long underground bypass, preserving the natural habitat and aquatic cover necessary for healthy fish and aquatic species. Furthermore, 21 acres of native vegetation would be planted along the river to cast shading over the stream, keeping waters cool for young fish.

An agreement among the stakeholders was ratified in 1998 to protect the Guadalupe River's sensitive habitat, but the agreement changed the scope of the Guadalupe project, and increased its budget to perform greater environmental enhancements. Federal approval of these changes was required—and obtained. In November 2001, Brig. Gen. Robert H. Griffin, the Corps of Engineers' director of civil works, signed off on the project. Construction on the Guadalupe project resumed in the summer of 2002.[24]

Launching FAHCE. The collaborative effort on the Phase Three mitigation plan would be mimicked in the broader, separate effort to address long-term fishery issues. Working with the state Department of Fish and Game, in

Eco-friendly features of the Guadalupe River Project

Gabions are rock-filled baskets that line the river's banks in a tiered manner (right), providing protection from erosion. The baskets fill with silt, allowing vegetation to establish itself. The growth will help shade and keep water cool for fish.

Below, **crib walls** use buried stacks of logs to stabilize the sides of the river. Native trees and shrubs are planted over the logs, which over time will decompose, but the vegetation will have developed a mature root system and will secure the embankments.

The underground **bypass channel** (left, under construction in 2004) will divert and convey high flows that would overbank the river's narrower portion; it converges again with the river at a wider spot where the flow can be handled. Bypass channels preserve habitat along the natural channel, saving it from construction activity.

1997 the Water District initiated FAHCE, the Fisheries and Aquatic Habitat Collaborative Effort. The same stakeholders were invited to resolve fish habitat issues using a "balanced approach to all beneficial uses of the local water source—including drinking water, flood protection, recreation and fisheries."[25] This project is further discussed in Chapter 15.

A celebrated accomplishment. The Water District's support of innovative design and eco-friendly features on the Guadalupe project catapulted the agency onto the national stage as a leader in both project design and policy setting. According to Robert Vining, chief of the programs management division of the Corps, the Water District established its reputation by "becoming proactive in the development of the Corps-local sponsor relationship; by contributing innovative ideas on water policy issues; and by designing a model project on the Guadalupe River that showed how urban flood protection measures could combine with recreational amenities and the preservation of riparian habitat."[26] Vining added that the Guadalupe project was truly groundbreaking in its approach and contributed to a new way of working on subsequent Corps projects.

The total cost of the Guadalupe River Park and Flood Protection Project was estimated at $253 million upon completion, an increase from $186.7 million before the Phase Three revisions. Of the increased figure, about $13 million was used for improvements to fish and wildlife habitat. Without the project, potential flood damage from a one percent flood in the San José city core alone could cost as much as $576 million.[27] Although many years and much collaboration went into the project, there remained concerns in the community of Alviso, where some residents still felt at risk. "After being flooded so many times,

> "These waters can be managed now for what they are—an asset and not a threat. This is one of the most important flood control projects that America has ever seen—today signed, sealed and delivered. It is a very historic occasion."
>
> ~ U.S. Transportation Secretary Norman Mineta

At center, U.S. Transportation Secretary Norman Mineta is flanked by Water District board directors (left to right) Larry Wilson, Sig Sanchez, Greg Zlotnick, Rosemary Kamei, Richard Santos and Tony Estremera. Absent: Board director Joe Judge.

"This is an accomplishment, a dream come true. It is a good example of how combining efforts works."

~ Chief Executive Officer Stan Williams, SCVWD

On January 14, 2005, the Water District, Corps and city of San José celebrated the completion of the downtown Guadalupe River Park and Flood Protection Project. Master of Ceremonies Stan Williams welcomed hundreds of dignitaries, Water District staff and retired staff, and community members. Umbrellas were distributed to the crowd to symbolize, "Let It Rain."

Dignitaries on stage included, left to right, 2005 Board Chairman Richard Santos of the Water District, Congresswoman Zoe Lofgren, U.S. Transportation Secretary Norm Mineta, Mayor Ron Gonzales of the city of San José, Major General Don T. Riley of the U.S. Army Corps of Engineers, and Chief Executive Officer Stan Williams of the Water District.

it's hard to have confidence that a project constructed upstream is going to protect you," explained Director Richard Santos, who represented the area and who himself had experienced the flooding.

Yet former mayor Tom McEnery looked back with satisfaction at the project. He said that while great plans often are not accompanied by great execution, the river park was an exception. McEnery, pointing to the egrets that swoop along the brushy river banks—a view he sees from his downtown office—said, "They show that we did something right."[28]

Vignette:
The Coyote Creek Flood Protection Project

Coyote Creek travels an impressive 63 miles from its headwaters east of Gilroy to its outflow into the southern San Francisco Bay. The creek drains the largest watershed in Santa Clara County, an area of nearly 320 square miles, including most of the eastern foothills, the city of Milpitas and parts of the cities of San José and Morgan Hill. A major tributary in this watershed is Berryessa Creek.[29]

Through the latter twentieth century, flooding on Coyote Creek occurred, on average, every four years. Prior to the construction of Coyote and Anderson reservoirs, flooding occurred even more frequently, with flood events in 1903, 1906, 1909, 1911, 1917, 1922, 1923, 1926, 1927, 1930 and 1931.[30] The reservoirs, built in 1936 and 1950, respectively, helped to absorb runoff in the area, thereby reducing—but not eliminating—flooding in this watershed. Flooding continued to occur, most significantly in 1982, 1983, 1986, 1995 and 1997.

The Coyote Creek Flood Protection Project shares much of the lengthy history of the Guadalupe project; Congress first identified it as a target project in 1941 under the Guadalupe River and Adjacent Streams Study.

The Coyote project rode the same roller coaster as the Guadalupe project for thirty years, being stalled by wars and federal disinterest. This lack of interest was easy to understand, given the largely rural nature of the Coyote watershed. In 1950, only ten square miles of the area were urbanized, with a population of barely 100,000. But rapid growth would occur here as elsewhere in Santa Clara County; by 2000, 100 square miles of the watershed were urbanized, with a population approaching one million.[31]

When the Guadalupe project was rekindled in the early 1970s, so was the Coyote project; from there it took its own path, with a series of studies conducted by the Corps. A "Plan of Study" was completed in 1973; "problem definition and alternative screening" was completed in 1974; more of the same was completed in 1978; a study of flooding in the baylands (the lower reach of Coyote Creek) was completed in 1979. As with the Guadalupe, it took the grim and substantial flooding in 1982 and 1983 for the project to merit not only studies but also congressional action. The Corps was urged to complete its studies, and the project won authorization for preconstruction planning, engineering and design under the Water Resources Development Act of 1986.[32]

The design of the Coyote Creek Flood Protection Project took particular aim at the unstable levees, constructed by early century farmers, which existed along the lower Coyote Creek. In this area, the communities of Alviso, northern San José and Milpitas were exposed to substantial flood risk. It was the overtopping and failure of these levees that was responsible for much of the flood damage in 1982 and 1983 (see Chapter 10 for discussion of these floods).

While waiting for federal funding after the disastrous '83 flood, the Water District worked on its own to address the flooded sludge ponds and rebuild the setback levees adjacent to the San Jose/Santa Clara Water Pollution Control Plant. In the summer of 1985, the Water District pro-

Opposite page:

Water District board directors Joe Judge and Sig Sanchez stand with Congresswoman Zoe Lofgren and General Manager Stan Williams at the January 13, 1996 celebration of the completion of the Coyote Creek Flood Control Project. The project was undertaken to address weak levees built by farmers of the early 1900s; the creek would frequently break through or overtop these antiquated and unstable barriers during high water flows. The right photograph shows the improved Coyote Creek channel handling storm flows that occurred in March 1995.

Summary:
Coyote Creek
Flood Protection Project

Location: San Francisco Bay to Montague Expressway

Total cost: $62 million

Description: The Coyote Creek Flood Protection Project is the first component of the greater Coyote/Berryessa Creek Flood Protection Project. The Coyote project entailed levee construction, excavation of a parallel overflow channel and extensive environmental mitigation. A study in 2001 estimated potential damages from a one percent flood on this creek at $138 million.

Status: Construction was completed in 1996. The Water District initiated a new Coyote Creek Watershed Study in 1999 to provide additional flood protection to areas still subject to the creek's overbanking, notably downtown San José. As of December 2004, the Water District continues to seek federal funding for the Berryessa Creek component.

Beth Redmond

161

posed a test levee for the soft mud to ascertain the best of various specialized construction techniques.[33] However, in September, when the Water District applied for permits to build additional levees, the regulatory branch of the Corps rejected the application. While the Guadalupe project was stalled by fish, it was the endangered salt marsh harvest mouse that slowed the Coyote project. Although the Water District provided what it considered to be an adequate environmental review of the project's impact on the mouse, the Corps requested a second review to satisfy national standards; this was completed in late 1986.[34] In complying with the Endangered Species Act, efforts were initiated in 1987 to improve habitat on 52 acres for the endangered salt marsh harvest mouse and to create a 16-acre

brackish water pond. The research conducted for this project led to successful mitigation work that became a model for flood protection projects elsewhere in the county.[35]

In addition to levee improvements, project objectives included widening Coyote Creek between the San Francisco Bay and Montague Expressway, and excavating a parallel overflow channel to preserve riparian habitat. The widening took place only on one side of the channel, helping to keep riparian habitat intact on the other side.

The entire Coyote Creek Flood Protection Project was completed in 1996. In 1997, homes in the project area were freed from the requirement for flood insurance.[36]

In retrospect, the environmental work of the Coyote project stands as one of its most notable features. Between 1993 and 2000, the Water District added 32 acres of trees and shrubs along Coyote Creek, substantially increasing the biological value of the area.[37] Furthermore, after flooding along the creek destroyed three homes in 1997 (upstream of the completed project and immediately downstream of William Street Park in San José), the Water District bought the homes, razed them and rebuilt the 1.5-acre site as an outdoor classroom. "From the devastation visited upon this site only a few short years ago, we now have a place where people can learn how to help prevent future flooding losses, and where tomorrow's leaders can learn what it takes to nurture our riparian environment," stated Director Tony Estremera, at the groundbreaking event for the Coyote Creek Outdoor Classroom. The $515,000 project was co-funded by the Water District and a grant from the state Department of Water Resources.[38]

The 1997 flooding came from a series of storms in January that generated record runoff in the Coyote watershed. Coyote Creek flooded several sites in San José and Morgan Hill, damaging homes and businesses and closing a portion of Highway 101. In downtown San José, several homes were inundated with more than six feet of water,

Severe storms in January 1997 caused Coyote Creek to flood (top), despite improvements that were completed in 1996. The Water District purchased the land where three homes were heavily damaged, and constructed the Coyote Creek Outdoor Classroom at this site in 2001 (bottom photo).

while a mobile home park and businesses adjacent to the Union Pacific Railroad tracks were flooded.[39] However, district officials noted that without the completed project downstream, the 1997 flooding would have backed up, creating 57 percent more volume, and "the resulting damage would have exceeded any flood disaster in the county's history."[40] As a result of the 1997 flood, the Water District proceeded to initiate a new Coyote Creek Watershed Study in 1999. As of 2004, this has not yet received federal funding.

Vignette:
Llagas Creek Watershed Project

On its journey to the Pajaro River at the county's southern end, Llagas Creek usually flows slow and lazy, passing open fields and the expanding cities of Morgan Hill and Gilroy. But during heavy storms, the Llagas—fed by many small tributaries that drain a 104-square mile watershed—can surprisingly fill and spill across fields, neighborhoods, commercial zones and important roadways.[41]

Like the Guadalupe River, Llagas Creek contributed to the infamous Christmas Week Floods of December 1955; that was the most extensive flood on this creek in recorded history (see Chapter 14). The 1982 Llagas flood, recorded as a one percent event, was also severe, with damages estimated at $8.5 million.[42] Work on the Lower Llagas portion of the project helped to reduce damage from floods in 1986, 1995, 1997 and 1998.

Efforts to provide flood protection along Llagas Creek began in 1954, when the Loma Prieta Resource Conservation District (RCD) applied for flood management assistance from the federal Soil Conservation Service, now referred to as the Natural Resources Conservation Service.[†]

Llagas is a PL-566 project. According to Fred Angelino, a long-time South County farmer and a member of the Loma Prieta RCD, the application was timed to take advantage of a new law, PL-566, the Watershed Protection and Flood Prevention Act of 1954.[43] The Service approved the application in 1957. The Santa Clara Valley Water District, which would become responsible for local-share and long-term maintenance costs, joined with the RCD and Service to work out a flood protection plan.[††]

Those were the days—as recalled by Jeff Rodriguez, a Service conservationist who administered the PL-566 projects in Santa Clara County—when highly trained engineers proceeded with their designs without engaging and educating the affected community.[44] So, although the plan was completed in 1962, when the farming community was invited to the only townhall meeting to view the final design, controversy erupted. Jack Sturla, whose family had been farming in South County since 1864, recalled the day:

> *At the meeting hall, the walls were covered with all kinds of maps and plans for rip rap, culverts and drop structures. When we saw the dimensions for the channel widening, well, we were stunned. The creek's natural width was about 60 feet; the plans called for widening it to 215 feet.*

Summary: Llagas Creek Watershed Project

Location: Wright Avenue (city of Morgan Hill) to the Pajaro River

Total cost: Lower Llagas—$52.6 million; Upper Llagas—$57.4 million

Description: The 16.6 mile-long project involved channel widening, installation of box culverts and 35 bridge replacements. A study in 1982 found a one percent flood could inundate 10,300 acres, and cost $8.5 million in damages. The potential amount of damages has significantly risen with increased urbanization in the area, and a restudy is underway at the time of this writing.

Status: The Lower Llagas project was completed in 1996. The Upper Llagas project is slated for completion in 2010.

[†] The Soil Conservation Service was formed under the Soil Conservation Act of 1935. This law enabled the formation of resource conservation districts, or RCDs, which operate in conjunction with the Service. With voter approval, any community may form a resource conservation district. As of 2005, two RCDs exist in Santa Clara County: the Loma Prieta RCD and the Guadalupe-Coyote RCD (formerly the Evergreen RCD).

[††] The Loma Prieta RCD and the Water District are among a handful of agencies in California that tapped into the PL-566 program. The Llagas project and a smaller Lower Silver Creek project (approved in 1983)—are the two PL-566 projects in Santa Clara County.

The district officials explained to us that while the cities of Morgan Hill and Gilroy were still relatively remote from the Llagas, the outskirts of these cities were pushing closer to the river. They talked about a 'one percent flood' and the catastrophic damage it could cause. But we thought it was pretty unlikely. The project was going to affect a lot of our land, so we were against it at the start; we saw that this was a huge project that would permanently change the landscape.[45]

Sturla and other community members who were unhappy with the proposal formed a committee and went before the Santa Clara County Board of Supervisors; they successfully delayed the project. They also requested many more meetings with the Water District. When Sturla was elected to the South Santa Clara Valley Water Conservation District (see Appendix A), his position on the project began to change. "It wasn't long before I understood the issues and what, exactly, a one percent flood would mean to the cities downstream," he said. Sturla reversed his stance and began promoting the project, educating farmers as to why the dramatically widened channel was needed. "It really was an issue of public understanding," noted Sturla.[46]

In 1967, separate work plans were prepared for the lower and upper portions of the creek, and federal funding was authorized in 1969.[47]

Channelization creates a stir. In 1974, when the long-awaited construction commenced, it was quickly halted when the project was found to have inadequately addressed environmental impacts, now required by the new National Environmental Policy Act (NEPA, passed in 1969), the California Environmental Quality Act (CEQA, passed in 1970) and the Endangered Species Act (ESA, passed in 1973). Fred Angelino recalled that during the 1970s, not only environmentalists within the county and

state, but as far away as Oregon, traveled to Santa Clara County to voice their opinions because of the proposed channelization methodology. The proposed project "was like waving a red flag in front of a bull because 'channelization' was seen as a dirty word," said Angelino.[48]

Channelization was the increasingly controversial process of straightening bends and widening a stream to increase its flow capacity, and often lining the channel with concrete. The approach reflected the major concern of flood management agencies in the 1950s and '60s: to convey floodwaters away from property as efficiently and cost-effectively as possible. At the time, this approach also had general public support; flood protection projects were built with scant attention to environmental impacts or aesthetics.

Channelization could increase the velocity of flows, and if unlined by concrete, such fast flows could lead to a scoured, deeper streambed with less stable banks. Environmentalists argued that this practice also destroyed too much habitat and caused more sediment to enter the stream. Angelino, along with project engineers, felt that some channelization was needed to achieve flood protection, and would provide for less costly maintenance. The Llagas Creek Citizens Advisory Committee was organized to develop a plan to minimize adverse impacts; this was completed in 1978 and presented for interagency review in 1979.

In March 1980, after numerous meetings, a restudy was proposed. The Soil Conservation Service and Water District completed this restudy of the Llagas Creek floodplain in 1982, taking into account environmental measures. Adverse impacts of construction on the riparian habitat would be mitigated by revegetation, installation of fish ladders, plunge pools and low-flow channels to allow the valley's small but still present steelhead trout population to continue their upstream migration.[49] The final Environmental Impact Report (EIR) was completed and construction was renewed in late 1982.

1986 flood proves project value. As planned, Llagas Creek was widened at some points to 215 feet. When a nearly one percent flood hit the area in February 1986, the project proved its value. "It was the most water I'd ever seen go by in that river in all the years I've lived here," said Sturla. "Without the channel widening, that water would have created a serious flood."[50]

In May 1987, the Water District secured an unusual source of funding for some elements of the Llagas project. Private developers Glen-Loma Farotte Construction Group of Gilroy, Arcadia Development Company and The William Lyon Company were building homes in the area, and they became concerned when told that progress on constructing culverts and bridges—which would help provide flood protection for the developers' properties—was being slowed because of inadequate funding. Recalled Bruce Wilson, a district project engineer at the time, "One developer asked me what it was going to take to get the project rolling. I explained that the district was short of seed money for the construction costs of the bridges, but would be reimbursed by the state subventions program within a few months of having completed the work. To my surprise, he said 'let's work out an arrangement.'"[51]

Shortly thereafter, the three developers advanced an interest-free $4.6 million loan to the Water District for the construction of five box culverts along Monterey Road and Leavesley Avenue. The loans allowed the Water District to begin work three years sooner than originally planned, providing flood protection to hundreds of existing and planned homes that much sooner.[52]

The nationwide PL-566 program was hit hard in the mid-1990s when federal appropriations to the program were slashed from $391 million in 1994 to $24 million in 1995. A backlog of $1.2 billion on PL-566 projects across the nation quickly mounted.[53] The Lower Llagas project was completed in 1996, but the upper portion was left in-complete. Consequently, floods in 1997 and 1998 affected homes in the vicinity of upper Llagas Creek. After the flood of 1997, over 100 community members attended a public meeting where they expressed frustration with the project's incomplete status and proposed schedule.

Because of PL-566 funding problems, in 1999 Congress approved the Water District's request to transfer federal construction authority from the Natural Resources Conservation Service to the U.S. Army Corps of Engineers. The Corps (which would now fund 50 percent of the costs on the Upper Llagas project) commenced a restudy of the area. Significant changes from the 1982 study included design consideration and mitigation for endangered species, such as the red-legged frog and steelhead trout.

In 2004, the Llagas Creek Watershed Project remains only 60 percent complete, providing flood protection to the Gilroy area but leaving Morgan Hill and San Martin unprotected. Completion of the project—expected in 2010—will provide flood protection to an additional 950 acres of urban land and about 1,300 acres of farmland.[54]

It was the most water I'd ever seen go by in that river . . . without the channel widening, that water would have created a serious flood.

Jack Sturla, whose family has been farming in South County since 1864, stands at the edge of a dry Llagas creekbed in June 1994. Sturla served as a board director and general manager for the former Gavilan Water District.

Summary: Matadero/Barron Creek Flood Protection Project

Location: El Camino Real (in Palo Alto) to the Barron Creek Sediment Basin

Total cost: $56 million (as of December 2004)

Description: The project entails construction of a floodwall, the Barron Diversion (3,000 foot-long underground bypass channel), and bridge and box culvert replacements. A one percent flood on this creek system could cause $370 million in damages, affecting more than 7,200 homes, apartments and businesses (2002 estimate).

Status: As of 2004, Phases One through Five are complete; phases Six and Seven are on hold. A remediation project was launched in 1999 to widen the channel and raise flood walls between Alma Street and the Palo Alto Flood Basin; the bridge at Louis Road was targeted for improvement as well. The remediation work was completed in December 2004.

Vignette: The Matadero/Barron Creek Flood Protection Project

For decades, neighborhoods in the vicinity of Matadero and Barron creeks, in the city of Palo Alto, braced for floods whenever heavy storms came along. Particularly significant floods occurred in the floodplain of these creeks in 1941, 1952, 1955, 1958, 1973 and 1983.

In the January 1983 flooding, heavy rains caused both Matadero and Barron creeks to overflow. When the Water District sponsored Measure F in 1986 to fund speedier construction of projects (Chapter 10), it would be Palo Alto voters who passed the measure with the highest margin in the county—more than a two-thirds majority.

This district-funded project would take place in a densely urbanized area as well as through a beloved neighborhood park. The Water District sought to work closely with the communites that would be affected. According to Doug Moran, president in 2003 of the Barron Park Association, while the community wanted flood protection, it was equally interested in preserving the "highly prized natural creek setting of their neighborhood."[55]

To accomplish the community's goal, district engineers came up with a design that would divert floodwaters from Barron Creek to Matadero Creek through the Barron Diversion—a 3,000-foot long underground bypass channel with a 10- by 6-foot dimension. Normal flows on the two creeks would continue to pass through their natural channels, but high floodwater would flow into the bypass and be conveyed into a concrete trapezoidal channel on the Matadero downstream of El Camino Real. The flow capacity of this downstream channel would also be increased by constructing floodwalls along the banks and replacing several bridges.[56]

The project, which began in 1988, was organized into seven phases relating to particular urban features. Each phase had its own challenges:

In Phase One, along Matadero Creek in mid-town Palo Alto, construction workers confronted an underground 60,000-volt electrical line, allowing only an 18-inch clearance at some points. Shutting off the line was not an option, as it supplied power to Hewlett Packard, Varian Associates and other high-tech businesses in the Stanford Research Park that could not incur interrupted service. Workers simply had to proceed carefully, and they did with success.

Similarly, in Phase Two, rail service could not be disrupted as workers installed a 50- by 20-foot pre-cast, concrete box culvert under the Southern Pacific (SP) railroad tracks crossing Matadero Creek. The solution was for contractors to coordinate with SP to alternate two-way train service on one set of tracks while workers quickly removed the other set, excavated for partial installation, back-filled, and replaced the tracks. A few days later, the same process was repeated on the second set of tracks.

In Phase Three, workers faced the ire of bicyclists, as construction alongside Park Boulevard required cyclists to use busy detours for several months. Phase Four also entailed detours as it focused on the installation of the previously-mentioned bypass under the six-lane, densely traveled El Camino Real. Coordinating with CalTrans, this took three years, with drivers enduring tedious changes of the detour from one lane to another every three to four months.[57]

Phase Five, begun in 1994, continued the installation of the Barron Creek Diversion under the popular Bol Park. The Water District did not own any rights-of-way there, and had to negotiate with numerous property owners for easements that granted access.

Construction challenges in the last phases, Six and Seven, were so daunting that the project was halted. Within the project area of these phases—specifically at the Hillview-Porter property along Matadero Creek—soil and groundwater contamination was severe enough to have the area designated as a Superfund site. Construction work was delayed and is still on hold at the time of this writing.

Perhaps more disappointing to both residents and the Water District, the innovative bypass would become a prolonged project: In 1996, when district staff applied to FEMA for a Letter of Map Revision, which would remove the insurance requirement on thousands of homes and businesses in the floodplain along Matadero and Barron creeks, some hydraulic calculation errors were discovered for the channel design in Phase One. Katherine Oven, an assistant operating officer for the Water District, explained that to comply with FEMA's freeboard height requirements, the floodwalls at various bridge crossings constructed in Phase 1 (between Highway 101 and Alma Street) would have to be raised an additional one to two feet, to a height as high as seven feet.[58]

Floodwall height was one of the most sensitive issues for the Palo Alto community. The Water District turned to its project planning consultant, Schaaf & Wheeler, for help.

The underground bypass was constructed

below the neighborhood's

beloved park . . .

At left is the underground bypass channel during construction in early 1994. The channel is now hidden from view as it lies beneath Bol Park (above photo).

Floods of the 1990s

January–March 1995

In 1995, a storm started on January 3 and lasted until January 14, delivering one of the Bay Area's wettest weeks on record. The night of January 9 was particularly intense—mudslides closed portions of several highways, while the Guadalupe River spilled into central San José. Floodwater on Highway 87 reached a depth of 15 feet at some underpasses. River Street at the edge of downtown flooded. Along Virginia Street, the river gushed into homes and pushed cars along the sidewalks. On Belmont Way, off Alma Avenue, firefighters used rafts to help evacuate residents, while others swam out. More than 300 residents fled their homes, and Red Cross shelters were prepared at three San José high schools. Across the county, power failed to about 75,000 county residents. President Bill Clinton declared the county a federal disaster area. Damage was estimated at more than $4 million.

Respite from the January storms was short-lived. On March 10, flows at the confluence of Los Gatos Creek and the Guadalupe River reached their highest peak on record—more than 10,000 cfs (cubic feet per second). The Guadalupe flooded 300 homes in downtown San José, leaving 339 people to sleep in a Red Cross shelter that night. Highway 87 was closed. Mayor Susan Hammer declared a state of emergency, and on March 13, President Clinton signed a national emergency declaration. Damages were estimated at $10 million.[102]

Highway 87 flooded, March 1995.

Courtesy San Jose Mercury News

River Street, downtown San José, March 1995.

William Street flooded by Coyote Creek, January 1997.

January 1997

In late January, Coyote Creek flooded several sites between Morgan Hill and San José, causing damage to homes and businesses. In parts of downtown San José, on January 26, several houses were inundated with more than six feet of water. Both a mobile home park and businesses adjacent to the Union Pacific Railroad tracks were flooded. However, had protective measures downstream not been completed by 1996, the flooding would have happened 40 percent faster and had 57 percent more volume; the resulting damage would have exceeded any flood disaster in the county's history.[103]

February 1998

In February, El Niño-driven rain drenched the valley. The district ran its Emergency Operations Center around the clock and distributed more than 1.1 million sandbags. On February 3, all ten reservoirs began to spill. Flooding was widespread; the most severe conditions occurred along San Francisquito Creek (city of Palo Alto), which inundated more than 11,000 acres and more than 1,100 homes, and also in Milpitas, where hundreds of homes and apartments flooded near the confluence of Calera and Berryessa creeks. The winter concluded as the third wettest on record with a total of 28.72 inches of rain. Total flood damages were estimated at more than $20 million.[104]

"It was the middle of the night. We heard a sound like the Niagara—floodwater that was roaring into our empty swimming pool. When we looked outside, water was rushing over the edge of the pool; at the rate it was moving, we figured we had about 15 minutes to get out. We will always wish we could have saved a few special things, but we were worried about getting electrocuted. After we fled, water filled the house to 14 inches deep. Before this flood, I liked the sound of rain, but now . . . I don't want to hear it anymore."

*~ Mary Schaeffer, Palo Alto resident,
recalling the 1998 flood on San Francisquito Creek.[105]*

Courtesy San Jose Mercury News

San Francisquito Creek jumped its banks before dawn on February 3, 1998 flooding hundreds of Palo Alto homes.

The consulting firm proposed conducting a risk-based analysis that, if successful, could keep the floodwall heights at a maximum of five feet. Adhering to the Corps' risk-based analysis procedure, the consultant performed thousands of hydraulic model computer runs using random combinations of flow and channel friction factors. The resulting findings: The modified channel would pass a one percent flood event with 95 percent reliability, meeting the Corps standard for levee certification. In 2002, in a rare move, FEMA accepted the analysis and approved the Water District's request to maintain floodwalls at the lower five-foot height; the agency also issued a Conditional Letter of Map Revision. Until this time, FEMA was not known to approve such requests from entities other than the Corps, and this reflected the credibility the Water District had gained with FEMA and the Corps, as well as other regulatory agencies.[59]

Similarly, the Water District was able to avoid an unsightly modification to the maintenance access ramps that slope from the street down to the channel at various bridge crossings. FEMA wanted the high point of these concrete ramps raised to the height of the floodwalls in order to help contain high flows in the creek. Considering that such a "hump" would result in unsightly and steeper ramps, the Water District instead proposed installing temporary floodwalls during the rainy season (October to April) every year. Lightweight overlapping panels would fit into posts flanking the concrete ramps, and would provide a seamless barrier to high waters in the creek. Such temporary floodwalls are common in the Midwest, where flooding is more predictable and there is adequate lead time to put the panels in place. As West Coast watersheds can generate high runoff within a few hours, the Water District proposed to install the temporary floodwalls across the maintenance ramps for the entire rainy season. After initial hesitancy, the proposal won FEMA's approval.[60]

While floodwall height and ramp design issues were successfully resolved, a newfound problem along the 1,200-foot section of Matadero Creek between Highway 101 and the Palo Alto Flood Basin added to project challenges. Maintenance in this stretch of the creek had been reduced since the 1970s, and what had once been a channel and floodplain with a 150- to 200-foot width was now a thick jungle of riparian shrubbery, reducing the channel to a 20-foot span. Any future high water flows coursing down the channel upstream of Highway 101 would encounter this wall of vegetation on the other side of the highway. The flow would likely backup along the creek and threaten residential areas with flooding.

District engineers set out to design a bypass channel that would convey high flows to the Palo Alto Flood Basin, yet minimize impacts to the lush riparian growth. This became the 4,500 foot-long Matadero Bypass, an open channel with a 12- by 12-foot dimension that used a minimal amount of concrete in order to maintain a pervious surface.[61]

Correcting the floodwall and bridge heights to satisfy FEMA and building the Matadero Bypass were all part of the Matadero Remediation Project, initiated in March 1999. Matadero Creek residents, who had earlier felt relief at the thought of being done with construction noise, inconveniences and $500-per-year flood insurance premiums, would now have to endure three more years of project planning and design, followed by two construction seasons. Completion of the project was successfully accomplished in December 2004.[62] Despite the aggravations and costs, as pointed out by Director Greg Zlotnick, elected to represent the Palo Alto area on the Water District board in 1997, "Given that a one percent event on Matadero and Barron creeks would likely flood more than 7,200 homes, apartments and businesses, proceeding with the remediation work was clearly worthwhile."[63]

Stream Maintenance:
10-Year Permit Models Environmental Commitment

Maintenance of the county's streams is an essential part of flood protection as the work aims to ensure the flood-carrying capacity of channels. By the 1990s, this work had become substantial: In an average year, maintenance workers were removing 80,000 cubic yards of sediment from streambeds; tending to vegetation on the approximate 3,500 acres of land abutting streams; repairing about 5,000 feet of eroding stream banks; and handling a miscellany of tasks such as cleaning out culverts, storm outfalls and the underside of bridges.[64]

Around 1990, the routine permit applications for maintenance work started becoming subject to greater environmental scrutiny. Increasing regulatory requirements turned the one-year permit cycle into a costly workload of perpetual applications and reviews, and any problem found by regulators could create a delay that left the county more vulnerable to flooding. "Everyone realized the process had become inefficient and was creating problems for all concerned," recalled Jim Fiedler, chief operating officer of the district's watershed management program, who in the 1990s oversaw the district's effort to switch to a multi-year approach. "Furthermore, the one-year permit cycle did not address the cumulative impacts of repetitive maintenance activities—the information that was really of concern to regulators."[65]

In 1995, the Water District collaborated with the regulatory agencies, cities and environmental groups to develop a more efficient and effective approach. The goal: a permit good for 10 years. The Water District would develop a Stream Maintenance Program with a projected 10-year scope of maintenance work, and would provide associated environmental review documents and a mitigation plan. While participants on all sides agreed that it was a good

concept, there was disagreement regarding the amount and kind of compensatory mitigation to be associated with maintenance projects.

Part of the challenge was that existing regulations did not differentiate maintenance work from construction projects. That meant the relatively new state requirement for "no net loss of wetlands" stood to apply equally to small-scale maintenance work. The State Water Resources Control Board interpreted the requirement to mean an acre-for-acre ratio for all impacts to wetlands, with existing conditions as the impact assessment baseline. But the Water District argued that the ratio was inapplicable where maintenance took place in channels that had been constructed for flood conveyance and then subject to ongoing maintenance. For example, several channels had been subject to regular sediment removal for decades.

The State Board determined the bottom line: The Water District would have to meet the regulations of the Clean Water Act, specifically Section 401 Water Quality Certification requirements enforced by the Regional Water Quality Control Boards, and Section 404 requirements enforced by the Corps. It would be up to the Water District to prove how their 10-year program would comply. To meet that challenge, district staff focused on a program that would "mitigate for [impacts to] special status species; address cumulative impacts through the CEQA process . . . and adhere to BMPs (best management practices) to significantly reduce the level of impacts related to routine maintenance compared to historical conditions."[66] The district would also mitigate for impacts of maintenance work in previously undisturbed wetlands or areas without a record of ongoing maintenance.

Frog delays work as El Niño approaches. One of the species that the Water District would have to watch out for on its maintenance projects was the red-legged frog. After the frog's designation in 1996 as a threatened species, all creek

SAN JOSE MERCURY NEWS ■ Local ■ MONDAY, OCTOBER 6, 1997

Flood control work loses out to frog

BY MARILEE ENGE
Mercury News Staff Writer

In a month or two, when the rains come and bone-dry stream-beds fill, the rare California red-legged frog will crawl from beneath leaves and up from rodent holes, stretch its legendary limbs and head for the water to propagate.

Biologists are encouraging that activity by protecting every creek and pond that might support the colorful frogs. But a year-old federal policy of nurturing the obscure amphibians has rankled

drawing board.

"Everybody was aghast that this red-legged frog seemed to have the power to interfere with the normal maintenance of our channel for flood control purposes," said Curtis Harrison, who has lived on the banks of Adobe Creek in Palo Alto since 1958.

At the center of the drama is *Rana aurora draytonii,* a rose-hued amphibian that can grow to five inches and likes ponds and slow-moving streams. The largest frog na

The red-legged frog policy has delayed storm control work on

and, second, if frogs can be found," said Doug Padley, a wildlife biologist with the water district.

Silt and overgrown vegetation can clog creeks and cause flooding during heavy rains. For creeks that seemed likely to support frogs, and where flooding also appears probable, the water district sought clearance to remove debris. Most places where the frogs live are in remote parts of the foothills, and most flood zones are on the valley floor,

When Mark Twain penned "The Celebrated Jumping Frog of Calaveras County" in 1865, many Californians knew the frog to which he referred: the red-legged frog, scientifically known as rana aurora draytonii. Today, a Californian would be lucky to find this little fellow, much less see him jump. In 1996, the frog leaped onto the U.S. List of Endangered and Threatened Species. In Santa Clara County, a few red-legged frogs remain, their small numbers belying their influence—protecting the frog's habitat became a force that affected all of the Water District's flood protection projects, as well as the location and design of multimillion dollar developments throughout much of California.

maintenance work had to account for the frog's habitat before it could proceed. In the fall of 1997, district biologists performed an extensive survey of frog habitat. They "walked every stream in the county, twice during daylight hours and twice at night . . . . They found the creatures in more than 100 locations, some that were previously unknown."[67] As a result of the findings, permits for storm work were denied in some areas. The decision caused consternation among residents in Palo Alto, where work was being delayed. The concern was amplified by the news of possible heavy storms relating to El Niño weather patterns—the strongest seen in 15 years (see inset, p. 122).

Executive staff of the Water District met with regulatory chiefs from the Corps, the state Department of Fish and Game, and the Regional Water Quality Control Boards to apprise them of the seriousness of the situation. No sediment removal had occurred during 1995 and 1996 due to permit delays, and the conditions of certain channels were ripe for flooding. In response, permits were issued for sediment removal at nine "Urgent Sediment Removal Projects." The district was also granted extensions to work in the creek channels past October 15, normally the last day allowed for in-stream maintenance work.[68] As it turned out, heavy storms struck the valley forcefully in February 1998 and caused high flows of muddy water in the county's waterways. In downtown San José, Highway 87 turned into a small lake at its intersection with I-280, while streets and homes flooded in Milpitas. The importance of the preceding fall's maintenance work was proven; while it didn't prevent flooding, it lessened the intensity by providing improved stream capacity.

10-year permit achieved. In 2001, the Water District submitted to regulators its proposal for a Stream Maintenance Program along with a draft environmental assessment of the program and an outline of proposed mitigation.[69] In exchange for a 10-year permit, the Water District would expend $41 million to preserve as much as 1,080 acres for stream and watershed protection; create 30 acres of tidal wetlands and 14 acres of fresh wetlands; and control giant reed in 125 acres of streams throughout the county.[70]

In the early spring of 2002, the San Francisco Bay Regional Water Quality Control Board and the Central Coast Regional Water Quality Control Board approved the proposal, and the Department of Fish and Game and the Corps issued a 10-year permit to the Water District for stream maintenance.[71] Noted Director Richard Santos, "This permit allows more time to focus on the important work of protecting people, property and environmental resources rather than on paperwork."[72] The Water District would not only spend less time on permit applications, it would also spend less money. The cost of the annual application process was approximately $100,000 per year, factoring in staff and consultants' time as well as application fees. Eliminating this expense for 10 years would provide a savings of approximately $1 million.[73]

The Water District's Stream Maintenance Program became the first such program in the nation. Craig Manson, assistant secretary for Fish, Wildlife and Parks for the U.S. Department of the Interior, lauded the district's effort as "an example of the 'new environmentalism' that focuses on consultation, communication and cooperation—all in the service of conservation." He added that achieving such a permit reflected much-improved "trust between the regulators and the community."[74]

Funding the Projects:
Challenges and Successes

In the mind of a property owner or resident, the most important flood protection project is the one that prevents flooding to his or her particular home or business. The stories of the Guadalupe, Coyote, Llagas and Matadero/

Barron projects are only a handful of the dozens of important flood protection projects under the purview of the Water District (see Compendium of Flood Protection Projects in Appendix C). But these projects are emblematic of the challenges faced by the officials and workers who set out to protect the valley from flood flows. Noted Director Larry Wilson in 2003, "When looking at the history of these projects, we can see how our agency advanced from a purely engineering viewpoint of controlling floodwater to a broad-based approach that considers community and environmental concerns. It's a striking progression."[75]

What also helped this progression was an active and concerned citizenry. By passing Measure F in 1986 (discussed in chapters 9 and 10), Santa Clara County voters put substantial muscle in the five-year-old Benefit Assessment Program, the local flood protection funding effort that would pay for creek maintenance and small projects, and leverage state and federal assistance on major projects. But while the valley had developed a local funding source, economic and political swings would affect the availability of state and federal assistance, regardless of ability to meet the local share requirement.

Financial savvy needed. On the federal side, the periodic changes in presidential administrations made it difficult to hold a project's funding status on course through the cycle of appropriation bills. To address this challenge, the Water District began working hard to cultivate its relationships in the nation's capital. Ronald Esau recalled that as assistant general manager in the early 1980s, his duties focused on this effort. When appointed as general manager in 1988, Esau continued in this public relations work, but recognized his need for help. With board approval, he developed a "two-AGM" structure at the Water District. Robert Smith, head of the flood control department was promoted to assistant general manager over the water utility functions, and recruitment began for

Our agency advanced from a purely engineering viewpoint of controlling floodwater to a broad-based approach that considers community and environmental concerns.

a second assistant general manager, one experienced in federally-funded flood protection projects.[76]

Stanley M. Williams from Tulsa, Oklahoma fit the bill, and joined the Water District in early 1990 as assistant general manager over the flood management program. In turn, Williams initiated recruitment for a new manager for the flood control department. P. Kay Whitlock was hired. As an engineer in Illinois, Whitlock had established ties with Corps officials and had experience in securing federal appropriations.

These managers and the board of directors undertook two strategies that provided a successful outcome for federal funding. First, according to Director Joe Judge, who joined the board in 1986, "We succeeded because we developed a strong presence in Washington D.C., and we established effective relationships with our congressional delegates who worked on our behalf."[77] And second, as pointed out by Whitlock, "We succeeded because we became proactive on the rules and environmental regulations associated with flood protection work."[78]

To increase the agency's presence at the federal level on flood and water supply issues alike, the Water District board hired Mia O'Connell in 1986 to work as a lobbyist in Washington D.C. One of her first tasks was to help the Water District pursue the new federal funding available under the 1986 Water Resources Development Act (WRDA). The WRDA is a bill that is typically passed by Congress every two years, but in 1986, the act ushered in greater funding as well as the objective of strengthening the partnership between the Corps and local project sponsors.[79]

The growing prominence of the valley's congressional representatives also helped the Water District's flood protection projects to gain momentum. During the 1980s and early 1990s, Congressman Norm Mineta (who had also served a term as mayor of San José during the 1970s), championed the Water District's priorities to the House

Public Works and Transportation Committee; between 1992 and 1994, he chaired this committee, which had the power to award federal dollars to various infrastructure projects.[80] "Norm was deeply familiar with the infrastructure needs of the Santa Clara Valley and was one of our greatest advocates," commented Director Judge.[81] Working with Mineta during this same timeframe was Congressman Don Edwards. These two men were well respected in the corridors of Washington D.C., and played a critical role in securing funding for Water District projects. Tom Campbell (during his terms in Congress from 1989 to 1993 and from 1995 to 2001), Zoe Lofgren (seated in Congress from 1995 through the time of this writing in 2005), Mike Honda (2000 through 2005), and Richard Pombo (1999 through 2005) have all continued this tradition of strong advocacy. This field of both Democrats and Republicans showed strong bipartisan support for obtaining federal funding for the Water District's work in Santa Clara County.

Furthermore, the agency's directors and managers pursued positions that could influence federal relationships and funding. For example, from 1984 to 1994, Director Jim Lenihan served as a gubernatorial appointee to the California Water Commission, and chaired that commission in 1993. The commission served as an advisory board to the state legislature on water supply issues and petitioned federal agencies and legislators for appropriations to flood protection projects. Also of note, in 1990 and 1991, Stan Williams, assistant general manager at the time, served as president of NAFSMA, the National Association of Flood and Stormwater Management Agencies. Through this organization, the Water District exercised leadership in helping to map out what the new partnership between the Corps and local project sponsors should look like—one of the objectives of the 1986 WRDA.[82] In 1999 and 2000, Kay Whitlock, who had become assistant general manager at the Water District, also served as president of NAFSMA.

As of 2004, the district continues to have a position on the NAFSMA board of directors.

With status as an economic engine for the nation; with experienced flood program managers and well-respected representatives in Congress; with directors appointed to influential commissions and managers leading national organizations; and with full-time lobbyists working to keep projects alive in Washington and Sacramento, construction on the valley's critical projects began to pick up pace. By 1994, federal projects included the $138 million Guadalupe River Park and Flood Protection Project, the $64 million Coyote Creek Flood Protection Project and the $63 million Llagas Creek Watershed Project. (These figures state the costs as estimated in 1994; the project vignettes discussed earlier in this chapter show costs as of 2004.) In addition, in 1994 the Water District was handling $47 million worth of projects that it solely designed and funded.[83]

Subventions help, then falter. To help with the high cost of flood protection projects, the state of California offered financial assistance through its Flood Control Subvention Program. This program was created in 1945 and directed by the state Department of Water Resources (DWR). After expending funds for the local share as well as fronting the portion of state share on federally-funded projects, the local sponsor could submit a claim to DWR for reimbursement.[84]

Unfortunately, beginning in 1990, the subventions program withered with economic downturns. Legislators attempted to revive subventions funding in 1990, 1992 and 1994 by authorizing general obligation bonds, but these efforts failed. In 1997, voters did approve Proposition 204, which included $60 million for subventions. Then, with an upbeat economy in the late 1990s, three legislative acts (the Budget Act of 1998, AB2784 of 1999 and the Water Bond measure of 2000) passed, and these bolstered the Flood Control Subvention Program.[85] But in December 2002,

subvention funding came to a screeching halt. California was reeling from the "dot-com bust" and facing its deepest budget deficits ever. Governor Gray Davis and the state legislature reverted all unexpended funds that they could to the state's General Fund, yanking about $58 million from the Flood Control Subvention Program.[86]

As of 2004, there is no reliable funding source for state subventions. Beneficiaries of this program, including the Santa Clara Valley Water District, must adjust their programs accordingly, or develop new revenue to shoulder more of project costs. But subventions made their mark on the success of California's flood management efforts. Between 1969 and 2004, the Water District received a total of $104 million in subvention reimbursements against filed claims totaling $120 million (the reimbursements pertained to projects on the Guadalupe River, Coyote Creek, Lower Silver Creek, Llagas Creek and Pajaro River).[87] Stated Chief Executive Officer Stan Williams, "Not all states have offered such a program, and California's was one of the first. The benefit to Santa Clara Valley residents is that it has greatly multiplied the use of their benefit assessment dollars, enabling us to leverage more federal funds and accomplish more work."[88]

Voters approve Clean, Safe Creeks measure. By the mid-1990s, it was clear that the local revenue provided by the Benefit Assessment Program had worked to the valley's advantage, and much was being accomplished in the area of flood protection; more than half of the parcels in designated flood hazard areas had gained protection and were freed of the FEMA insurance requirement. However, the program's sunset in 2000 loomed, and more flood protection work was needed. (Assessments would actually continue as long as 2030, but only to repay old debt obligations; no new expenses could be incurred.)

Staff at the Water District began considering ways to continue generating a local revenue stream for flood

Subventions helped us to greatly multiply the use of our taxpayers' benefit assessment dollars, enabling us to leverage more federal funds and accomplish more work.

We were facing a tough two-thirds voter approval requirement; we knew our proposal had to reflect the concerns and values of community members and businesses.

protection. At one point, they considered asking voters to simply extend the existing Benefit Assessment Program. But after district officials floated this idea before the cities and towns of Santa Clara County and groups such as the League of Women Voters, there was little enthusiasm for the proposal. Williams noted that without endorsements from these critical groups, securing voter approval would be unlikely.[89]

Looking for a new strategy, the district decided to hire a professional public opinion research firm. Explained Director Greg Zlotnick, "We were facing a tough two-thirds voter approval requirement;[†††] we knew our proposal had to reflect the concerns and values of community members and businesses."[90] In May 1997, a field survey of voters in Santa Clara County was conducted. The results showed that high on the list of concerns were clean water and careful fiscal management. Using this community input, the Water District prepared a new 15-year Clean, Safe Creeks Program that would take over where the Benefit Assessment Program left off—though with significant changes in direction.

The proposal, which became Measure B on the ballot, entailed a parcel tax based on contribution to runoff, with an average annual rate of $39 per household. District staff estimated that this rate would generate approximately $25 million (1999 dollars) annually for the 15-year lifespan of the measure. The revenue would fund nine projects to safeguard approximately 16,000 parcels including 13,600 homes, 1,040 businesses and 43 schools and public facilities. Rather than the zone-by-zone funding approach of the Benefit Assessment Program, the new plan was applied

countywide (at least one flood protection project was proposed in each of the five major watershed areas, but the goal was to obtain funding that was not geographically restrictive). The new plan also differed from the Benefit Assessment Program in that it was a pay-as-you-go program, and did not enable debt-financing.

The Clean, Safe Creeks Program offered to restore creek ecosystems, improve water quality, remove trash and develop 70 miles of creekside trails and 100 acres of habitat. Reflecting the public's desire for greater accountability in government expenditures, the Measure B package included an external, independent monitoring committee that would review and report on the progress and expenditures of the program yearly.[91] (This would eventually be headed by Susanne Wilson, a former Santa Clara County Supervisor and long-time valley leader).

On November 7, 2000, the needed two-thirds of voters in Santa Clara County approved Measure B.[92] Noted Zlotnick, board chairman in 2000, "This proposal passed because it reflected the community's own priorities."[93] Both the expiring Benefit Assessment Program and the Clean, Safe Creeks Program testify to the power of a motivated community. As of 2003, a total of $358 million in benefit assessment dollars had been collected across the life of the program, and the number of parcels in designated flood-prone areas was reduced from a high of approximately 165,500 to 77,000.[94] The latter number is left to be tackled by the Clean, Safe Creeks program and whatever assistance the Water District can obtain from state and federal agencies—although state government, in particular, was no longer a dependable ally.

[†††] In November 1996, the voters of California passed Proposition 218, a constitutional initiative that took aim at controlling how various governing entities developed revenue through general taxes, special taxes, parcel taxes, assessments, fees, etc. The new Clean, Safe Creeks measure had to comply with the rules of Proposition 218, which included securing a two-thirds voter approval for a special tax.

State grabs local funds. In dealing with its budget woes of the 1990s and early 2000s, the state not only cut subvention funding, but also began siphoning funds from local governments. In fiscal year 1992-93, the state permanently shifted ten percent of the property tax revenue stream from special districts and local governments to schools. The loss to the Santa Clara Valley Water District from this particular action was $1.8 million in 1992, but escalated annually to $3.7 million by 2004.[95o]

It was a frustrating situation. The Water District pressed its case in Sacramento through its legislative representative, Ron Davis, who was hired in 1992 to represent district interests in the state capital. Davis called the state's penchant for shifting revenues from infrastructure programs to schools "a Band-Aid approach to problems." He pointed out that the bond ratings of local governments were negatively affected by less capital being available for infrastructure improvements; this, in turn, negatively affected the state's economic recovery.[96]

The state did not heed such arguments. In fiscal year 1993-94, some legislators proposed another shift of local funds, but this failed to pass. However, in mid-2004, the state successfully pursued a large raid of local government funding. Governor Arnold Schwarzenegger's administration and local government, including special districts, negotiated an agreement whereby $1.3 billion of local property tax receipts would be shifted to the state annually for two years, with special districts paying $350 million each year. In exchange, the governor agreed to support a constitutional amendment to make it more difficult for the legislature to raid local coffers in the future. California voters approved this amendment in 2004.

In this arrangement, the Water District had expected to lose, at worst, $22 million in property tax revenue. But in late November of 2004, district officials were given a shock: They learned that the state had raised the Water District's contribution to $51 million over the next 17 months—an amount more than double what had been considered the district's maximum forfeiture.[97] The Santa Clara Valley Water District would thus take the largest hit under "the deal," paying $18 million more than any other special district in California.

Director Joe Judge, chairman in 2004, expressed the district board's reaction: "We were stunned. We agreed to pay our fair share to the state, and then the rules were changed with no advance warning."[98]

The district's share was effectively increased when the state began to exempt certain types of special districts, e.g., fire districts, mosquito abatement districts and other districts relating to public safety from having to participate in the state/local government revenue-shifting agreement. Water and wastewater districts ended up shouldering upwards of 85 percent of the special district burden ($350 million per year for two years). The Santa Clara Valley Water District was hit hard, in particular, because of its dual functions, the Water Utility Enterprise and the non-enterprise Flood Control Program. Both sides of the agency were required to forego receipt of property tax revenue. Stated Director Greg Zlotnick, "In the Santa Clara Valley, we took steps to become a consolidated, streamlined agency handling multiple responsibilities—we ended up getting penalized for this in the state's formula for property tax contributions."[99]

Unless district officials can find a way to ameliorate the state's proposal, the agency will be left to reduce its work plans and programs. The proposed $51 million shift represented about 10 percent of the Water District's total revenues over two years. One possible remedy to the loss of revenue was a water rate increase. The district board of directors rejected the idea of a mid-year increase in water rates in November 2004, after hearing and discussing the news of the state's plans. Nevertheless, Richard Balocco,

In dealing with its budget woes, the state not only cut subvention funding, but also began siphoning funds from local governments.

vice president of San Jose Water Company, saw a future increase as likely. "This is bad news for water customers," he commented. "The state is forcing the Water District to find alternative funding sources to maintain flood protection and water quality projects—which could ultimately mean an increase in water rates."[100]

Flood Protection
Involves Public Awareness

Just as the Water District worked to educate the public on water supply and conservation issues (Chapter 11), it also developed outreach and education programs relating to flood protection. When the El Niño phenomenon ushered in particularly wet winters in the mid-1990s, the Water District stepped up its public outreach efforts and inaugurated its "FloodSAFE" program. During the winter of 1996, slides with flood safety tips ran in movie theaters, ad-

vertisements showing sandbag locations were placed in community newspapers, and a children's play, "The Great Flood on Sesame Street," debuted at schools and libraries.

In 1997, the Water District began to feature Noah, builder of the famous ark, in advertisements and brochures that promoted flood safety efforts. Explained Teddy Morse, then-public information officer, the choice of the world's most well-prepared flood victim as a spokesperson allowed the use of subtle humor in dealing with the serious issue of flooding.[101] The toll-free 1-888-HEY-NOAH was set up for easy access to flood information.

The media attention given to El Niño provided the Water District with a unique opportunity to link the district's water supply and flood protection in one public outreach campaign. Noah appeared on radio and in newspaper ads, asking the "chief" if this El Niño would bring drought or floods. The message to Santa Clara County residents was that we must always be ready for both.∎

Will El Niño bring drought or floods?

The message from Noah to Santa Clara County residents was that we must always be ready for both.

SOURCES, CHAPTER 12:

[1] Williams, Stan and Whitlock, Kay. "Digging in at Last," *Aquafacts*, Winter 1993, p. 4.

[2] Sanchez, Sig. Interviewed by Cheryl Wessling, April 1, 2004.

[3] Association of Bay Area Governments (ABAG) Web site: www.abag.ca.gov (go to Flood Insurance Rate Map Background Information); also, Federal Emergency Management Agency Web site: www.fema.gov

[4] Ibid; also, Zlotnick, Greg (SCVWD board director). Comments to draft book re insurance costs, April 18, 2005.

[5] Oven, Katherine (SCVWD staff). E-mails to Kathleen McNamara, Aug. 22, 2003 and to Cheryl Wessling, Sept. 9, 2003.

[6] Klemencic, Marc (SCVWD staff). Comments to draft book, Dec. 13, 2004.

[7] Guadalupe project information from: *Status Report: 2003*, p. 6*; also, "Restoring the Guadalupe," *Valley Water News*, SCVWD, 2003, p. 2; also, SCVWD Web site: www.valleywater.org/water/watersheds

[8] *Guadalupe River Flood Control Project*, groundbreaking handout, SCVWD, March 30, 1992; also, Grant, Joanne. "Founders would hail flood control plan," *San Jose Mercury News*, p. 2B, circa 1992.

[9] Bamburg, Bonnie. Interviewed by Kathleen McNamara, April 22, 2003.

[10] Williams, Stan and Whitlock, Kay. "Digging in at Last," *Aquafacts*, Winter 1993, p. 3.

[11] McEnery, Tom. Interviewed by Kathleen McNamara, Sept. 3, 2003.

[12] Regarding the city-Corps-SCVWD negotiation process, Whitlock, Kay. Interviewed by Cheryl Wessling, Feb. 29, 2004.

[13] Williams, Stan and Whitlock, Kay. "Digging in at Last," *Aquafacts*, Winter 1993, p. 5.

[14] Ibid.

[15] *Status Report: 1991-91*, March 1991, p. 23.*

[16] *Final General Re-Evaluation Report for Proposed Project Modifications, Guadalupe River Project, Downtown San José, California,* Vol. 1, February 2001, pp. 1-2.

[17] Krieger, Lisa. "Flood project restores Guadalupe gracefully," *San Jose Mercury News*, Oct. 7, 2003, p. 1F.

[18] Schoenberg, Steven, U.S. Fish and Wildlife Service staff biologist as quoted in "Flood Project Threatens Fish, Foes Say" by Gaura, Marcia Alicia, *San Francisco Chronicle*, July 15, 1996.

[19] Guadalupe project files of Chief Executive Officer Stan Williams, accessed December 2004.

[20] Letter to SCVWD General Counsel Tony Bennetti from lead attorney Richard Roos-Collins, Natural Heritage Institute, dated May 22, 1996, re Notice of Citizen Suit Under Section 505 of the Clean Water Act (33 U.S.C. § 1365)—Guadalupe River Flood Control Project. SCVWD files.

[21] Bernardi, Nancy as quoted in "Flood Project Threatens Fish, Foes Say" by Gaura, Marcia Alicia. *San Francisco Chronicle*, July 15, 1996.

[22] Kamei, Rosemary. Interviewed by Cheryl Wessling, Nov. 5, 2003.

[23] Estruth, Jerry. Interviewed by Cheryl Wessling, phone conversation, Oct. 25, 2004.

[24] Guadalupe project files of Chief Executive Officer Stan Williams, accessed December 2004.

[25] *Fisheries and Aquatic Habitat Collaborative Effort, Summary Report*, SCVWD, Feb. 26, 2003, p. 2.

[26] Vining, Robert. Interviewed by Cheryl Wessling, April 13, 2004.

[27] *Status Report: 2003*, 6-8*; also, SCVWD News Release, "Key Silicon Valley flood protection project wins approval from Bush administration," Nov. 21, 2001; also, SCVWD News Release, "Work resumes on project to restore an urban stream through Silicon Valley, create habitat for threatened fish and provide riverside recreation," June 18, 2002.

[28] McEnery, Tom. Interviewed by Kathleen McNamara, Sept. 3, 2003.

[29] Coyote project information from: *Status Report: 1991-92*, March 1991, p. 10*; also, *Status Report: 2001*, April 2001, pp. 32-34, 54-55*; also, SCVWD News Release (no title), Aug. 10, 1983.

continued

* Refers to the annual "Status Report: Federal Projects for Santa Clara County, California, and Federal Appropriation Statements of Support." These are produced by SCVWD and submitted to the U.S. Army Corps of Engineers to support federal funding requests.

SOURCES, CHAPTER 12 - *continued*:

[30] *Status Report: 1993-94,* March 1993, p. 8.*

[31] Coyote watershed urbanization noted in "Urban Runoff Management Plans Move Forward," *Progress* (newsletter), Water Environment Research Foundation at: http://www.werf.org/press/Opgr_sp/ 0sp_urbn.cfm

[32] *Status Report: 1990-91*, March 1990, pp. 29-30.*

[33] *Review/Outlook, 1984/1985*, SCVWD, p. 6.

[34] *Review/Outlook, 1985-1986,* SCVWD, p. 16.

[35] *Status Report: 2000,* March 2000, pp. 31-32*; also, *Coyote Creek Flood Protection Project Early Success*, internal document, SCVWD, p. 2.

[36] Ortiz, Jose. Interviewed by Kathleen McNamara, May 2, 2003.

[37] *Status Report: Fiscal Year 2003*, March 2002, p. 41.*

[38] SCVWD News Release, "Outdoor 'classroom' rises from site of devastating 1997 flood on Coyote Creek," Nov. 15, 2001.

[39] *Clean, Safe Creeks and Natural Flood Protection*, July 25, 2000, Section 2.18.

[40] *Coyote Creek Flood Protection Project Early Success*, internal document, SCVWD, p. 1.

[41] SCVWD Web site: www.valleywater.org/water/watersheds

[42] *Status Report: Fiscal Year 2004,* April 2003, p. 17.*

[43] Angelino, Fred. Interviewed by Kathleen McNamara, April 25, 2003.

[44] Rodriguez, Jeff. Interviewed by Kathleen McNamara, April 23, 2003.

[45] Sturla, Jack. As quoted in "Pl-566 helps communities keep dry—and more," by Cheryl Wessling and Timmy Yung, *Aquafacts*, Summer/Fall, 1994, p. 17.

[46] Ibid.

[47] *Llagas Creek Watershed Final EIS/EIR,* SCVWD, May 1982, pp. 1-7.

[48] Angelino, Fred. Interviewed by Kathleen McNamara, April 25, 2003.

[49] Wessling, Cheryl and Yung, Timmy. "PL-566 helps communities keep dry—and more," *Aquafacts*, Summer/Fall 1994, p. 15.

[50] Sturla, Jack. As quoted in "Pl-566 helps communities keep dry—and more," by Cheryl Wessling and Timmy Yung, *Aquafacts*, Summer/Fall, 1994, p. 17.

[51] Wilson, Bruce (retired SCVWD staff). Comments to draft book, March 21, 2004.

[52] *Review/Outlook, 1986-1987*, SCVWD, p. 6; also, SCVWD News Release (no title), June 8, 1987.

[53] Wessling, Cheryl and Yung, Timmy. "PL-566 helps communities keep dry—and more," *Aquafacts*, Summer/Fall 1994, p. 16.

[54] *Status Report: Federal Projects for Santa Clara County, California*, SCVWD, March 2000, pp. 5-7, 23-24; also, same report dated March 2002, pp. 14-17.*

[55] Moran, Doug. Interviewed by Kathleen McNamara, April 16, 2003.

[56] Oven, Katherine (SCVWD staff). Comments to draft book, March 29, 2004; also, *Matadero/Barron Creeks Long-Term Remediation Planning Study, Final Engineer's Report-Project No. 102109,* SCVWD, October 2002; also, Hsueh, Nai and Russell, Alison. "Behind the Scenes: Challenges of Palo Alto's Matadero Creek Flood Control Project," *Aquafacts*, Summer/Fall 1994, pp. 18-19.

[57] Author unknown. "Flood-Control Project Causes Customer Trickle," *Palo Alto Weekly,* May 25, 1994.

[58] Oven, Katherine (SCVWD staff). Comments to draft book, December 2004.

[59] Ibid.

[60] Ibid.

[61] Ibid.

[62] Teresi, Joe. Interviewed by Kathleen McNamara, April 16, 2003.

[63] Zlotnick, Greg. Interviewed by Cheryl Wessling, Dec. 22, 2003.

[64] SCVWD News Release, "Program for improved long-term stream maintenance advances," April 6, 2001.

[65] Fiedler, Jim. Interviewed by Cheryl Wessling, March 17, 2003.

* Refers to the annual "Status Report: Federal Projects for Santa Clara County, California, and Federal Appropriation Statements of Support." These are produced by SCVWD and submitted to the U.S. Army Corps of Engineers to support federal funding requests.

[66] "Briefing Materials for Meeting with RWQCB Executive Officer on the Maintenance Program Regulatory Project," Memorandum from Deborah Amshoff, SCVWD, April 21, 1997.

[67] Enge, Marilee. "Flood control work loses out to frog," *San Jose Mercury News*, Oct. 6, 1997.

[68] *Heads Up*, internal newsletter, SCVWD, Sept. 9, 1997.

[69] SCVWD News Release, "Program for improved long-term stream maintenance advances," April 6, 2001.

[70] SCVWD News Release, "Regional board pays tribute to SCVWD," Dec. 12, 2003.

[71] SCVWD News Release, "Waterway management plan for Santa Clara County nears approval," Feb. 27, 2002.

[72] Santos, Richard. Interviewed by Cheryl Wessling, Oct. 6, 2003.

[73] SCVWD Memorandum, "Benefits of Multi-Year Stream Maintenance Program," Jan. 7, 2004.

[74] Manson, Craig. As quoted in E-mail to Mike DiMarco (SCVWD staff), Aug. 29, 2002.

[75] Wilson, Larry. Interviewed by Cheryl Wessling, Sept. 25, 2003.

[76] Esau, Ronald. Interviewed by Cheryl Wessling, March 1, 2004.

[77] Judge, Joe. Interviewed by Cheryl Wessling, March 13, 2004.

[78] Whitlock, Kay. Interviewed by Cheryl Wessling, Feb. 27, 2003.

[79] O'Connell, Mia. Interviewed by Cheryl Wessling, April 13, 2004.

[80] Profile on Norm Mineta obtained from: www. abcnews.com/ sections/politics/DailyNews/profile —mineta.html.

[81] Judge, Joe. Interviewed by Cheryl Wessling, March 13, 2004.

[82] Vining, Robert. Interviewed by Cheryl Wessling, April 13, 2004.

[83] Wessling, Cheryl. "Local flood control construction activity hits peak level," *Aquafacts*, Summer/Fall, 1994, p. 5.

[84] *Flood Control in the Santa Clara Valley: An Overview*, SCVWD, circa 1992, p. 35; also, *Annual Performance Report 1995-1996*, SCVWD, p. 13.

[85] Mansfield, Liz, Deputy Assistant, Flood Control Subventions Program, Sacramento. E-mail to Kathleen McNamara, August 4, 2003.

[86] Ibid.

[87] Wilson, Scott (SCVWD staff). E-mail to Cheryl Wessling, Nov. 15, 2004.

[88] Williams, Stan. Interviewed by Cheryl Wessling, Nov. 21, 2003.

[89] Ibid.

[90] Zlotnick, Greg. Interviewed by Cheryl Wessling, Dec. 22, 2003.

[91] Magill, Mala (SCVWD staff). E-mail to Cheryl Wessling, Jan. 14, 2003; also, *Clean, Safe Creeks and Natural Flood Protection*, SCVWD, July 25, 2000. p. 1.3.

[92] League of Women Voters of California archives, Measure B, Clean, Safe Creeks and Natural Flood Protection, Special Parcel Tax, information accessed at: www.smartvoter.org; also, *Capital Improvement Plan*, SCVWD, available at: www.valleywater.org

[93] Zlotnick, Greg. Interviewed by Cheryl Wessling, Dec. 22, 2003.

[94] Record of benefit assessment revenue from Grasso, Norma (SCVWD staff). E-mail to Cheryl Wessling, April 7, 2004; also, parcel figures from Nguyen, Ngoc (SCVWD staff). E-mails to Kathleen McNamara, August 2003.

[95] *Annual Report 1992-1993*, SCVWD, p. 18; also, *Annual Report 1993-1994*, SCVWD, p. 29.

[96] Davis, Ron. "Legislative News," *Aquafacts*, Spring 1993, p. 19.

[97] SCVWD News Release, "Tax Raid Puts Local Water Programs at Risk," Nov. 19, 2004.

[98] Judge, Joe, as quoted in ibid.

[99] Zlotnick, Greg. E-mail to Cheryl Wessling, April 29, 2005.

[100] Balocco, Richard, as quoted in ibid.

[101] Morse, Teddy. Interviewed by Donna Krey, March 19, 2003.

[102] *Status Report 1995-96*, March 1995, p. 3; also, *Status Report Fiscal Year 2002*, April 2001, p. 8.*

[103] *Coyote Creek Flood Protection Project Early Success*, SCVWD, p. 1.

[104] *Annual Performance Report 1997-1998*, SCVWD, p. 13; also, *Status Report Fiscal Year 2002*, April 2001, p. 40.*

[105] Schaeffer, Mary. Interviewed by Kathleen McNamara, July 8, 2003.

Agriculture in the Delta region, 2002.

CHAPTER 13

Dealing with the Delta—Our Imported Supply

By Walt Wadlow, Chief Operating Officer, and Cheryl Wessling

From the 1980s forward, the Santa Clara Valley Water District found itself increasingly engaged—and at times embroiled—in issues centered on the Sacramento-San Joaquin Delta, an area located roughly 70 miles northward of San José. What interest could local water officials have in this largely agricultural place, with its islands of wheat, alfalfa and tomatoes, and the occasional water-skier being towed through its channels? Of what concern are the distant water quality problems of the Delta to busy Silicon Valley residents, executives and political leaders?

"We are inextricably linked to the Delta, by both geography and our reliance on the Delta as the conveyance hub for about half of our water supply," explained Director Greg Zlotnick of the Water District board. "How the inflow of fresh water in the Delta is managed affects the quality and reliability of a major portion of Silicon Valley's supply."[1]

"How the inflow of fresh water in the Delta is managed" became one of California's greatest controversies during the latter half of the twentieth century and carried into the twenty-first century as well. As discussed in Chapter 10, the 1982 Peripheral Canal proposal involved the entire state in a bitter fight over the distribution of the Delta's inflow. The defeat of the proposal did not end the debate. Instead, Delta water quality and supply issues became a permanent statewide concern.

By the early 1990s, nearly two-thirds of all Californians were drinking water that was pumped through the Delta, and about five million acres of farmland were irrigated by water directly from or conveyed through the Delta as well.[2] This water supply had become essential to all sectors of the state's economy—and was likewise essential to wildlife and fisheries in the Bay-Delta environment. The heart of the problem was that as more water was pumped through

By the early 1990s, nearly two-thirds of all Californians were drinking water that was pumped through the Delta.

Map B. San Francisco Bay-Delta Estuary

➤ **Estuaries** are places where rivers empty into seawater, creating a habitat influenced by the mix of freshwater flows and ocean tidal action. The San Francisco Bay-Delta Estuary is one of the world's largest such places, covering 1,620 square miles. It includes the entire San Francisco Bay, the smaller San Pablo and Suisun bays, and the Sacramento-San Joaquin Delta.

➤ **The Delta** is, specifically, the point where California's two largest rivers, the Sacramento and San Joaquin, funnel through a maze of channels surrounding 57 manmade islands before flowing through the Carquinez Strait and into Suisun Bay.

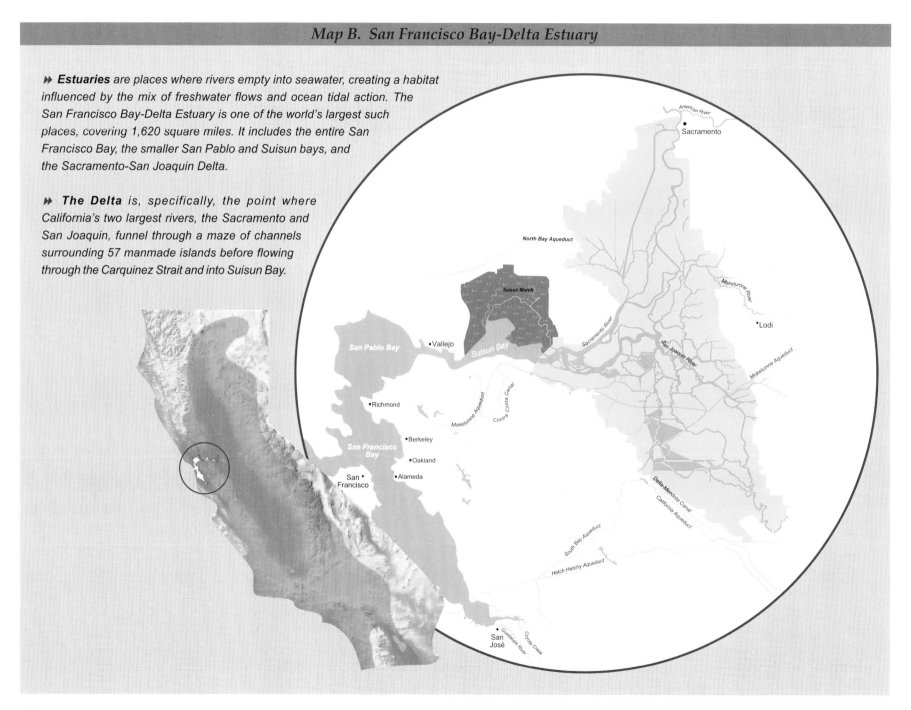

the Delta to consumers, less fresh water was left to flush through the outlet to the bay, enabling salty seawater to intrude and allowing pollutants from surrounding agricultural lands to concentrate. With these conditions, a troublesome chain reaction took place: Several plant and animal species in the estuary became endangered; regulations that protected endangered species were enacted; pumping operations in the Delta water were periodically shut down; and serious water quality and supply reliability problems resulted for the many recipients of Delta water.

Along with roughly 22 million other Californians, citizens of the Santa Clara Valley had a stake in how the Delta's resource problems would be resolved.

The Delta is a Conveyance Hub

As discussed in earlier chapters, the Santa Clara Valley Water District is the only urban agency in the state to hold contracts with both the State Water Project (SWP) and federal Central Valley Project (CVP). During the 1980s and onward, anywhere from half to two-thirds of the water used in Santa Clara County was imported (see Table F in Chapter 11 for imported water deliveries to the valley). "Our stake in the continued delivery of imported water is significant," commented Director Larry Wilson. "However, the district board has always taken a position of advocating the protection of the Delta environment, as well as protecting the quality of water flowing through this environment."[3] As discussed in Chapter 7, the Tri-County agencies that had worked together to secure CVP water through the San Felipe Project had pledged to conduct importation so "as to avoid degradation of Delta waters." At the same time, the Water District had invested heavily in these systems, and could not easily afford to lose the promised supply. Under contractual agreements, the Water District would pay

annually for the cost of facilities and operations regardless of the actual amount delivered.

It is important to note that the CVP and SWP contracts held by many water utilities, including the Santa Clara Valley Water District, are not for water from the Delta per se, but rather for water that originates in the rivers that flow into the Delta. Water delivered through the SWP and CVP originates as precipitation and snow melt from the Sierra Nevada and coastal range. Large dams, such as the one at popular Lake Shasta (a CVP facility), were built along Sierra rivers to capture this flow of icy water. The water is released from reservoirs as needed throughout the year, back into the rivers that eventually empty into the Delta. The Delta thus functions as a large, open-ended reservoir, where CVP and SWP pumping stations move the water into canals or aqueducts—facilities built to convey water to the state's farmlands and cities.

Over the years, the CVP and SWP increased their water exports as California grew to become the nation's most prosperous and populated state. With roughly $1.3 trillion in annual economic activity, California stands as the world's fifth largest economy, behind the United States, Japan, Germany and Great Britain (2004 data). And as of July 1, 2004, census estimates showed California with almost 36 million residents; in second and third place, respectively, were Texas with roughly 22 million people and New York with roughly 19 million people. At the time of this writing, the state grows more than 200 crops, including 45 percent of the nation's total produce and close to 100 percent of several specialty crops such as almonds, artichokes and lettuce. In addition to farmland irrigation, the SWP has supported continued growth in California's cities, which account for about 75 percent of the state's economic activity. Specifically in Santa Clara County, the water provided by the SWP and CVP has been an essential ingredient to high tech manufacturing, supporting the

Along with roughly 22 million other Californians, citizens of the Santa Clara Valley had a stake in how the Delta's resource problems would be resolved.

185

emergence and growth of Silicon Valley, a "global engine" of technology and research.[4]

In short, the CVP and SWP systems have played an important role in supporting California's and Silicon Valley's remarkable economic expansion and population growth. Unfortunately, the systems' increasing export of fresh water, particularly in the 1970s and '80s, has been one of the major factors in dwindling wildlife and fishery populations and in water quality problems in the Delta environment. These water quality problems affect not only the estuary, but must be dealt with at the treatment level by all the agencies and cities that receive water conveyed through the Delta (see Chapter 10).

Problems of Concern in the Delta Region

The water that flows into the Delta has been tapped by farmers and cities for more than 150 years. However, the increasing diversions during the 1970s and '80s, along with pollution, are pointed to as the key factors that have contributed to serious degradation of the Delta environment, leading to the designation of several endangered species.

Diversion of freshwater flow. The amount of fresh water flowing through the Bay-Delta estuary is astounding: About 40 percent of California's entire rainfall and snowfall ends up draining through the estuary. In an average rainfall year, 24 million acre-feet (MAF) of water flows through the Delta. In the wettest years, as much as 69 MAF may rush through the area; the driest years may have flows as low as 6 MAF.[5]

Also impressive is the number of rights to divert portions of this freshwater flow: In addition to the CVP and SWP, there are about 7,000 diverters holding permits upstream in the watershed that feeds the estuary. Of the total diverted water, 80 to 94 percent (depending on how water

use is measured) is applied in farmland irrigation and the raising of livestock. (It should be noted that some of this use results in return flows to water systems).[6] As the largest diverter, the CVP delivers, on average, about 7 MAF to contractors. The SWP delivers between 3 and 4 MAF to its contractors in normal years. These two systems alone divert about 45 percent of the Delta's freshwater flow in years of normal rainfall.[7]

Increases in diversions over the years led to problems. Exported water became saltier, as the reduced freshwater flow from rivers enabled ocean and bay water to intrude further into the Delta and even upstream into the rivers.[8] In addition to a higher salt content, reduced freshwater flows also diminished the flushing of pollutants and natural organics from the Delta system, leading to a higher concentration of these substances in exported water. A frustrating point to the Water District and other contractors is that the quality of water at its source—Sierra runoff—is usually very good. But as this water flows to the Delta, it is diverted, used and returned to the tributaries as treated wastewater and storm water, laden with urban and agricultural residues. Added to this soup is the organic matter that leaches from the Delta's peat soils.

Droughts, such as the one from 1987 to 1992, reduce the freshwater flow even further. Both SWP and CVP systems during the 1976-1977 and 1987-1992 droughts were unable to deliver full contract entitlements to their customers; the water that was provided exceeded, at times, the allowable levels of sodium. Former Director Patrick Ferraro recalled that in 1977, the sodium content of imported water was so high that the Water District ceased to recharge this supply in the percolation ponds. The high sodium concentration could cause the sediments in the ponds to harden to a "near concrete-like layer, sealing the ponds and destroying their ability to recharge the groundwater basin."[9] (The ionic exchange between sodium-laden

---

> ➤ *How much water is the Delta's average flow of 24 million acre-feet?*
>
> Think of one million acre-feet (MAF) by first thinking of one acre-foot—one foot of water covering one acre. Then stack one million of these on top of each other. This would be one million feet high, equal to 189.4 miles. The Delta's average annual flow of 24 MAF would thus be:
>
> *A one-acre column of water that is 4,545 miles high!*

Urbanization ... drought ... dredging ... and 1100 miles of unstable levees affect the water quality of the Delta.

Urban sprawl in the Delta region (Butte County in 2002).

Drought, 1988, at Lake Folsom, a CVP facility that releases water into the Delta.

Flooded levee in the Delta area (Twitchell Island, 1998).

Dredging in the Delta, 2004.

All photos courtesy California Department of Water Resources

Large dams, such as this one at Lake Shasta, capture runoff and icy snow melt. The water is released from reservoirs as needed throughout the year, back into the rivers that empty into the Delta.

Courtesy California Department of Water Resources

From the Tracy Pumping Plant (left), the Delta-Mendota Canal (below) conveys water to San Luis Reservoir. These facilities are part of the federal Central Valley Project (CVP).

Both photos courtesy US Bureau of Reclamation

The Central Valley Project

The Central Valley Project was conceived by State Engineer Edward Hyatt in the early 1930s; endorsed by the state legislature in 1933; and sustained by California voters in a December 1933 referendum. But in the era of the Great Depression, California had no hope of financing the project's $500 to $600 million price tag. State leaders turned to the federal government for help. President Franklin D. Roosevelt, who welcomed any opportunity to create jobs, helped the state to secure congressional approval for the project. However, it would commence under the direction of the U.S. Bureau of Reclamation, a young federal agency that, in 1935, had just completed construction of the impressive Hoover Dam on the Colorado River. The CVP thus became a federally controlled project.

The Bureau began construction of the CVP in the late 1930s; the system would grow to include more than 20 dams, 11 power plants and 500 miles of conveyance facilities. The Bureau became the largest water provider in the western United States; the CVP became its largest project.

As of 2004, 300 entities, primarily agricultural water agencies, held contracts for CVP water. The Santa Clara Valley Water District is the largest of the system's few urban contractors. The San Felipe Water Project is the arm of the CVP that brings water from San Luis Reservoir into Santa Clara County.[54]

The *Santa Clara Valley* taps *two* of the *world's largest* water projects—both *rely* on the *Delta.*

The State Water Project

At the end of World War II, with CVP water flowing mainly to farmland, the state's booming cities remained concerned about water supplies. In the early 1950s, the state legislature approved appropriations to begin building what would become the State Water Project. In 1959, at the urging of Governor Edmund G. "Pat" Brown, the legislature approved the Burns-Porter Act, making a full commitment to develop the project. The next year, Californians agreed to invest in the SWP by narrowly approving the $1.75 billion bond measure specified in the Act. About two-thirds of the SWP supply would head to urban areas; the rest to agricultural customers.

Water supply agencies across California eagerly signed contracts for SWP water. Contractors agreed to repay the full costs, including interest. The Santa Clara Valley Water District was the first recipient of SWP water in 1965, the year that the South Bay Aqueduct was completed. San Joaquin Valley contractors began receiving their SWP water in 1966, after Lake Oroville filled to its 3.5 million acre-feet capacity for the first time. And in 1972, SWP supplies began flowing into southern California.

Today, the 660-mile SWP stands as the largest state-built water system in the nation and counts among the world's largest water distribution systems. The system is operated by the state Department of Water Resources.[55]

The Harvey O. Banks Pumping Plant, above, is located at the southern end of the Delta, where it pumps water into the South Bay Aqueduct (left). The aqueduct conveys the water to the Penitencia Water Treatment Plant in San José.

Both photos courtesy California Department of Water Resources

of a salinity standard, featured largely in the unfolding political decisions and underpinned, finally, what would become "the largest, most comprehensive water management program in the world . . . the most extensive ecosystem project ever proposed . . . one of the most intensive water conservation projects ever attempted."[22]

The path to this monumental effort—the CALFED Bay-Delta Program—began in the late 1970s with the first serious step toward setting water quality standards for the Delta. In 1978, the State Water Resources Control Board (State Board) adopted a revised "Water Quality Control

---

Designated Uses of the Waters of the San Francisco Bay-Delta Estuary

Pursuant to state law, the designated uses for waters of the Bay-Delta estuary are:

• Agricultural Supply
• Cold and Warm Freshwater Habitat
• Estuarine Habitat
• Fish Migration
• Fish Spawning
• Groundwater Recharge
• Industrial Process Supply
• Industrial Service Supply
• Municipal and Domestic Supply
• Navigation
• Water Recreation
• Commercial and Sport Fishing
• Preservation of Rare and Endangered Species
• Shellfish Harvesting
• Wildlife Habitat

Plan for the Sacramento-San Joaquin Delta and Suisun Marsh" and related measures in Decision-1485. The five-member State Board, appointed by the governor, is vested with broad authority to "allocate water rights, adjudicate water rights disputes, develop statewide water protection plans and establish water quality standards" for the designated uses of California's water sources (see inset below). The Clean Water Act mandates the State Board to develop a water quality control plan for the various water bodies that it oversees; update these plans every three years; and submit them to the federal Environmental Protection Agency (EPA) for approval.[23]

In the 1978 Water Quality Control Plan, the State Board took a stronger position on protecting natural resources than in previous plans. It called for a standard that would maintain Delta conditions "as they would exist in the absence of the CVP and SWP"—certainly a goal that could affect project operations.[24] The Water Quality Control Plan also required monitoring and study of the Delta aquatic resources. Nevertheless, the EPA found the plan's provisions inadequate for the protection of fish and wildlife, and particularly objected to the absence of salinity standards. The Fish and Wildlife Service and the National Marine Fisheries Service also weighed in on the inadequacies of the state's water quality standards.

This would mark the beginning of a lengthy debate between federal regulators and State Board staff as to what constituted adequate criteria to protect estuarine habitat. Far from collaborating on the development of an adequate and balanced plan, stakeholders would file or threaten lawsuits against whatever proposals regulators and the State Board were able to develop—depending upon the impacts to their particular interests. Sixteen years would pass before the involved parties would agree upon a package of proposed water quality standards and other actions—those embodied in the historic 1994 Bay-Delta Accord.

Between 1978 and 1994, as state and federal regulators grappled with setting standards, several events along the way were of importance to the Santa Clara Valley's imported water supply and involved the Water District:

SCVWD drumbeat. By the end of 1982, with the Peripheral Canal defeated (Chapter 10) and no alternative in place, Water District leaders became even more vocal on the need for improved water quality standards for Delta exports. In a resolution and letter to the Association of California Water Agencies, the district board of directors urged the association to demand "in the strongest possible terms" establishment of reasonable standards. The letter stated that the "condition of uncertainty caused by official inaction is intolerable."[25] In May 1984, the board turned to state legislators to demand safe, healthful and adequate water supplies from the State Water Project. The board authored a letter to legislators, propounding that "surface supply of local and imported water should be protected from all sources of pollution and degradation."[26]

Frustrated by the lack of action, the Water District began to work with other urban agencies to influence a positive outcome. The district became a member of California Urban Water Agencies in 1990, and joined the Bay-Delta Urban Coalition shortly thereafter. To specifically address CVP contractor issues, in 1992 the Water District helped to form the San Luis & Delta-Mendota Water Authority, a joint powers union of 32 contractors that were concerned with CVP operations south of the Delta. In this group, the Water District stood out as the only major urban supplier, but all members (as well as all contractors on the SWP and CVP systems) would share the same drumbeat: *quality* and *reliability*. To protect public health, the environment and economy, water exported through the Delta must be of good quality and reliable supply.

The CVPIA (1992). While efforts at the state level were paralyzed during the 1980s, a movement was taking place at the federal level that sought, among other goals, to reverse the environmental degradation attributed to CVP diversions. A report entitled *Restoring the Waters* characterized the historic conditions of California's Central Valley wetlands:

> *Prior to the Gold Rush of 1849, California's great Central Valley included four million acres of wetlands. That acreage shrank more than 90 percent to roughly 350,000 acres by 1990. Construction of the CVP was one of a variety of factors contributing to wetlands decimation . . . .*[27]

The coalition of groups that worked together for a law that would mandate changes to CVP operations included environmental groups, commercial and sport fishermen, duck hunters, waterfowl organizations, Native Americans and urban and business interests. Their efforts succeeded: In October 1992, President George Bush signed the controversial Central Valley Project Improvement Act (CVPIA), thereby changing the priorities and operations of the CVP. Allocations for the environment were now on par with irrigation and domestic uses, and 800,000 acre-feet (about 14 percent) of CVP water was dedicated to fish and wildlife. The Act also established an environmental restoration fund through new water user fees, expecting to raise $50 million annually.[28] Officials at the Water District opposed the CVPIA, primarily because of operational and financial impacts—it would reduce the reliability of the CVP supplies while increasing its costs.[29]

At the time of this writing in 2004, the CVPIA has been enacted for 12 years, and the water set aside for the environment has provided some hoped-for results. The dedicated water supplies have coincided with dramatic increases of migrating waterfowl. Biologists in the Department of the Interior have been able to secure flow improve-

All contractors on the SWP and CVP systems would share the same drumbeat: quality and reliability.

ments for salmon and other fish in major Central Valley rivers since 1993. In 1995, the Sacramento River fall run of Chinook salmon was strong, with almost 268,000 returning spawners, the highest number in more than 25 years.[30]

On the downside, CVP contractors have been left frustrated by the lack of progress made in the implementation of another CVPIA section, one that aimed to develop replacement water for contractors who were affected by the dedication of flow to the environment.

Member Agencies of the CALFED Bay-Delta Program

State of California agencies:
- Department of Fish & Game
- Department of Food & Agriculture
- Department of Health Services
- Department of Water Resources
- California Environmental Protection Agency
- California Resources Agency
- Delta Protection Commission
- State Reclamation Board
- State Water Resources Control Board

Federal agencies:
- National Marine Fisheries Service
- Natural Resources Conservation Service
- U.S. Army Corps of Engineers
- U.S. Bureau of Land Management
- U.S. Bureau of Reclamation
- U.S. Dept. of Agriculture
- U.S. Dept. of the Interior
- U.S. Environmental Protection Agency
- U.S. Fish and Wildlife Service
- U.S. Forest Service
- U.S. Geological Survey
- Western Power Administration

EPA proposes standards (1993). Back at the state level, with still no acceptable Water Quality Control Plan in place, the door was open for federal regulators to assert jurisdiction and begin directing actions on Delta operations. Pushed by a court order, in December 1993, the EPA issued the proposed "Water Quality Standards for Surface Waters of the Sacramento River, San Joaquin River and San Francisco Bay and Delta of the State of California," and published that these would become effective February 23, 1995. Included was the intention to list the Sacramento splittail as a threatened species, and reclassification of the winter-run Chinook salmon from threatened to endangered. With these listings would come controls over the pumping of water in the Delta. The writing was on the wall: Exports were to be limited for the benefit of estuarine habitat and salinity standards were to be implemented.

While environmentalists could possibly live with the EPA's rules, no other group wanted the EPA controlling Delta exports; the EPA standards would reduce up to 3 MAF of water supply annually, with no proposed replacement supply. It was at this juncture that co-author Walt Wadlow became directly involved:

> Early in 1994, as a water quality engineer at the Water District, I reviewed the proposed EPA standards. District staff and the board of directors had no doubts about opposing the proposal. We found it to be reactive, again taking a species-by-species approach that focused almost solely on actions to reduce exports. What was desperately needed was a comprehensive plan that accounted for water supply reliability as well as the ecosystem.

The Water District not only opposed the EPA's proposal, but Wadlow began working with members of the

California Urban Water Agencies coalition to develop a better option. Together, they developed a flexible salinity standard that worked on a sliding scale according to real-time conditions. This differed from the EPA's proposed fixed standard that simplistically reflected the water year type—wet year, dry year, etc. The goal was to find a way to achieve the same water quality objectives while lessening the impact on water supply.[31]

While the coalition's efforts to devise a more balanced proposal were not immediately rewarded, and operational problems in the Delta would continue through the 1990s, the heart of this alternative was ultimately adopted in the 2000 CALFED Record of Decision, the document that outlined the management plan for the Delta (see section entitled, "CALFED Fix Unveiled").

Battle Gives Rise to CALFED

In mid-1994, a truce amongst the warring water factions was finally reached. The truce took the form of a Framework Agreement that stakeholders and regulators signed. The document aimed at three major objectives: formulation of a new Water Quality Control Plan acceptable to both the EPA and State Board; coordination of SWP and CVP operations so as to rapidly respond to environmental conditions in the Delta with an adaptive management approach; and implementation of a long-term plan for the estuary that would balance water supply reliability and environmental protection.[32]

What motivated each stakeholder group to move forward with a compromise? Director Greg Zlotnick, having closely followed these issues, offered this opinion:

In my view, the 1994 agreement was a shotgun compromise. The federal EPA was stepping in with a draconian plan that used the Endangered Species Act to trump state primacy on water allocation. If 22 million Californians and millions of acres of profitable farmland were to be cut off from water to save a few hundred endangered fish, folks in the environmental community could see that unwanted reform of the ESA might follow. In the other corner, the agricultural community was realizing that they would never get a reliable supply of water unless ecosystem improvements were made to the Delta. For these two most contentious groups, acceptance of compromise was acknowledged—begrudgingly—as necessary.[33]

Factions sign Bay-Delta Accord (1994). Six months later, on December 15, 1994, stakeholders also signed the Bay-Delta Accord. This more specifically provided the interim water quality standards that would remain in effect for three years—enough time (it was thought) to hammer out the long-term plan identified in the Framework Agreement. To create that plan, state and federal agencies joined sides and the CALFED Bay-Delta Program was born (see inset, opposite page).[34]

The Accord also called for early implementation of certain ecosystem restoration projects. Funding for these projects came from Proposition 204, passed by California voters in 1996; the California Bay Delta Environmental Enhancement Act, passed by Congress also in 1996; and voluntary contributions from urban water agencies.[35] These contributions included a $30 million guarantee ($10 million per year for three years) from the Metropolitan Water District of Southern California for Category III programs (environmental measures that didn't "cost water"). The Santa Clara Valley Water District also made a contribution of $500,000 in 1995, and again in 1996 (the Water District was the only agency in the state except for Metropolitan to make a contribution in the second year).[36]

Concerns of Contractors
South of the Delta

Pumping was restricted

to avoid killing the Delta

smelt, creating a conflict

between the water needs

of Silicon Valley and this

tiny fish.

After the 1994 Accord was signed, CVP and SWP contractors hoped they would see at least the beginnings of the CALFED Program's objective to balance water supply reliability and environmental protection. But operational troubles in the late 1990s showed that water supply reliability was not being adequately addressed, and many contractors were continuing to experience chronic water shortages.

Small fish vs. Silicon Valley (1999). Pumping operations in 1999 exemplified the problem of continuing to operate the Delta export pumps under the rigid standards embodied in the individual species biological opinions required by the Endangered Species Act. The first few months of 1999 were quite wet—enough to classify 1999 as a wet year. But the ensuing spring was extraordinarily dry. The Delta smelt, a small fish listed as endangered, then behaved as if it were a drought year, swimming in the vicinity of the pumps long past their usual departure in May. So although June and July were the months that CVP pumping normally increased in order to fill San Luis Res-

A Delta smelt.

Courtesy California Department of Water Resources

ervoir, the Fish and Wildlife Service placed tight restrictions on early summer pumping to prevent the entrainment of the smelt in the pumps, as well as to help meet water quality requirements in the Delta.[37]

This action affected both the quality and availability of water supply for Santa Clara County and other south-of-Delta contractors. By July's end, 500,000 acre-feet of water had been withdrawn from an already-low San Luis Reservoir. With no re-supply headed to the reservoir, the rapid drawdown caused concern among engineers about the integrity of the dam. The decline of storage levels also left users of San Luis supplies (Santa Clara and San Benito counties and agricultural customers in the San Joaquin Valley) with very poor quality water. The Santa Clara Valley Water District, in particular, was challenged to treat the algae-laden water from the shallows of the reservoir. With high-tech industries in Silicon Valley requiring high quality water, meeting this challenge was all the more important.[38]

In response to the drawdown of San Luis Reservoir, in December 1999, the Water District helped the Bay-Delta Urban Coalition to release a bluntly worded report: *California's Bay-Delta Water Quality Dilemma: It's Getting Worse—Not Better.* The evidence in the report pointed to a serious lack of attention to quality and reliability concerns by CALFED and regulators. Delta water continued to contain "high levels of organic carbon and six times the national average level of bromide," and "1.5 times more salinity (salts) than the national average." These problems "imposed substantial costs on the California economy and undermined public confidence in the water supply." With that said, the report pointed to federal regulatory actions that were particularly troublesome, such as the restrictions that had caused the 1999 San Luis Reservoir drawdown.[39]

At issue was the timing of pumping. The best quality water was available in spring, when the concentration of total dissolved solids (salts) was low. But spring was also the time when fisheries needed substantial protection. Consequently, ESA regulations forced CVP and SWP operators to pump during the fall, when the concentration of dissolved solids was high. The shift in pumping to the fall months resulted in an additional 17,000 tons of salt in the water supply sent to south-of-Delta contractors via San Luis Reservoir.[40]

Users of San Luis Reservoir water were not alone in these types of impacts. Contra Costa Water District had similar problems at its new Los Vaqueros Reservoir, which—like San Luis—is filled with water conveyed through the Delta. Contra Costa County voters had approved this $450 million project in order to improve their water quality and supply reliability.[41]

Clearly a more flexible approach to CVP/SWP system operations was needed if water quality and financial investments were to be protected along with fish.

CALFED Fix Unveiled

On July 21, 2000—22 years after the State Board and EPA began their struggle over setting water quality standards and five years after the Bay-Delta Accord was signed—CALFED officials unveiled the "Delta fix." It was outlined in a mammoth, 6500-page final programmatic EIS/EIR with an associated Record of Decision (ROD). The ROD, signed in August 2000, outlined a long-term plan with specific actions to improve the Bay-Delta. The plan also earmarked $1 billion for improving the water quality and environmental health of the Delta region; the schedule for fully implementing the plan spread across 30 years—or more. Given the project's large scope, state legislators established, in January 2003, a new agency to provide the Bay-Delta program with a formal governance structure: the California Bay-Delta Authority.[42]

Of particular interest to the Water District are the references in the ROD which discuss exploring solutions to the concerns of SWP and CVP contractors. Members of the earlier-mentioned San Luis & Delta-Mendota Water Authority pointed to poorly developed state and federal regulations as the primary reason for shortages experienced by their members. Stated Director Larry Wilson (who, along with Director Sig Sanchez, has represented the Water District's interests on the Authority's board), "It is sadly ironic and unnecessary that shortages are imposed on south-of-Delta contractors even in wet years, when water north of the Delta is abundant."[43] Since federal and state laws provide for broad discretion in implementing regulations in a balanced and efficient manner, the Authority advocated that this discretion include consideration of water supply objectives as well as meeting fishery needs and water quality mandates.[44]

EWA helps. The 2000 CALFED ROD included a new water management tool—the Environmental Water Account (EWA)—to help meet competing demands on the system projects. Devised by the Natural Heritage Institute, a nonprofit legal group working on environmental projects, the EWA functions as "a water district for the environment."[45] As described in the above section regarding the Delta smelt, rigid restrictions on water project operations were based on typical hydrologic and biologic conditions. This methodology did not account for real-time events; it did a poor job of protecting fish; and it certainly did not promote water supply reliability. The EWA was designed to promote better real-time management while protecting water supplies for Delta exporters.

With the EWA, regulators use the water banking concept and purchase and store water "assets." The water is then released as needed for the benefit of endangered fish—or to pay back the projects for supplies lost during fishery-related shutdowns of the pumps. As an example of the former, in October and November of 2001, supplemental EWA water was released from Folsom Reservoir to coincide with the flow and temperature needs of spawning Chinook salmon. Operations in 2003 also illustrated the value of the EWA. During February and early March, the relative absence of fish near the pumps enabled system operators to pump and store supplies south of the Delta. Later in the season, when fish were in greater need of protection, pumping was curtailed, but the previously stored EWA water was available to water users. Thus, fish were protected while maintaining water supply service to the urban and agricultural economy.[46] Stated Director Greg Zlotnick, "The EWA has been a significant step in improved resource management. It has provided fisheries with the water needed to protect them from jeopardy—while our economy receives greater certainty in its water supply."[47]

San Luis low point problem. Built in 1962, San Luis Reservoir, with a 2.1 million acre-feet capacity, is the largest offstream storage facility in the world. Delta water is conveyed to the reservoir via the California Aqueduct and Delta-Mendota Canal, and stored there for release to CVP and SWP users, according to their contracts (see Table F in Chapter 11 for contracted deliveries). But the reservoir has a design problem: In the late summer and early autumn, the water level may drop lower than the outlet that supplies Silicon Valley. When this happens, about 200,000 acre-feet of usable water is left out of reach—enough water to supply about one million people for a year. (For the benefit of fish, the reservoir is required to maintain year-round a minimum pool of 79,000 acre-feet; the 200,000 acre-feet at issue is in addition to this minimum pool requirement.)[48]

The CALFED ROD identified the need to address this low point problem, and in 2002, the Water District received a $14 million Proposition 13 grant to begin performing studies on a fix. By 2004, the district had identified several options for solving the problem, including: 1)

lowering the pipe that links San Luis to the San Felipe Project—the system that brings water to Silicon Valley; 2) enlarging nearby Pacheco Reservoir; 3) building a bypass pipeline that would, in dry times, divert water around San Luis Reservoir to San Felipe pipelines; or 4) combining some degree of these facility improvements with alternative water supplies. In the 2004 federal reauthorization bill discussed in the next section, the San Luis Reservoir Low Point Project was listed as a potential recipient of funds earmarked for water conveyance projects, and staff at the Water District were optimistic that environmental studies on these options could proceed and be completed by 2006.[49]

Moving Forward with the CALFED Plan

As of 2004, the CALFED Program is in Stage 1, the first seven years of the 30-year implementation period. Stage 1 includes a number of actions aimed at ecosystem restoration, water use efficiency, levee stability, water quality, watershed management and water transfers. Responsibility for implementation has been shared by water contractors through a system of mitigation credits; environmental fees attached to contractor costs; and the development of the Environmental Water Account.[50]

The ROD specified an intent to finance the full program with roughly equal contributions from federal, state and local sources. During fiscal years 1998 to 2000, Congress appropriated $220 million under the 1996 Bay-Delta Act. That money, along with state and local contributions, allowed CALFED to implement early ecosystem restoration actions while the long-term plan was under development. However, it is state funding that has largely carried the objectives of CALFED. The state has provided, as of February 2004, over $1.5 billion, with taxpayer-supported bond funds and general funds.[51]

In October 2004, some federal funding was again obtained through the leadership of Senator Dianne Feinstein and Congressman Richard Pombo. President George W. Bush signed their $395 million reauthorization bill to be spent over three years for the CALFED Program. The fact that CALFED supporters had hoped to have $3 billion authorized speaks to the political difficulties Feinstein and Pombo faced in garnering support for the program. To meet the goals of CALFED's 30-year implementation schedule, the state Legislative Analyst's Office has estimated that $9.2 billion is needed to complete the program; about two-thirds of this funding has yet to be identified.[52]

While the price tag appears high, the CALFED actions to improve the estuary are critically needed, and are expected to generate between $2 million and $21 million annually in net economic benefits to commercial and recreational fisheries, with significant employment gains in that industry. The package of actions to protect the estuary will also produce the benefit of "increased certainty regarding water supplies from the Delta; this allows for more informed water management planning and investments."[53]

Californians may remain largely unaware of their stake in the long-troubled Sacramento-San Joaquin Delta, but they are fortunate that progress on protecting their main water supply, if slow in coming, has arrived. With the CALFED Program, a mechanism is in place to manage the entire Delta system, supported by a systematic manner for developing scientific data and proposed actions. The Santa Clara Valley Water District supports this program as beneficial to the long-term interests of Silicon Valley and the whole of California. While some level of environmental challenges and system uncertainties appear to be a permanent feature of Delta operations, and while controversy and litigation may continue to swirl around the issues and reshape some particular actions, the majority of Delta stakeholders are committed to moving forward, eschewing the grueling years of disagreement. If they prevail, and if the CALFED Program continues to receive state and federal funding, then the future holds promise for better water quality conditions for both estuarine creatures and for contractors who rely on the Sierra water that travels through the amazing Sacramento-San Joaquin Delta.■

Californians may remain largely unaware of their stake in the long-troubled Sacramento-San Joaquin Delta, but they are fortunate that progress on protecting their main water supply, if slow in coming, has arrived.

SOURCES, CHAPTER 13:

[1] Zlotnick, Greg. Interviewed by Cheryl Wessling, Dec. 22, 2003.

[2] "Facts About the Bay-Delta," CALFED Web site: http://www.calwater.ca.gov/Archives/Newsroom/FactSheets_1999/about_bay_delta.pdf; also, *Fishery Fact Sheet*, California Water Resources Association, circa 1992.

[3] Wilson, Larry. Interviewed by Cheryl Wessling, Sept. 25, 2003.

[4] Legislative Analyst Office Web site: http://www.lao.ca.gov/2002/cal_facts/econ.html; also, U.S. Census Bureau Web site: www.census.gov; also, McClurg, Sue, "Delta Debate," *Western Water*, March/April 1998, p. 6.

[5] "Facts About the Bay-Delta," CALFED Web site: http://www.calwater.ca.gov/Archives/Newsroom/FactSheets_1999/about_bay_delta.pdf.

[6] Environmental Protection Agency Web site: http://www.epa.gov/fedrgstr/EPA-WATER/1995/January/Day-24/pr-54DIR/fulltext.html; also, *Environmental Entrepreneurs Update*, newsletter, July 2003, available at: http://www.e2.org/ext/document.jsp?id=3045

[7] CVP total deliveries obtained from U.S. Bureau of Reclamation Web site: http://www.usbr.gov/dataweb/html/cvp; also, SWP total deliveries obtained from Cotton, Frank (SCVWD staff). Comments to draft book, April 22, 2004.

[8] Fowler, Amy (SCVWD staff). Comments to draft book, April 5, 2004.

[9] Ferraro, Patrick. Comments to draft book, March 26, 2004; also, Iwamura, Tom (retired SCVWD staff). Comments to draft book, March 17, 2004; also *Review/Outlook 1983-84*, SCVWD, p. 2.

[10] Hoose, Seena (SCVWD staff). E-mail to Cheryl Wessling, Dec. 6, 2004.

[11] *Fishery Fact Sheet*, California Water Resources Association, circa 1992; also, McClurg, Sue. "Delta Debate," *Western Water*, March/April 1998, p. 6.

[12] "Facts About the Bay-Delta," CALFED Web site: http://www.calwater.ca.gov/Archives/Newsroom/FactSheets_1999/ about_bay_delta.pdf; also, San Joaquin River Group Authority Web site: http://www.sjrg.org/EIR/supplemental/ sup_chapt20.html

[13] Environmental Protection Agency Web site: http://www.epa.gov.fedrgstr/EPA-WATER/1995/January/Day-24/pr-54DIR/fulltext.html; also, San Francisco Estuary Project Web site: http://www. abag.ca.gov/bayarea/sfep

[14] *Fishery Fact Sheet*, California Water Resources Association, circa 1992.

[15] Leavenworth, Stuart. "Dire warning for Delta's future," *Sacramento Bee*, Oct. 5, 2004.

[16] James, Roger and Wessling, Cheryl. "The CCMP: The plan to improve, protect and manage California's—and Santa Clara County's—most important water source," *Aquafacts*, Winter/Spring 1994, SCVWD, p. 8.

[17] Snow, Lester as quoted in *The Delta Dilemma*, video, CALFED Bay-Delta Program, 1996.

[18] McClurg, Sue. "CALFED and the Delta Fix," *Western Water*, January/February 1999, p. 7.

[19] *Review/Outlook 1990-91*, SCVWD, p. 8.

[20] Webster's New Collegiate Dictionary.

[21] Zlotnick, Greg. Interviewed by Cheryl Wessling, Dec. 22, 2003.

[22] *Programmatic Record of Decision*, CALFED Bay-Delta Program, Aug. 28, 2000, p. 1.

[23] State Water Resources Control Board Web site: www.swrcb.ca.gov

[24] San Joaquin River Group Authority Web site: www.sjrg.org

[25] *Review/Outlook 1983-84*, SCVWD, p. 2.

[26] Ibid.

[27] Natural Resources Defense Council Web site: http://www.nrdc.org/water/conservation/rrestor.asp

[28] Ibid.

[29] Maher, Joan.(SCVWD staff) Comments to draft book, May 20, 2004.

[30] Natural Resources Defense Council Web site: http://www.nrdc.org/water/conservation/rrestor.asp

[31] Wessling, Cheryl. "EPA proposes Bay-Delta standards; water agencies offer more water-efficient alternative," *Aquafacts,* Winter/ Spring 1994, SCVWD, pp. 16-17.

[32] CALFED Web site: http://www.calwater.ca.gov/AboutCALFED/ ProgramHistory; also, Environmental Protection Agency Web site: www.epa.gov/fedrgstr/EPA-WATER/1995/January/Day-24/ pr-54DIR/fulltext.html

[33] Zlotnick, Greg. Interviewed by Cheryl Wessling, Dec. 22, 2003.

[34] San Joaquin River Group Authority Web site: http:// www.sjrg.org/EIR/supplemental/sup_ chpt20.html

[35] Ibid.

[36] Zlotnick, Greg. Comments to draft book, May 22, 2004.

[37] *California's Bay-Delta Water Quality Dilemma: It's Getting Worse, Not Better*, Bay-Delta Urban Coalition, December 1999, p. 17; also, Nelson, Daniel, Executive Director, San Luis & Delta-Mendota Water Authority. "CALFED Opportunities: Conveyance and Coordination Between Federal and State Water Projects and Refuges," testimony to Subcommittee on Water and Power, June 28, 2003, found at: www.sldmwa.org

[38] Ibid.

[39] *California's Bay-Delta Water Quality Dilemma: It's Getting Worse, Not Better*, Bay-Delta Urban Coalition, December 1999, p. 18.

[40] Ibid.

[41] Ibid, pp. 20-22.

[42] McClurg, Sue. "CALFED and the Delta Fix," *Western Water*, January/February 1999, p. 4-7; also, McClurg, Sue. "Delta Debate," *Western Water*, March/April 1998, p. 4.

[43] Wilson, Larry. Interviewed by Cheryl Wessling, Sept. 25, 2003.

[44] Nelson, Daniel, Executive Director, San Luis & Delta-Mendota Water Authority. "CALFED Opportunities: Conveyance and Coordination Between Federal and State Water Projects and Refuges," testimony to Subcommittee on Water and Power, June 28, 2003, found at: www.sldmwa.org

[45] Natural Heritage Institute Web site at: http://www.n-h-i.org/ Projects/WaterResources/WaterResources.html

[46] *Environmental Water Account Expenditures for Protection of the Delta Smelt in Water Year 2003,* U.S. Fish and Wildlife Service, found at: http://science.calwater.ca.gov

[47] Zlotnick, Greg. Interviewed by Cheryl Wessling, Dec. 22, 2003.

[48] Arends, Kurt (SCVWD staff). Phone conversation with Cheryl Wessling, March 29, 2004; also, Rogers, Paul. "Federal funds target San Luis design flaw," *San Jose Mercury News*, pp. 1B, 4B; also, SCVWD Web site at: www.valleywater.org

[49] Rogers, Paul. "Federal funds target San Luis design flaw," *San Jose Mercury News*, p. 4B.

[50] CALFED Web site: www.calwater.ca.gov; also, Environmental Protection Agency Web site: http://www.epa.gov/fedrgstr/EPA-WATER/1995/January/Day-24/pr-54DIR/fulltext.html

[51] CALFED funding status available at the state Legislative Analyst's Office Web site at: http://www.lao.ca.gov/ analysis_2004/ resources/res_ 02_cc_calfed_anl04.htm

[52] Ibid; also, Zlotnick, Greg. Comments to draft book, April 18, 2005.

[53] Environmental Protection Agency Web site: http://www.epa.gov/ fcdrgstr/EPA-WATER/1995/January/Day-24/pr-54DIR/ fulltext.html

[54] Hundley, Norris. *The Great Thirst*, second edition, 2002, p. 257; also, Stene, Eric. *The History of the Central Valley Project*, (no date) found at U.S. Bureau of Reclamation Web site: www.usbr.gov; also, number of CVP contractors in 2004 provided by Cotton, Frank (SCVWD staff). Comments to draft book, April 22, 2004.

[55] *The State Water Project*, brochure, State Water Contractors, 2001; also, McClurg, Sue. *Water and the Shaping of California*, 2000, p. 85.

Almaden Reservoir, 2004.

Cait Hutnik

CHAPTER 14

Strengthening and Protecting the Local Supply

By Elizabeth Emmett

As the long-awaited storms washed away the 1987-1992 drought, the plan for Santa Clara County's water supply came into question. The strategy outlined in the 1975 Water Supply Master Plan was to meet the valley's water demand through 2020 by supplementing the local supply with imported water. But imported water deliveries from the State Water Project (SWP) and federal Central Valley Project (CVP) had proven unreliable during the drought. And even after the drought ended, regulations governing water exports through the Delta left the contractors of these giant water systems with significantly reduced supplies (see Chapter 13).

From 1991 to the time of this writing in 2004, deliveries to the Santa Clara Valley Water District from the SWP system have fallen far short of the contracted amount, which has ranged between 94,000 and 100,000 acre-feet. The project's average annual delivery during this time has been 48,000 acre-feet, representing an approximate 50 percent loss of expected supply.

Likewise, as of December 2004, the San Felipe Water Project of the CVP has never delivered—not even closely—the Water District's annual allotment of 152,500 acre-feet. The largest amount ever received was 123,000 acre-feet in 2002. The average delivery between 1987—the year that San Felipe came on-line—and 2002 was about 90,000 acre-feet, representing a 41 percent loss of expected supply. (See Table F in Chapter 11 for year-by-year imported water deliveries.)

While Water District officials hoped to someday regain full contract deliveries, they also recognized the critical need to strengthen and carefully manage local water sources. There was also a need to address water quality issues. Chlorination had become a problematic treatment process because of the undesirable byproducts that it produced. And the discovery of Superfund sites in the 1980s had made it clear that the quality and safety of groundwater—even below the thick clay layers of the valley floor—could not be taken for granted. During the 1990s,

It became clear that a new approach to the multi-faceted issues of water management and water supply planning was needed.

while strengthening local water sources, the Water District would also launch new efforts to protect the quality of those sources and to improve the water treatment process. In tackling this work, it became clear that a new approach to the multi-faceted issues of water management and water supply planning was needed. Befitting an agency that worked to integrate its water supply and flood management operations, and that was dealing increasingly with environmental issues, in the mid-1990s, the district board would adopt a method of planning known as *integrated water resource planning.*

Strengthening the Local Water Supply

In 1990, Water District staff engaged in the traditional process of updating the 1975 Water Supply Master Plan (previously updated in 1983, as discussed in Chapter 9). The 1990 update was developed as a Draft Water Supply Overview Study. But members of the district board were uncomfortable with the study, and even by late 1992 could not arrive at a consensus on it. Part of the problem was that the study outlined supply alternatives based on least cost analysis, and did not engage board members in the development of those alternatives.[1] The overview study was largely tabled for the next two years.

A new way to plan ahead. In 1994, newly-appointed General Manager Stan Williams and members of the district board engaged in a two-day review of the agency's work approaches. Williams introduced the integrated water resource planning concept, a technique that was gaining global acceptance.[2] Around the world, the challenges involved in freshwater management were becoming increasingly common: how to allocate limited water supplies between agricultural, municipal and environmental uses; how to protect the quality of water; and how to respond to changing water supply conditions. Out of this universal

need to sensibly address these challenges was born *integrated water resource planning.* Because the process is tailored by those who engage in it, the method has no single definition. But this description of integrated resource planning (applicable to any natural resource) provided by the American Water Works Association captures the essence of the process:

> *IRP [Integrated Resource Planning] is a comprehensive form of planning that attempts to consider all direct and indirect costs and benefits of demand management, supply management and supply augmentation by using alternative planning scenarios; analyses across disciplines; community involvement in the planning, decision-making and implementation process; and consideration of other societal and environmental benefits.*
>
> *IRP includes planning methods to identify the most efficient means of achieving the goals while considering the costs of project impacts on other community objectives and environmental management goals.*[3]

At the Water District, an integrated water resources plan (IWRP) could function as an adaptive blueprint offering options to meet future external events, such as drought, and would comprehensively address board and community concerns beyond least-cost analysis. Board members agreed to the new process.

Their first step was to reexamine the core goals of the Water District, and by 1995, they had identified six priority areas for the development of strategies and related policies— these remain in place at the time of this writing in 2004:

1) Insure a reliable, high quality water supply;
2) Keep our communities floodsafe;

3) Protect natural resources;

4) Solve complex water problems (addressing inter-relationships between competing water supply, water quality, flood control, environmental and recreational issues);

5) Inform and involve the community; and

6) Manage district funds in a sound manner.[4]

Reflecting priority 5, in March 1996, the board approved initiating a stakeholder process for the formal development of an Integrated Water Resources Plan. Jim Fiedler, the IWRP executive project manager (and later chief operating officer over watersheds) explained that foundational to the IWRP, "the selected strategy must respond to community concerns in order to succeed."[5] Representation from every segment of the county was therefore invited: the academic community; agriculture and environmental groups; League of Women Voters and chambers of commerce; water retailers and more. These stakeholders were put to work on shaping the county's future water supply plan within a framework guided by Water District staff.

Water District board members could attend the IWRP stakeholder workshops, but didn't speak at them. Recalled Director Rosemary Kamei:

IWRP participants were visibly startled when told that it would be their opinions that would shape the water supply planning strategies. It wasn't that the board was relinquishing its powers, but rather that we had been trying to communicate with groups and city jurisdictions for some time that when it came to water issues,

We wanted a broad-based public perspective about what path our valley would now take in securing its water supply.

Both photos: Alison Russell

Level 1 stakeholders in the IWRP process played a major role in the development of the 1997 IWRP preferred strategy.

Left to right: Professor Burton Dean, Leode Franklin, Craig Breon, Scott Yoo, Ronald Alexander, Dean Chamberlin, Doug Nakamura, Art Jensen, Elizabeth Zimmerman, Steve Ritchie, Marcia Allen, Lorrie Gervin, James Tucker and Nancy Richardson. Not pictured: Connie Martinez, Paul Romero, Peter Van Dyke, Fred Angelino, Suellen Rowlison, Julia Bott and Louis Garcia.

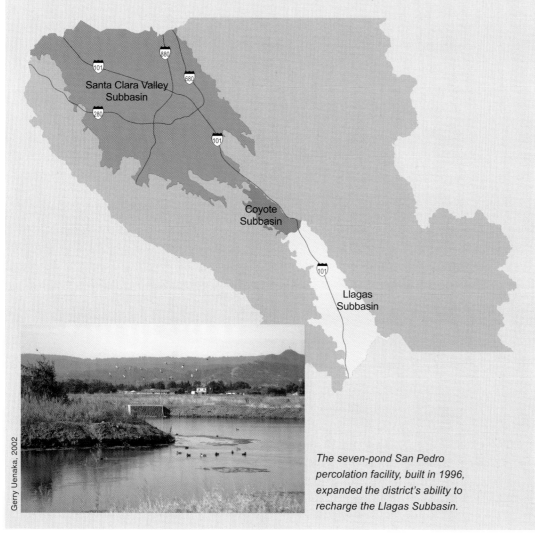

Map C. Subbasins of the Santa Clara Valley

The valley's groundwater basin is comprised of three subbasins: the northern Santa Clara Valley Subbasin, the mid-valley Coyote Subbasin and the southern Llagas Subbasin. As discussed in Appendix D, the total capacity of the three subbasins is quite large, with 530,000 acre-feet of "operational storage." Given the potential for land subsidence, far less is pumped into the county's water supply. From the mid-1980s to the time of this writing in 2005, in a typical year about 175,000 acre-feet is pumped and replenished.

The seven-pond San Pedro percolation facility, built in 1996, expanded the district's ability to recharge the Llagas Subbasin.

Gerry Uenaka, 2002

we were in this together—we wanted a broad-based public perspective about what path our valley would now take in securing its water supply.[6]

The key issues to address were Santa Clara County's population growth and the ability to meet water demand in the event of another prolonged drought. District staff projected that the county's population would grow to almost two million by 2020. Regarding future countywide water demand, many variables could affect the projection—fluctuations in weather patterns; variance from the predicted development and growth; and conservation programs that might save more or less water than expected. District staff therefore developed an estimated range of demand: between 350,000 and 500,000 acre-feet by 2020. If rainfall remained average or above through 2020, existing water supplies could probably meet demand, even with projected population growth. But another severe drought could create a shortfall of 100,000 acre-feet in needed supply.[7] (Readers should note that these numbers are historical, representing the analysis made in 1997; in subsequent years, the IWRP would be updated.[†])

In December 1997, the district board unanimously accepted the preferred strategy recommended in the final IWRP report. The preferred strategy established a course of multiple actions intended to meet the range of demand up to 500,000 acre-feet while balancing a variety of objectives. The actions included: more groundwater recharge, more water recycling, more conservation and the establishment of water banking and water transfer arrangements.

[†] In a 2003 update to the IWRP, countywide demand in 2020 was estimated at 425,000 acre feet, and no shortfall would occur during a drought if full implementation of various strategies were followed. Any reader interested in more current information should contact the Water District.

More groundwater recharge. Even before the IWRP process was started, the Water District knew it needed to improve the groundwater recharge system—a system that by 2003 would include 70 recharge ponds across the county with the capacity to recharge about 138,000 acre-feet annually.

Improvements focused on South County where groundwater is the only source of water supply. In the early 1980s, Water District planners saw that the recharge facilities replenishing the Llagas Subbasin (see Map C, opposite page) were inadequate to meet the area's future needs. Projections indicated an annual demand of 72,000 acre-feet on the Llagas and Coyote subbasins by 2020—well exceeding the existing production of about 50,000 acre-feet a year.[8]

In the 1983 South Santa Clara County Water Supply Plan, Water District staff evaluated two alternatives: 1) greater groundwater recharge efforts, or 2) construction of a water treatment plant that would enable distribution of treated local and imported water. Expanding the district's groundwater facilities was by far the less expensive option; as water percolates into the ground, it is naturally filtered by the layers of soil, gravel and rocks, and is purified to the extent that it can usually be pumped directly into the water supply, thus saving the many costs that come with planning, building and operating a treatment plant. Acting on the 1983 plan recommendations, in the mid-1980s the Water District purchased 80 acres of land near San Pedro Avenue and Hill Road for seven new percolation ponds. Known as the San Pedro facility, the construction effort included two pipeline turnouts from the Santa Clara Conduit, enabling imported CVP water to be used in recharge operations.

With the project's completion in 1996, district officials estimated that groundwater supplies in South County would remain sufficient to meet the area's water needs through 2020.[9]

More water recycling. The idea of using recycled water was controversial and had been bandied about by water officials since the 1950s (see Chapter 6). But drought had made water reuse—for nonpotable purposes—imperative. In 1991, the Water District teamed with the city of San José on a $2.16 million study of potable and nonpotable uses of recycled water. From this study, the city launched the ambitious $236 million South Bay Water Recycling program (SBWR). The program evolved into a regional effort, supported financially by the cities of San José, Milpitas and Santa Clara, as well as the five sanitary agencies whose wastewater is treated by the San Jose/Santa Clara Water Pollution Control Plant. The U.S. Bureau of Reclamation and the Water District also provided funding for the program. Construction of recycled water system elements started in 1996 and 60 miles of purple-colored recycled water pipeline was in place by 1999. Since then, the SBWR system has continued to expand.[10]

The Water District's primary interest in SBWR was to supplement the county's water supply by diverting recycled water from the San Jose/Santa Clara plant to large-scale landscapes such as industrial parks, sports fields and golf courses. But the involved cities had a different impetus for supporting the project: The vast amount of purified effluent emptying into the southern San Francisco Bay was jeopardizing the salt marsh habitat there by diluting it and making it less saline; environmental regulations required that the plant reduce its effluent. The San Francisco Regional Water Quality Control Board set a limit of 120 mgd (million gallons per day) of wastewater flow into the Bay. The limit applied specifically to the "Average Dry Weather Effluent Flow"—that is, the seasonal months without any rainfall occurrences.[11] Exceeding the limit could "trigger a halt to continued development and growth in Silicon Valley."[12] (See also discussion of the multi-agency urban runoff program in Chapter 15.)

The Water District's interest in recycled water was to supplement the local water supply, but the involved cities had a different motivation: reduce the outpour of treated effluent into the southern Bay or risk being shut down.

Table G. Water Recycling Partnerships

In the late 1990s, the Water District offered financial and technical assistance to entities interested in expanding the use of recycled water. Several partnerships were formed, as listed below. By 2004, these partnerships collectively provided almost 500 customers with 10,000 acre-feet of recycled water per year:

* Santa Clara. The city of Santa Clara initiated the first Recycled Water Reimbursement Agreement with the Water District in 1995. *Goal:* 450 acre-feet of annual recycled water by 2000. Santa Clara's effort later folded into the SBWR program (below).

* Sunnyvale. The city of Sunnyvale, operator of the Sunnyvale Water Pollution Control Plant, signed a Joint Participation Agreement with the Water District in 1997. *Goal:* 500 acre-feet of recycled water per year starting in 2000; 2,000 acre-feet per year by 2010; and 3,000 to 4,000 acre-feet per year by 2020.

* Gilroy/Morgan Hill. The cities of Gilroy and Morgan Hill and the South County Regional Wastewater Authority signed an agreement with the Water District in 1999. *Goal:* 500 acre-feet of recycled water per year in 2000; 1,200 acre-feet per year by 2010; and 4,000 to 5,000 acre-feet per year by 2020.

* San José/Santa Clara/Milpitas. This is the South Bay Water Recycling (SBWR) program, including the three named cities and the five sanitary agencies whose wastewater is treated by the San Jose/Santa Clara Water Pollution Control Plant. *Goal:* 8,000 to 14,000 acre-feet of recycled water per year by 2010; 17,000 acre-feet per year by 2020.

* Palo Alto/Mountain View. In early 2005, the Water District signed a Memorandum of Understanding with the cities of Palo Alto and Mountain View for using recycled water use from the Palo Alto Regional Water Quality Control Plant.

In 1996, Water District board directors Patrick Ferraro, Rosemary Kamei, Tony Estremera, Bob Gross and Jim Lenihan helped celebrate the groundbreaking of the South Bay Water Recycling project. A typical use for recycled water is irrigation at large landscapes and golf courses, such as the Eagle Ridge Golf Course in Gilroy (bottom photo).

Purple pipes indicate a recycled water system, as shown at the SBWR facility.

As of 2004, more than 400 customers, including the San Francisco 49ers and the Great Mall of the Bay Area, were receiving recycled water from SBWR for nonpotable uses. Their collective usage has been enough to keep the San Jose/Santa Clara plant's discharges within the state limit. Water District planners project that by 2010, SBWR will provide 8,000 to 14,000 acre-feet of recycled water per year, and 17,000 acre-feet per year by 2020.[13]

The Water District's partnerships with SBWR and other recycled water producers underscored a greater commitment to supplementing the local supply with recycled water. In 1997, the district board passed a policy supporting the expanded use of recycled water, directing that: "By the year 2010, water recycling accounts for 5 percent of the total water use in Santa Clara County," and "By the year 2020, water recycling accounts for 10 percent of the total water use in Santa Clara County."[14] To help achieve these targets, the Water District offered a payment of $115 for every acre-foot of recycled water used (see Table G for the partnerships that developed from this offer).[15]

A significant development in water recycling came about in January 2002 when the Water District board met jointly for the first time with the San José City Council. Board directors and council members agreed to share the cost of a $26 million, five-mile pipeline extension into Coyote Valley; the Water District's share would be 25 percent of the pipeline cost, in return for one-third of the pipeline capacity, up to five million gallons per day. The pipeline would supply recycled water as a coolant to the Metcalf Energy Center, a power plant being built by Calpine Corp. at the time of this writing (the plant is expected to come on-line in 2005).[16] Director Larry Wilson explained the benefits of using recycled water at the Metcalf plant: "It will help the city of San José reduce its wastewater discharge into the Bay, thereby helping to protect aquatic habitat; it will provide Calpine with a relatively low-cost water supply for coolant; and it will help the Water District meet its long-term goal of extending the valley's potable water supply."[17]

While state regulations permitted recycled water to be used for agriculture and irrigation, drinking water aquifers in the Coyote Valley are unusually close to the surface and need careful guarding. City and Water District officials, at the time of their discussions in 2002, agreed that while using recycled water as a coolant for Calpine was acceptable, no other use of recycled water in Coyote Valley would be allowed—unless studies first concluded that such use could be done in a manner that protected the quality of groundwater.[18] By the end of 2004, such studies were completed. Using the study results and with the help of consultants, district staff determined that the appropriate level of treatment for recycled water used in irrigation in the Coyote Valley should be "advanced treatment with a membrane process and ultra-violet disinfection."[19] As of March 2005, the Water District was proceeding with pilot work on this process.

More water conservation. Low-flow showerheads, ultra-low-flush toilets, drought-tolerant gardening techniques, landscape irrigation audits—these and other "demand-side management" programs were aggressively launched by the Water District in response to the 1987-1992 drought. As discussed in Chapter 11, the district had signed the state MOU Regarding Urban Water Conservation and by 1992 was working to implement 16 state-mandated best management practices (BMPs) for urban water use.

As a contractor for CVP water, the Water District also became subject to federal water conservation mandates. With the passage of the Central Valley Project Improvement Act in 1992, all CVP contractors were mandated to meet water conservation criteria established by the U.S. Bureau of Reclamation. As CVP water is predominantly used in agriculture, the focus of the criteria was agricultural

The target: By the year 2020, water recycling accounts for 10 percent of the total water use in Santa Clara County.

Efficient Water Management Practices, or EWMPs. Although agriculture had become a small part of Santa Clara County's overall water demand and was already relatively efficient, as a CVP contractor, the Water District was obligated to identify and encourage water-use efficiency measures in this sector. These measures are discussed along with the urban BMPs in Chapter 11.

The Water District's conservation programs aimed to satisfy not only these state and federal mandates, but also to meet the agency's local objectives identified in the IWRP. Altogether, the various conservation strategies could yield an estimated annual 46,000 acre-feet in water use reductions by 2020. Conservation thus stood as a key strategy in assuring an adequate water supply for the valley.[20]

Regional efforts. As demonstrated by the 1991 MOU, conservation would be enhanced through regional coordination. In 2002, the Bay Area Water Agencies Coalition (BAWAC) formed to specifically address water management issues throughout the Bay Area region. BAWAC members (see inset), have shared resources and engaged in research to bolster conservation across the region. In 2003, BAWAC began an important effort to develop an Integrated Regional Water Management Plan—much like the district's earlier mentioned IWRP, but with a regional scope. In the fall of 2005, BAWAC will likely receive grant funding under Proposition 50 to proceed with an intensive regional plan.

Water banking, transfers and trading. In addition to interagency coordination, interagency transactions became a normal part of managing the local supply. Just as some people may bank money "for a rainy day," prolonged droughts have inspired water utilities to bank water "for a dry day." *Water banking* involves the leasing of space to store surplus water supplies. One agency "deposits" some of its water supply during wet years with another agency that possesses ample storage facilities; the depositor

agency then "withdraws" its water during dry years of need. A banking agreement can be based on using water transmission facilities to convey surface water, or it may entail groundwater recharge.

In 1997, the Santa Clara Valley Water District entered its first long-term banking agreement with the Semitropic Water Storage District, near Bakersfield. Semitropic, an SWP contractor, has developed an extensive groundwater banking program using surface water distribution facilities and groundwater recharge and pumpback facilities. Of Semitropic's total one million acre-feet of storage capacity, 35 percent—or 350,000 acre-feet—was reserved for the Santa Clara Valley Water District. Eight years later (as of March 2005), the Water District had banked nearly 145,000 acre-feet of its SWP supply. Per the original agreement, the maximum rate of withdrawal is 35,000 acre-feet per year. The arrangement between the two agencies is known as an *in-lieu* banking method: When the Water District chooses to make a withdrawal, it will not withdraw the specific SWP supply that it has banked at the Semitropic facilities, but instead will receive the appropriate portion of Semitropic's own SWP supply from conveyance facilities that bring the water southward. In 2005, the Water District board is scheduled to negotiate the agency's continued level of participation in Semitropic's program.[21]

Water transfers differ from water banking in that they involve the direct purchase of water from other agencies. The Water District first participated in water transfers during the drought, when it purchased additional supplies from the state's Emergency Drought Water Bank and from Yuba County (see Chapter 11). In 1993, the Water District also entered a one-year option agreement with the Dudley Ridge Water District for transfer of up to 30,000 acre-feet. The option was not exercised, however, because other supplies were available at the time. The following year, 1994,

Bay Area Water Agencies Coalition (BAWAC)

Members:
- Alameda County Water District
- Bay Area Water Users Association*
- Contra Costa Water District
- East Bay Municipal District
- San Francisco Public Utilities Commission
- Santa Clara Valley Water District
- Zone 7 Water Agency

* *This association represents 29 cities, Water Districts and other agencies located in San Mateo, Santa Clara and Alameda counties.*

the Water District purchased 9,000 acre-feet from the SWP as part of a pilot program for possible longer-term transfer agreements in the future. As of 2004, the board policy for water transfers is to consider and evaluate each opportunity as it arises.[22]

Water banking and water transfer agreements of the 1990s fostered a new spirit of cooperation among water entities throughout the state. In that spirit, the Water District joined with the San Francisco Water Department (SFWD) to develop a project that would facilitate the *trading* of water between the two agencies. The SFWD's Bay Division Pipelines that carry Hetch Hetchy water through Santa Clara County and up the Peninsula lay but a short stretch from the Water District's distribution system, specifically, the giant Milpitas Pipeline. The proximity of the pipelines made the idea of an intertie feasible, and the two agencies began discussing the project in the early 1990s.

"Connecting two entirely separate water systems was a technical challenge for the San Francisco PUC and Santa Clara Valley Water District," said Patricia Martel, general manager of the San Francisco Public Utilities Commission, which oversees SFWD operations. "The intertie was 10 years in the making and attests to our joint commitment to supply reliable drinking water to Bay Area customers."[23] Construction began in 2000, and involved laying about 1,000 feet of 42-inch pipe and constructing a pump station, a chemical-injection system and a maintenance yard. Commented Director Robert Gross at the groundbreaking ceremony in October 2000, "This project will benefit hundreds of thousands of Bay Area residents, both in Santa Clara County and along the greater Peninsula."[24]

Even before its completion, the intertie pump station proved helpful to the South Bay water system. When one of the Water District's treatment plants was off-line for construction upgrades, the district was able to pull water from the partially completed intertie pump station in the summer

of 2001 to augment deliveries to areas in Milpitas and northern San José.

In 2003, the SCVWD/SFWD Intertie was completed with a capacity to deliver 40 million gallons of water per day to either agency's system. The intertie will be used during emergencies and planned or unplanned outages in either system. The cost of the project, $9.1 million, was evenly split between the two water agencies.[25]

Improving the Water Treatment Process

Throughout the 1990s, the Water District would prove its commitment to the mission of providing valley residents with safe drinking water. Improving the water treatment process became a top priority and included investment in an experimental laboratory; this would lead to major upgrades of the district's three treatment plants.

Treatment experiments begin. In 1990, the Santa Clara Valley Water District joined with neighboring Alameda County Water District in the search for new treatment technologies that could solve the trihalomethanes (THMs) problem as well as handle the burgeoning list of substances that required monitoring (as discussed in Chapter 10, the federal list had grown by more than 100 substances by 1991). The two agencies worked to prepare a Disinfection Byproduct Action Plan and to build a small pilot treatment plant that would test alternative treatment options, including ozone gas and granular activated carbon.

The pilot plant on which the water managers pinned their hopes was a small, nondescript building, placed into service in February 1993 at the Vasona Pump Station in Los Gatos. Equipped with several loops of pipes, filters, reservoirs and chemical application points, the pilot plant—which cost less than $200,000 to design and build—was set up to simulate various treatment processes. The goal was to identify a process that would reduce THMs and that would meet

Water banking and water transfer agreements of the 1990s fostered a new spirit of cooperation among water entities throughout the state.

the new regulations for other constituents.[26] Walt Wadlow, who oversaw the experimental plant as a supervising engineer (and later became chief operating officer over the Water Utility), explained the small facility's role: "The pilot plant enabled us to assess treatment alternatives as well as design criteria and cost estimates for modifications to our three treatment plants. It was the only pilot plant of its kind in California, reflecting our board of directors' support for staying ahead of the regulations curve."[27]

Between 1993 and 1994, the pilot plant engaged in various tests, changing the contact point for chlorine in an effort to minimize THMs, and testing the viability of ozone gas as a disinfectant. The results of those tests ultimately led the Water District to plan for upgrading its treatment plants to ozonation technology. Alameda County's water agency also opted to install ozone disinfection when its newest treatment plant was built in the early 1990s, and Contra Costa Water District and Metropolitan Water District of Southern California made similar moves—all such projects costing in the range of $50 million to $200 million.[28]

Also in the mid-1990s, Water District staff tested a theory proposed by Bob Howard, then-head of the Water District's Treated Water Operations: If chlorine had less time to interact with organics, then perhaps THMs would be reduced. At the Rinconada Water Treatment Plant, Howard's idea was tested. Jeff Micko, a district engineer, designed a "chlorine grid" system that was installed at the midpoint in each of Rinconada's four clarifier basins; in these 20-foot deep, two million-gallon basins, much of the heavy organic matter in the water settled to the bottom. With approval from the state Department of Health Services, rather than adding chlorine at the Rinconada inlet valve vault as done in the past, chlorine was released evenly and horizontally as the water passed through Micko's grids in an upward flow. Rinconada Plant Super-

visor Ken Baker recalled that the new approach resulted in a consistent drop in THMs by 25 percent or more.[29]

For water suppliers, at the heart of the THMs issue was how to balance the risks from microbial pathogens such as *Giardia* and *Cryptosporidium* versus the risks from disinfection byproducts. Pathogens can cause diseases such as typhoid fever and cholera; chlorination has been the key to wiping out these deadly diseases in the United States. Yet the byproducts that result from the application of chlorine have their own health risks, as noted in the discussion of THMs in Chapter 10. In 1996, amendments to the Safe Drinking Water Act directed the Environmental Protection Agency (EPA) to establish rules that would help water utilities eliminate pathogens while simultaneously reducing disinfection byproducts and associated public health risks.[30]

To further address this issue, the EPA formed the Partnership for Safe Water in the late 1990s. Signatories to the Partnership, primarily local water suppliers, voluntarily agreed to enhance the performance of their water systems for greater control of microbial contaminants.[31] As a partner, the Water District agreed to allow independent experts to scrutinize its treatment practices and propose improvements or enhancements; any findings would be reported to the public.

Onward with ozonation. Armed with two years of research from its pilot plant experiments, in the mid-1990s, the Water District began planning for the most ambitious, locally-funded capital project in its history: the $285 million Water Treatment Improvement Project (WTIP). Underway at the time of this writing with completion expected in 2009, WTIP is switching the Water District's disinfection method from chlorine to ozone gas. Ozone offers many advantages as a disinfectant. It attacks *Giardia* and *Cryptosporidium* as well as bacteria and virsuses, and it helps control algae-based tastes and odors. Importantly, it disinfects water without creating THMs and other undesir-

Upgrading to ozonation for water treatment

Upgrades at all three of the Water District's treatment plants included the construction of a building to house the ozone contactor and ozone generation equipment. At left is construction of this building in April 2004 at the Penitencia plant in east San José. Above: the completed building in April 2005.

▶▶ **How it works:** Inside the building, ozone generators (right photo) will produce 400 pounds of ozone each day to disinfect the Penitencia plant's daily average of 50 million gallons of drinking water. Ozone is produced by energizing oxygen molecules so that the bonds recombine to form ozone. The ozone is piped to deep contactor basins where it bubbles up through water that has been cleared (flocculated) of dirt and larger particles. After 16 minutes of "ozone bubbling"—which provides disinfection—the water moves to a filtration tank that contains layers of sand and carbon to remove any tiny particles. A small dose of chlorine is still added after filtration to provide long-term disinfection of the water as it moves through the distribution system.

able byproducts that are common when disinfecting water with chlorine. The improvement project also provides for retrofitting the Penitencia Water Treatment Plant for better seismic tolerance, and increasing the capacity of the Rinconada plant from 80 to 100 mgd.[32]

Commenting on the significance of the upgrades, Director Tony Estremera stated in 2004, "Upgrading our treatment plants to ozonation and other plant retrofits represents an investment in the health and welfare of our community. Our citizens will reap the benefits for decades to come."[33] As mentioned earlier, other water agencies in the state have also switched to ozonation. In the Bay Area, the Santa Clara Valley Water District's effort stands to be the largest in the region. Contra Costa Water District has a total treatment capacity of 115 mgd; in the Santa Clara Valley, the three treatment plants will have a total capacity of 240 mgd. (The Penitencia plant has a capacity of 40 mgd; Rinconada will upgrade from 80 to 100 mgd; and the Santa Teresa Water Treatment Plant has a capacity of 100 mgd.)

Upgrading
the Water Quality Laboratory

In addition to upgrading treatment plants, the Water District board supported a major upgrade and site change to the water quality laboratory (see also inset on p. 119 for more information regarding the lab). Although the lab's original 1,280-square-foot space at Rinconada had expanded to 2,600 square feet by 1987, a study that same year found far more space was needed to accommodate the increasing workload associated with new regulations. By 2003, 17 lab employees were working to monitor treatment processes, and were performing more than 138,000 tests each year for bacteria, turbidity, hardness, pH, trihalomethanes, organic substances, metals, pesticides, fertilizers and toxic chemicals. The budget for this level of work exceeded $3 million

annually. The lab holds one of the highest levels of certification available from the state Department of Health Services, both for the number of tests it can perform and for analytical accuracy.[34] "Twice a year we get blind water samples to test—we don't know what's in them or at what concentration," said Jim Scott, laboratory unit manager, in 2003. "For the last 10 years, we've identified the constituents in the samples within a 98 to 100 percent accuracy range."[35]

Given this growth in lab work, the District board approved the idea of adding a new laboratory to the headquarters campus on Almaden Expressway in south San José, and increasing staff to 24 analysts as well. By early 2006, construction is expected to be complete on a $13.4 million, 18,400-square-foot laboratory building at the northeast end of the campus. The lab may also be available to the county's water retailers, providing services on a fee basis.

Protecting
Local Water Sources

While the Water District had established programs to address the problem of leaking underground storage tanks and abandoned wells in the 1980s (Chapter 10), there emerged new threats to local water quality. The Water District—like many other water management agencies in the country—would have to contend with four major contaminants of concern in the 1990s and early 2000s: nitrates, MTBE, perchlorate and mercury.

Nitrates in rural areas. In contrast to the leaking chemical and fuel tanks associated with the high tech industries of the northern county, it was agriculture and livestock that presented water quality challenges in South County. Routine tests in the southern subbasin were showing high levels of nitrates, which can be associated with health problems and can be especially troublesome for infants, leading to "blue baby syndrome." Typical sources of nitrogen in groundwater are livestock waste, fertilizers and septic systems.

Tom Iwamura, a former Water District geologist, recalled that the problem of nitrates in groundwater was recognized as far back as the late 1950s. Through the years, as more wells tested in excess of the drinking water standard for nitrates, the concern became more acute.[36] By 1995, the Water District had developed a comprehensive Nitrate Management Plan. In following that plan, the Water District offered residents information and assistance on topics such as well location and construction; septic system use; and fertilizer selection and use. In 1998, the Water District offered free nitrate testing to more than 2,000 well owners in South County (benefiting well owners as well as providing the District with the opportunity to compile accurate data). About 600 well owners accepted the offer. Test results showed that about half of their wells had nitrate levels above the state drinking water standard of 45 ppm. Armed with this information, well owners could decide how to tackle their individual nitrate concerns.[37]

MTBE, gasoline additive. More politically complicated than nitrates—and a greater threat to groundwater and public health—was MTBE. To satisfy a federal clean-air regulation, California began using "oxygenates" in its gasoline to produce cleaner-burning fuel. Since 1992, the oxygenate used in gasoline was methyl tertiary butyl ether, or MTBE. Unfortunately, MTBE—a potential carcinogen—began showing up in shallow groundwater aquifers around the state, primarily near underground fuel storage tanks that were leaking. Although targeted against air pollution, the toxicity of MTBE, coupled with its mobility in groundwater, made it an immediate threat to aquifers

statewide. By 2002, MTBE contamination had forced the closing of drinking water wells in the cities of Santa Monica, South Lake Tahoe, Sacramento, Cambria, Temecula, and in Kern and Ventura counties.

In the Santa Clara Valley, the Water District began investigating the potential for MTBE contamination in 1995. Testing found MTBE in the soil at 292 sites (primarily at gas service stations) throughout the county, and at low levels in local reservoirs.[38] MTBE had most likely made its way into the reservoirs from boat and jet ski engines, runoff from streets and parking lots, and/or in rainfall.

The Water District took quick action. By 1997, staff had written the state's first guidelines for owners of leaking underground fuel tanks on how to identify and clean up MTBE contamination before it reached groundwater. The District also worked with the Santa Clara County Parks and Recreation Department to develop guidelines for boating on reservoirs. This included a phased reduction of the number of boats and jet skis on a reservoir based on MTBE levels in the water. In August 1998, after suspending two-stroke engines on Calero Reservoir for a seven-week stretch, the average MTBE levels in water samples dropped from 15.7 ppb in June to 3.7 ppb[††] in August—the restrictions obviously worked.[39]

In January 1998, Great Oaks Water Company, which serves a portion of South San José, chose to close one of its drinking water wells when trace amounts of MTBE were detected. As of 2004, this and one other well of the valley's 600-plus public drinking water wells were the only ones in which MTBE has been detected.

In the view of the Water District, and most other water utilities in the state, the best way to protect ground-

The toxicity of MTBE, coupled with its mobility in groundwater, made it an immediate threat to aquifers statewide.

[††] Drinking water standards for MTBE are a primary Maximum Contaminant Level (MCL) of 13 ppb and a secondary MCL of 5 ppb. The primary MCL is based on health and safety; the secondary MCL is based on aesthetics—taste, odor and appearance.

Perchlorate is a serious

issue, and is now the

number one water quality

problem in many areas

of the United States.

water from MTBE was to ban the additive. Taking charge of the MTBE issue locally was Director Robert Gross. Under his leadership, the Water District lobbied state and federal officials to ban MTBE from California's gasoline. Gross became an expert on the subject, speaking and meeting with scientists, medical doctors and researchers throughout the United States, Europe and Australia.[40]

In July 1999, a Blue Ribbon panel of the EPA recommended a "significant reduction" in the nation's use of MTBE, lending momentum to the Executive Order by Governor Gray Davis to phase out the additive in California by December 31, 2002. However, on March 15, 2002, Davis announced an extension to the deadline, allowing the gasoline industry more time to transition from MTBE to another oxygenate.[41] While the delay could possibly help keep gas prices from skyrocketing, Director Rosemary Kamei noted that it also meant taxpayers in Santa Clara County "would continue to shell out nearly a million dollars a year to protect groundwater from MTBE contamination."[42] The district cost to find and oversee cleanup of MTBE-contaminated sites and to perform monitoring tasks was roughly $900,000 per year. Fortunately, for the safety of drinking water supplies throughout the state, the ban on MTBE officially went into effect on January 1, 2004.

Perchlorate, a toxic salt. Perchlorate is a type of salt used in the production of rocket fuel, safety flares, fireworks and other products. It is also a substance known to cause severe thyroid disorders, cancer in adults and birth defects in developing fetuses. Perchlorate was discovered at high levels in groundwater in the early 2000s, mostly in western states. Because perchlorate quickly dissolves and spreads, it is difficult and expensive to clean up, requiring the pumping and treatment of vast quantities of groundwater.

After taking samples in January 2003, the Water District and the Santa Clara County Public Health Department announced that "as many as 450 private wells in

southern Santa Clara County could potentially have low levels of perchlorate."[43] The source of the perchlorate was believed to be Olin Corp., a manufacturer of flares that had operated for more than 40 years in Morgan Hill. It was estimated that the plume had spread four miles in the southern subbasin. Public reaction was cautious at first: "San Martin residents stay calm about contaminated wells," read a January 18 headline in the *San Jose Mercury News*. But three weeks later, on February 7, headlines reflected greater dismay: "Concern grows on tainted wells; South County problem spreading." Director Rosemary Kamei, who had been representing South County since 1993, recalled that concern among residents was great enough to generate the largest public meeting in Water District history; that February, more than 700 South County residents attended a District-sponsored informational meeting.[44]

Although the contamination was a regulatory issue under the jurisdiction of the Central Coast Regional Water Quality Control Board, Kamei noted that "the Water District went above and beyond its legal duty to assist the South County communities with the perchlorate problem—and appropriately so." The Water District began with tests on hundreds of wells and assisted Olin and the Regional Board in their investigation and remediation efforts. In April 2003, the Water District provided a portable treatment plant, capable of treating water and removing perchlorate at a rate of 450 gallons per minute through the process of ion exchange. Eventually, the city of Morgan Hill and Olin each installed similar treatment facilities on public wells serving Morgan Hill and San Martin. The Water District also held press conferences and public meetings; established a perchlorate hotline; published information in both English and Spanish on the Water District Web site; and, provided bottled drinking water for those whose wells tested above the interim 4 ppb regulatory standard.[†††45] Between January and July of 2003, the cost to the Water

District for the bottled water was $450,000.[46] As the investigation progressed, Olin eventually took over the responsibility of providing bottled water. By July of 2003, the perchlorate plume was estimated to be more than eight miles long.

Perchlorate has proved even more problematic than MTBE. In southern California, perchlorate plumes were discovered near Simi Valley, in San Gabriel Valley and in San Bernardino County. At the time of this writing, in Nevada, a plume of the toxic salt is slowly percolating into Lake Mead and the Colorado River, threatening the drinking water supply for millions of people.[47] "Perchlorate is a serious issue, and is now the number one water quality problem in many areas of the United States," said Jim Crowley, who led the Water District's program on leaking underground storage tanks and associated groundwater protection efforts. "One unburned road flare can contaminate more than 2 acre-feet of groundwater, and 40 metric tons of flares were used or burned in Santa Clara County in 2003 alone. We are still trying to understand all the sources of perchlorate contamination."[48]

In an effort to counter the problem, Assemblymember Hannah-Beth Jackson of Ventura County initiated the Perchlorate Contamination Prevention Act in July 2003; Governor Gray Davis signed it into law in September. This act requires any facility that manufactures or stores perchlorate to monitor the area under the facility to prevent contamination of groundwater supplies. It also requires the state Department of Toxic Substances Control to create regulations that specify best management practices for the handling of perchlorate materials.[49]

Mercury, miners' toxic legacy. Mercury, also known as quicksilver, was mined for many decades in several parts of California. It served as an efficient magnet for something miners were even more interested in: gold. The globules of silvery mercury helped to amalgamate gold particles in the muddy sluices used in gold mining operations. While helpful in extracting gold, the miners' use of mercury left a poisonous legacy. An approximate 10 percent of the estimated 65,000 tons of mercury mined in the state between 1850 and 1920 was lost to streams in the Sierra and coastal mountains. In these streams, naturally occurring bacteria converts mercury to a more toxic form, methylmercury, which is easily absorbed by plants and fish—and by any humans who eat such fish.[50]

Locally, mercury was mined in the area where Almaden Quicksilver County Park now stands—the rolling hills here were once home to more than 1,800 miners and their families. The mines have been sealed, but remnants of mining structures remain in the park. Unfortunately, also remaining are remnants of the extracted mercury, having settled in the sediments of streams leading out of this watershed. Alamitos Creek, Guadalupe Creek and Guadalupe River as well as Almaden, Calero and Guadalupe reservoirs have long been designated as containing mercury-contaminated sediments, and the fish in these streams and reservoirs are considered unsafe to eat (warnings against consuming fish are posted along these streams and reservoirs). In 2002, the San Francisco Bay Regional Water Quality Control Board sponsored a study of mercury, and some fish sampled from Anderson and Stevens Creek reservoirs—as well as from eight other

---

††† In March 2004, the state Office of Environmental Health Hazard Assessment announced a public health standard of 6 ppb for perchlorate. Roughly 70 percent of the wells tested in South County were between 4 ppb and 6 ppb; none were above 6 ppb. Comparatively, in areas next to jet facilities, perchlorate was found at 260 ppb in Sacramento County and 159 ppb in Los Angeles County. Regardless of the standard, both the Water District and Regional Board committed to cleaning up groundwater in South County to a zero level for perchlorate.

Anderson Reservoir is one of the local reservoirs where sampled fish were found to contain an unhealthful level of methylmercury. The source appeared to be mercury particles that are emitted with the burning of fossil fuels and industrial waste and that fall back to the earth, as well as naturally-occurring mercury in geologic formations. In this March 1995 photo of Anderson, the reservoir, swollen with runoff from a severe storm, is spilling over into Coyote Creek (see also flood photos in Chapter 12).

Scott Ludwig

218

reservoirs in the Bay Area—were found to exceed human health guidelines for methylmercury.[††††] The source of mercury in Anderson and Stevens Creek reservoirs (as well as for many water bodies throughout California's coast range) appeared to be naturally-occurring from geologic formations, combined with atmospheric deposition—mercury discharges into the air when fossil fuels and industrial waste are burned, falling back to earth when it rains.[51]

In response, the Santa Clara County Public Health Department distributed fish-consumption guidelines for Anderson and Stevens Creek reservoirs.[52] And in 2003, the Water District began working with the Regional Board on a $1 million study to identify sources of mercury, and to calculate how much mercury "load" the water system can absorb and still meet water quality standards. The study, funded by the District's Clean, Safe Creeks Program (see Chapter 15), provided a scientific basis for developing a plan to reduce mercury in fish in the Guadalupe watershed. Using the information from this local study, the Regional Board and Water District will develop a plan for controlling mercury. The plan for cleaning up mercury in Santa Clara County will tie in with the broader effort by the Regional Board to reduce by half the existing amount of mercury in the San Francisco Bay, as well as control the sources of mercury pollution to the Bay. By 2004, an estimated 140,000 pounds of mercury had settled in the Bay's sediments and food web. In addition to reducing the flow of mercury out of Santa Clara County's historic mining district, the Regional Board is working with water boards in the Central Valley to reduce mining-related mercury, as well as monitoring the mercury used in Bay Area oil refineries. The plan to halve the mercury load in the Bay is estimated to take 120 years.[53]

Security. Sadly, pollutants aren't the only threat to a water source. After the terrorist attacks of September 11, 2001, the major water utilities in the Bay Area joined with intelligence groups and law enforcement agencies, and formed the Bay Area Security Information Collaborative (BASIC). Through BASIC, agencies developed emergency response procedures and conducted regional exercises.

In its own operations, the Water District has always attended to the security of its systems, but in the post 9/11 era, the agency toughened and expanded its safety measures, adding a 24-hour presence of security guards at critical facilities and installing video surveillance, sensors and alarms at all key facilities. Public tours of plants and buildings were suspended; use of employee and visitor identification safeguards were reinforced; and daily inspections occurred at every major facility.

The Water District also worked with the federal Environmental Protection Agency and the state Department of Health Services in conducting security-related vulnerability assessments. The District then updated the emergency response plan it already had in place, developed to deal with many types of emergencies, from natural disasters to terrorist attacks and bomb threats.[54]

~

The 1990s and early 2000s reflected an intensified, multi-level effort to bolster and protect local water sources for the mission of providing Santa Clara County with safe and adequate drinking water. As discussed in the next chapter, efforts to protect source water in the early twenty-first century would become even broader in scope, and would involve many entities.■

[††††] In addition to finding mercury in the fish, the Regional Board study also found polychlorinated biphenyls (PCBs), a group of industrial chemicals. Although PCB manufacturing ended in 1977, the chemicals remain in the environment for years. Like mercury, PCBs can accumulate in fish tissues.

SOURCES, CHAPTER 14:

[1] Williams, Stan. Interviewed by Cheryl Wessling, July 27, 2004.

[2] Ibid.

[3] American Water Works Association, White Paper on Integrated Resource Planning, 1993, as quoted in, "Water Demand Management Within the Integrated Resource Planning Process" by William O. Maddaus, accessed on Nov. 7, 2004 at: http://www.isf.uts.edu.au/whatsnew/Demand_Mgmt_IRP.pdf

[4] *Annual Performance Report, 1995-96*, SCVWD, pp. 2-13.

[5] Fiedler, Jim. Interviewed by Cheryl Wessling, March 17, 2004.

[6] Kamei, Rosemary. Interviewed by Cheryl Wessling, Nov. 5, 2003.

[7] *Integrated Water Resources Plan, Final Report*, SCVWD, January 1997, p. ES-1.

[8] Ahmadi, Behzad (SCVWD staff). E-mail to Cheryl Wessling regarding subbasin capacity and pumping, and South County groundwater projections, July 8, 2005.

[9] *Review/Outlook 1983-84*, SCVWD, p. 5; also, *Review/Outlook 1984-85*, SCVWD, p. 16; also, *Water Supply and Distribution Facilities*, brochure, SCVWD, updated July 1997, p. 3.

[10] *Annual Report 1990-91*, SCVWD, p. 8; also, John, Pam (SCVWD staff). Comments to draft book, January 2005.

[11] John, Pam (SCVWD staff). E-mail to Cheryl Wessling, April 26, 2005.

[12] *The South Bay Water Challenge*, brochure, South Bay Water Recycling program, City of San José, April 2000.

[13] Ibid; also, *Urban Water Management Plan*, SCVWD, April 2001, p. 59.

[14] Resolution No. 97-60 as stated in *Urban Water Management Plan*, SCVWD, April 2001, p. 56.

[15] *Annual Performance Report, 1994-1995*, SCVWD, p. 5.

[16] *Urban Water Management Plan*, SCVWD, April 2001, p. 56; also, Metcalf Energy Center Web site: www.metcalfenergycenter.com

[17] Wilson, Larry. Interviewed by Cheryl Wessling, Sept. 25, 2003.

[18] Mercury News Staff Report, "State's High Court Dismisses Suit to Block Plant," *San Jose Mercury News*, May 22, 2003, p. 3B; also, Wilson, Larry. Comments to draft book, Feb. 16, 2003.

[19] John, Pam (SCVWD staff). E-mail to Cheryl Wessling, April 26, 2005.

[20] *Integrated Water Resources Plan, Final Report*, SCVWD, January 1997, pp. 7-2 to 7-4.

[21] Maher, Joan (SCVWD staff). E-mail to Cheryl Wessling, Dec. 7, 2004; also, *Urban Water Management Plan*, SCVWD, April 2001, p. 63. Regarding banked amount, data provided by Kao, Cindy (SCVWD staff), e-mail to Cheryl Wessling, July 25, 2005.

[22] *Urban Water Management Plan*, SCVWD, April 2001, p. 56.

[23] Martel, Patricia. As quoted in SCVWD News Release, "Pump station links Santa Clara County, San Francisco drinking water systems," May 13, 2002.

[24] Gross, Robert. As quoted in SCVWD News Release, "Work to link Santa Clara County, Hetch Hetchy water supplies begins," Oct. 23, 2000.

[25] SCVWD News Release, "Pump station links Santa Clara County, San Francisco drinking water systems," May 13, 2002.

[26] *Review/Outlook 1992-93*, SCVWD, p. 9.

[27] Wadlow, Walt. Interviewed by Elizabeth Emmett, April 28, 2003.

[28] *California's Bay-Delta Water Quality Dilemma: It's Getting Worse, Not Better*, Bay-Delta Urban Coalition, December 1999, pp. 12-13.

[29] Baker, Ken. E-mail to Cheryl Wessling, April 21, 2005; also, Scott, Jim. Interviewed by Elizabeth Emmett, Jan. 21, 2004.

[30] Environmental Protection Agency Web site: http://www.epa.gov/safewater/mdbp/ieswtrfr.pdf; also, Brewster, Francis, et al. Comments to draft book, March 26, 2004.

[31] Environmental Protection Agency Web site: http://www.epa.gov/safewater

[32] "Ozonation: A Better Way to Disinfect Our Water," SCVWD brochure, 2005; also, Brewster, Francis, et al (SCVWD staff). Comments to draft book, including cost and year, March 26, 2004.

[33] Estremera, Tony. Interviewed by Cheryl Wessling, Feb. 6, 2004.

[34] *New Water Quality Laboratory Project Plan*, SCVWD, August 2003, p. 1.

[35] Scott, Jim. Interviewed by Elizabeth Emmett, Jan. 21, 2004.

[36] Iwamura, Tom (retired SCVWD staff). Comments to draft book, March 16, 2004.

[37] SCVWD News Release, "High nitrate readings showing up at many private wells in South County," May 14, 1998.

[38] *Review/Outlook, 1997-98*, SCVWD, p. 5.

[39] SCVWD News Release, "Two-stroke watercraft allowed back on Calero Reservoir as long as levels of gasoline additive MTBE remain within limits," Aug. 21, 1998.

[40] SCVWD News Release, "Alviso native pledges to provide county residents with continued water, flood protection services," Jan. 10, 2001.

[41] California Energy Commission Web site: http://www.energy.ca.gov/mtbe/index.html

[42] Kamei, Rosemary. "Delay in eliminating MTBE is going to cost the valley," *San Jose Mercury News*, editorial opinion, March 22, 2002.

[43] SCVWD Press Conference Statement, internal document, Jan. 16, 2003.

[44] Kamei, Rosemary. Interviewed by Cheryl Wessling, Nov. 5, 2003.

[45] Stuenkel, Lori. "Well users wary of new standard," *Morgan Hill Dispatch*, March 16, 2004; also, comments on perchlorate and its ppb levels from Hall, Stephen. *A Comprehensive Examination of the CALFED Program and Ways to Increase and Improve Water Supply, Reliability, Availability and Quality*, Testimony to House Subcommittee on Water and Power, July 1, 2003.

[46] *The Pinnacle*, week of June 27, 2003, p. 1.

[47] Pitzer, Gary. "Confronting a Legacy of Contamination: Perchlorate," *Western Water*, May/June 2003, pp. 4-5; also, News Release, "Jackson Bill to Prevent Perchlorate Contamination of Water Supply Passes With Bipartisan Support," July 2003, accessed at: http://democrats. assembly.ca.gov/members/a35/press/p352003014.htm

[48] Crowley, Jim. Interviewed by Elizabeth Emmett, Aug. 18, 2003.

[49] News Releases (two): "Jackson Bill to Prevent Perchlorate Contamination of Water Supply Passes With Bipartisan Support," July 2003, and "Assemblymember Jackson's Bill to Prevent Perchlorate Contamination of Water Supply Signed by Governor," both accessed at: http://democrats.assembly.ca.gov/members/a35/press/p352003026.htm

[50] Santa Clara County, Department of Parks and Recreation Web site: www.parkhere.org

[51] SCVWD News Release, "Anglers advised to limit consumption of fish caught from local reservoirs; water for drinking, other household uses remains safe," Oct. 14, 2004.

[52] Ibid.

[53] Drury, Dave (SCVWD staff). Comments to draft book, Jan. 27, 2005.

[54] Yep, Ray (SCVWD staff). E-mail to Cheryl Wessling, April 24, 2005; also, *Issues: 2002*, newsletter, SCVWD, p. 1.

Volunteers in the Adopt-A-Creek program clean up a stretch of Uvas Creek.

Jim McCann, 2005

CHAPTER 15

Embracing Environmental Stewardship and Collaboration

By Cheryl Wessling

Managing water in the Santa Clara Valley is an evolving effort, as readers of this history will, by now, have grasped. Looking back at the fledgling Water District of the early 1930s, there was a two-person operation that focused solely on operating reservoirs for groundwater recharge. Its jurisdiction covered only the north central portion of Santa Clara County. After consolidations with other water entities (see Appendix A), the district evolved into a countywide agency with a full-time staff, in 2005, of about 815.[1] In addition to the objective of recharging groundwater, the agency now focused on imported water operations, flood protection, water treatment, water quality protection, environmental enhancements, and community uses of district facilities, such as recreation on reservoirs and trails along flood protection projects. The agency had also become an established leader in state and federal arenas, helping to shape policy, regulations and legislation on all of these issues.

Comprehensive and successful as it was, there was room for improvement to the modern Water District. Changes to the agency's internal organization and the way work was accomplished—for staff, managers and the governing board—would take place. The stories of the major flood protection projects in Chapter 12 show how public values, regulatory pressures and board policy initiatives reshaped the agency's approach to the environmental component of its work—shifting the district's stance from merely compliant to proactive. Ultimately, the Water District would embrace environmental stewardship as a third official mission, making it a unique agency with chartered responsibility for water supply, flood protection and environmental stewardship in the county's watersheds.[2]

Furthermore, in a groundbreaking manner, the Water District began to address the objectives of its three missions through one comprehensive approach: *integrated watershed*

Several exciting collaborations would emerge between the 1990s and early 2000s.

It was an extraordinary time. We were rolling out new programs and running full speed with the workload.

management. This approach was not undertaken by the Water District alone, but rather through collaborative partnerships with local governments, state and federal regulators, and community and environmental stakeholders. Several exciting collaborations emerged between the 1990s and early 2000s. The Water District spearheaded the Fisheries and Aquatic Habitat Collaborative Effort, the Santa Clara Valley Urban Runoff Pollution Prevention Program and the Water Resources Protection Collaborative. It also became a key participant in the federally-driven Santa Clara Basin Watershed Management Initiative and the landmark South Bay Salt Ponds Restoration Project.

Reorganizing the Approach to Water Management

The period between 1980 and 2005 was a time of rapid expansion in the Water District's facilities, programs and responsibilities, matched by recruitment of people to do the work. In 1980, there were 300 employees; in 1995, approximately 600; by early 2004—as previously noted—there were 825.[3] Ronald Esau, who served first as assistant general manager and then general manager from 1980 to 1994, explained this expansion: "It was an extraordinary time," he said. "We took over the operations and maintenance of the newly constructed San Felipe Water Project; built and began operating the new Santa Teresa Water Treatment Plant; and greatly expanded the In-County Distribution System. Concurrently we dealt with a succession of events—leaking chemical storage tanks, floods, diminished imported water supplies and environmental regulations. We were rolling out new programs and running full speed with the workload."[4]

With the multiplicity of new programs, it was time to take a fresh look at the way the Water District was doing business. That became the first assignment for Stan Williams, who became general manager in 1994, after serv-

ing as an assistant general manager for four years. (Note: The title of "general manager" changed to "chief executive officer" in July 2001.)[5]

Reorganizing the agency. Several forces were driving the need for reorganization. Reductions in state and federal funding were causing budgetary challenges, particularly for flood protection projects. New strategies were needed for dealing with the permits and environmental issues associated with these projects (Chapter 12). The uncertainty of imported water supplies was also calling for new supply strategies, leading to the Integrated Water Resources Plan (Chapter 14). And the ever-present responsibility of a public agency to work for greater cost efficiencies and save taxpayer dollars remained a driving concern. After identifying these forces, staff worked with an independent consultant to assess the district's structure and recommend improvements. "The proposal of a major reorganization created anxiety for many employees. We opted for a third-party analysis to help diffuse emotions and to keep us focused on what constituted a better structure and how to get there," said Williams.[6]

By mid-1995, the recommendations were approved and under implementation: The district's eight "compartmentalized" departments, which historically had separate planning and design staff for the water supply and flood management operations, were streamlined into five groups—essentially integrating the planning and design engineering staff so as to be available to all projects.[7] Stated Director Joe Judge, "Taking an integrated approach to the valley's water supply, water quality, flood management and environmental issues was more than a planning process. It was an organizational goal as well. We needed to see that integration in the structure of our agency."[8]

Cultural values, new headquarters. As the Water District grew and evolved, so did its commitment to equal opportunity and a discrimination-free work environment. The

Employees, managers and board directors gather at the groundbreaking of the new Water District headquarters, 1998.

Scott Ludwig

Excerpts from
Board Governance Policies

These two excerpts are among the directives stated in the *Governance Policies of the Board of Directors*, November 1, 2002:

▶▶ *Global Governance Commitment, Adopted October 19, 1999.* The purpose of the board, on behalf of the people of Santa Clara County, is to see to it that the District protects the public health and safety and enhances the quality of living within Santa Clara County by comprehensively managing water resources in a practical, cost-effective and environmentally-sensitive manner.

▶▶ *Governing Style, Adopted March 27, 2001.* The Board will govern with an emphasis on: a) outward vision, b) encouragement of diversity in viewpoints, c) strategic leadership more than administrative detail, d) clear distinction of Board and chief executive roles, e) collective rather than individual decisions, f) future rather than past or present, and g) proactivity rather than reactivity.

agency formed an Equal Opportunity Programs Unit to assist "in creating a diverse organization where respect, empowerment and inclusion are an integral part of the way business is conducted."[9] This extended from ensuring diversity in hiring practices to the participation of small and local businesses in the district's contracts and procurement activities.

This diverse and growing organization soon expanded beyond its headquarters at 5750 Almaden Expressway. The Water District necessarily turned to leasing space at satellite offices around Almaden Valley. In 1998, with the goal of consolidating most of the satellite locations, the Water District broke ground on a new, larger headquarters just north of the old complex on the same site. The building was completed in 1999. Staff spread into both the old and new headquarters, enabling more employees to work in proximity of each other. District managers anticipated that the cost-savings in lease expenses would pay for the new headquarters within 16 years.[10]

New governance structure. The board of directors also undertook improvements to the way it accomplished its work. As discussed in Chapter 14, the board had already clarified the agency's goals by engaging in the comprehensive integrated water resource planning process in the mid-1990s. In 1999, under the leadership of then-chair Larry Wilson, the board also adopted a set of "Governance Policies," an evolving compilation of the board's governance practices and its broad policy goals (see inset).[11] "We needed a framework that gave us a clear and firm approach to policy-setting, not the details of policy implementation, which is the job of the agency's administration," said Wilson.[12] Five years later, in 2004, board members agreed that the governance policy framework is beneficial.[13] "We don't always agree on the issues and there remain plenty of split votes, but with the clear guidance derived from our policy statements, we collectively understand our objectives and we work well together," said Director Tony Estremera.[14]

A key issue that board members agreed needed to be addressed was how the agency responded to the many environmental considerations of its projects and operations.

A Collaborative for Fish Highlights Environmental Approach

As told in Chapter 12, progress on key flood protection projects was faltering in the early 1990s, primarily because of environmental issues. Phase Three of the Guadalupe River Park and Flood Protection Project was a particular turning point in the Water District's approach to environmental mitigation. In that phase, the interest of constructing the project directly squared off against the interest of protecting fish.

To recap the events, in July 1996, several organizations concerned with fisheries notified the Water District of their intent to sue the agency in a federal court for violations of the Clean Water Act, citing impacts from construction of the Guadalupe project. Additionally, they filed a complaint against the Water District with the State Water Resources Control Board, stating that because of its reservoir operations, the Water District was failing to provide water for the benefit of fisheries on local streams and should have its water rights amended. Of primary concern were the small populations of Chinook salmon and steelhead trout in the Guadalupe River, Coyote Creek and Stevens Creek. Both listed as threatened, these salmonid species had somehow managed to prevail "alongside Silicon Valley's freeways, industrial zones and high density neighborhoods," swimming in streams "subjected to dam and bridge construction; flood protection projects; and no small amount of litter and dumping."[15]

The State Board, with authority to define the designated uses of the state's waterways, could rule on how the Water District allocated its water supply:

The use of water for recreation and preservation and enhancement of fish and wildlife resources is a beneficial use of water. In determining the amount of water available for appropriation for other beneficial uses, the board* shall take into account, whenever it is in the public interest, the amounts of water required for recreation and the preservation and enhancement of fish and wildlife resources.

~ California Water Code 1243
(* State Water Resources Control Board)

While the Water District had faced lawsuits before, this was the first time the agency faced a serious challenge to its water rights. The Water District's response was to resolve the complaint—but in a manner that balanced all public interests in the water resource. In early 1997, the Water District and the state Department of Fish and Game invited the complainants—the Guadalupe-Coyote Resource Conservation District, Trout Unlimited and the Pacific Coast Federation of Fisherman's Associations, all represented by the Natural Heritage Institute, to join with other stakeholders (the city of San José, the Santa Clara Valley Audubon Society and regulatory agencies) to participate in formulating a plan of action. Called the Fisheries and Aquatic Habitat Collaborative Effort, or FAHCE, the participating stakeholders worked together for five years to reach an agreement (and are continuing to collaborate on the implementation of that agreement).

The FAHCE process was intensive. As stated in the collaborative's Summary Report in 2003, stakeholders would develop "a comprehensive scientific record through field studies that would identify the causes for degradation of salmonid fisheries." They would evaluate the merits of alternative remedies and seek a balance of competing uses for water. Following the studies, participants would then

"negotiate solutions consistent with the scientific record and applicable laws and policy in the form of a proposed Fish Habitat Management Plan." The plan would serve as the basis for a settlement between the complainants and the Water District, if accepted by all parties and approved by the State Water Resources Control Board.[16]

If there had been any doubts about the Water District's willingness to address fishery needs, the Fish Habitat Management Plan that resulted from the FAHCE process allayed them. In 2003, the plan stood among the most comprehensive, long-term fisheries agreements developed in California.

The plan also did much to improve the working relationships between the Water District and regulators. At the mid-point of the Guadalupe flood protection project, staff from the U.S. Fish and Wildlife Service (FWS) had expressed little faith in the Water District's plans to provide adequate mitigation for habitat impacts. But in 2003, Watershed Planning Branch Chief Mark Littlefield of the FWS had this to say: "The collaborative nature of FAHCE enabled the Service to develop a level of trust regarding the outcomes of the studies and to support the recommendations on how to best manage for salmonid species."[17]

To improve conditions for salmonid species, FAHCE focused on flow and non-flow actions on the Guadalupe River, Coyote Creek and Stevens Creek. Flow-related actions involved orchestrating releases from the Water District's reservoirs for improved flows and cooler stream temperatures, timed to benefit spawning fish and the habitat needs of juvenile fish. Non-flow actions included promoting fish migration (removing barriers and/or installing fish ladders) and a healthy habitat that supported reproduction (enhancing gravel beds for spawning fish and maintaining riparian canopy to provide needed shade). These actions were based on the substantial work performed by the FAHCE Technical Advisory Committee. This was a group

The interest of constructing the project directly squared off against the interest of protecting fish.

In 2004, the **Fish Habitat Management Plan** *of FAHCE*

was among the most comprehensive, *long-term* ***fishery agreements*** in California.

What began as a complaint against the Santa Clara Valley Water District evolved into a collaborative effort to address fishery habitat on the Guadalupe River, Stevens Creek and Coyote Creek. After several years of scientific studies and evaluations, the Fisheries and Aquatic Habitat Collaborative Effort (FAHCE) produced a 30-year plan that provided for improved streamflow management, as well as non-flow measures, such as removing barriers to fish migration and plantings that will create more shade over the streams.

Left: In October 1998, four rock vortex weirs were installed on the Guadalupe River to help fish navigate the change in stream elevation caused by the Hillsdale Avenue bridge. Above: Biologists perform habitat typing on Guadalupe Creek, August 2002. During a fish survey that year, a steelhead trout is caught, examined and then released.

of biologists and technical experts in the areas of fisheries and aquatic resources, assembled from the participating FAHCE agencies and including hired consultants.[18]

To fund the fishery plan, the Water District agreed to provide as much as $126 million over a thirty-year period. "This signaled the Water District board's long-term commitment to environmental stewardship," said Walt Wadlow, who served as the district's lead negotiator for the FAHCE talks.[19] The Water District furthermore committed a portion of its water supply to FAHCE: The operational impact was estimated at 2,000 acre-feet per year of local surface water being used for fish habitat needs rather than for drinking water supply. It fell to the district's Integrated Water Resources Plan (Chapter 14) to determine how to best replace the lost drinking water supply.[20]

FAHCE would work synergistically with other efforts along the West Coast that aimed to facilitate the rebound of salmonid species—a challenging goal. As of February 2003, more than 106 West Coast salmon runs were extinct; another 214 were at risk of extinction. Analysts for the fishing industry estimated that commensurate with the loss of salmonid habitat was the loss of about 72,000 salmon-related jobs.[21] Addressing this problem was an important part of the CALFED Bay-Delta Program, which defined measures to protect and restore salmonid species in the San Francisco Bay-Delta Estuary, California's largest fishery (see also Chapter 13).

Environmental Stewardship Becomes Official Mission

The circumstances surrounding FAHCE—and the Stream Maintenance Program as well (see Chapter 12)—showed that the Water District's two missions of providing an adequate water supply and protecting the valley from floods could not be well accomplished without also protecting fishery and wildlife habitat. Recognizing this, the Water District's board of directors began directing policies to include environmental stewardship. Both former Assistant General Manager Kay Whitlock and Director Greg Zlotnick recalled a "revolutionary" moment when, during a 1997 board workshop, board members agreed that while the number one priority in flood protection work remained the protection of life and property, it was time to incorporate environmental considerations and benefits whenever feasible. "References to environmental benefits had existed in our policies, but this was the first time where I had seen the board elevate environmental benefits to becoming a major consideration of how we would conduct our work," recalled Whitlock.[22]

One of the earliest directives, included in the above-mentioned *Board Governance Policies*, built on this policy swing, specifically articulating that district work reflect an "an ongoing commitment to conserving the environment":

The District is a steward of the watersheds of Santa Clara County, the streams and the natural resources therein, and will strive to ensure their benefits to the community's quality of life are protected and when appropriate, enhanced or restored. Consistent with the District's primary responsibility to provide for public health and safety, water quality, and water supply, the District's approach in flood management and the water utility shall reflect an ongoing commitment to conserving the environment as a priority in the District's mission of comprehensive public service. ~ Board Governance Policies, GP-1, section 1.5. Adopted October 19, 1999.

With this statement in place, Director Greg Zlotnick, also a practicing attorney, saw the need to expand the district's charter to make environmental stewardship a third official

The two missions of providing an adequate water supply and protecting the valley from floods could not be well accomplished without also protecting fishery and wildlife habitat.

With adoption of environmental stewardship as a third mission, projects would now include "an ethic that places environmental protection as fundamental to the work."

mission. "Stewardship was the direction our work was taking, yet this pursuit was not acknowledged in our charter. Furthermore, it was important to 'lock in' the environmental component to provide future boards with a clear directive."[23]

Board members agreed, and asked state Senator Byron Sher to help propose legislation that would amend the Water District's 72-year-old chartering act. The bill, SB449, provided for three amendments that 1) clarified the district's ability to capitalize on the use of recycled water; 2) added the responsibility of protecting the county from tidal flooding, and 3) reflected the district's commitment to environmental stewardship throughout the county and provided the authority to enhance, protect and restore streams, riparian corridors and natural resources.

On August 9, 2001, Governor Gray Davis signed the amended district charter into law, making environmental stewardship a third official agency mission.[24]

Refining the mission statement*. To better reflect the charter's intent, the board also rewrote the agency's mission statement. The original mission statement was first set by the Water District board in 1974.[25][†] By the early 1990s, the mission statement focused on the dual missions of water supply and flood protection, stated as:

> The District's mission is: *To provide high quality water at the wholesale level in sufficient quantity for beneficial uses by the county's land and population, and to manage flood and storm waters, thereby providing for public safety and the protection of property and natural resources.*[26]

On August 6, 2002, the seven-member board voted unanimously to adopt the following revised mission statement, which framed water supply, flood protection and environmental stewardship within the concept of watershed management:

> *The mission of the District is a healthy, safe and enhanced quality of living in Santa Clara County through watershed stewardship and comprehensive management of water resources in a practical, cost-effective, and environmentally sensitive manner.*[27]

With the district charter and mission statement thus amended, Director Zlotnick noted: "The approach to the environmental considerations of a project are no longer simply driven by regulations, but by an ethic that places environmental protection as fundamental to the work."[28] Zlotnick also pointed out the uniqueness of the Water District's inclusion of a "quality of living" objective in its mission statement, placing a focus not just on services to be performed (the traditional focus of mission statements) but *why* these services were important.

Environmental staff come aboard*. Reflecting the growing priority of environmental work, several fishery biologists and environmental specialists were hired by the Water District, an agency historically composed of engineers and support staff. Dr. Bernie Goldner, head of the environmental unit until his retirement in 1995, recalled that for many years, he worked as the Water District's lone

---

[†] In February 1985, the board officially updated the language describing the agency's objectives, but left the mission statement intact. The 1974/1985 version stated that the broad purpose of the Water District was to conduct a sound water management program that served the community, and this was to be fulfilled through three missions: (1) Provide a supply of water, adequate as to both quantity and quality, needed to meet the desired quality of life in the community; (2) Provide protection against flooding in a manner that maintains the desired quality of life in the community, and (3) Coordinate all other community water-related programs to achieve full water management.

environmental specialist. Hired in 1972, about two years after the passage of the California Environmental Quality Act (CEQA), Goldner's main focus was writing environmental impact reports (EIRs) for district construction projects. "Like other entities in the state, the district was now responsible for producing EIRs on its projects. For a couple of years, the agency assigned the task of producing these reports to engineering staff, but the environmental community began to express dissatisfaction, wanting to see more thorough analyses—that's when I was hired," recalled Goldner.[29]

By the 1990s, Goldner was overseeing a staff of five biologists and environmental planners, and most EIRs were produced in-house. With the launching of FAHCE and the new environmental mission, the Water District added even more fishery biologists, thus saving the expenses associated with hiring consultants. By the end of 2004, the water district was utilizing a staff of 24 environmental planners and 14 biologists to handle the many environmental aspects of district work.[30]

The future will show how the addition of environmental stewardship to the Water District's missions will play out. But the mission's potential for positive outcomes for the environment is being hailed. As noted in the 2003 Watershed Action Plan of the multi-jurisdictional Santa Clara Basin Watershed Management Initiative (p. 233):

The Santa Clara Valley Water District's water supply and flood control operations and facilities comprise the most significant influence on stream habitats. Amendment of the Water District's purposes creates unprecedented new opportunities to integrate stream and riparian restoration into the Water District's capital construction projects and its maintenance operations.[31]

Integrated Watershed Management: A National Trend

"An ounce of prevention is worth a pound of cure." That adage is what *integrated watershed management* is largely about, although the range of concerns covered by watershed management is wide. To some it is a way to keep source water clean, rather than using expensive treatment processes to remove contaminants from the drinking water supply. For those interested in fisheries and wildlife, it is a means to establishing protections over entire ecosystems, gravitating from the controversial species-by-species approach of the Endangered Species Act. For facilities which discharge wastewater, it is a crucial component of meeting

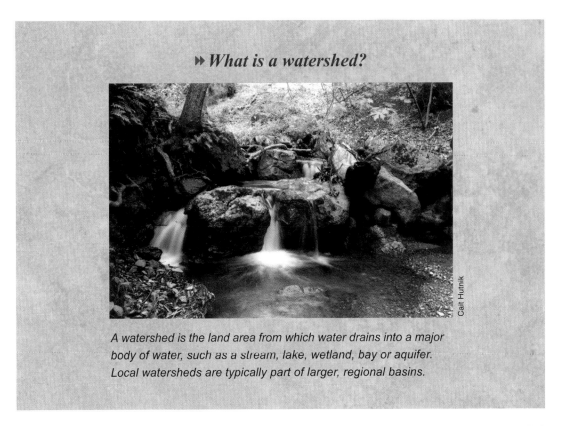

➤ *What is a watershed?*

A watershed is the land area from which water drains into a major body of water, such as a stream, lake, wetland, bay or aquifer. Local watersheds are typically part of larger, regional basins.

Cait Hutnik

It was the first time

our agency had to

consider the health

of the southern San

Francisco Bay as part

of its scope of work.

regulations on the chemical content of effluent that pours into bays and oceans. Where flood protection is needed, watershed management can help establish practices that reduce stormwater flows. For the Water District, with its missions of water supply, flood protection and environmental stewardship, watershed management includes all of these things—and has become an opportunity to address the interrelationship of these issues.

The federal Natural Resources Conservation Service (NRCS), formerly the Soil Conservation Service, is an arm of the U.S. Department of Agriculture and one of the earliest promoters of watershed management, emphasizing land and water management practices that would prevent soil erosion. The Water District's first project entailing watershed management was the NRCS-sponsored Llagas Creek Watershed Project initiated in 1954 (see Chapter 12).[32]

Watershed management efforts slowly picked up more credence through the next few decades. But in the late 1990s, the concept was kicked into high gear. On October 18, 1997, the twenty-fifth anniversary of the Clean Water Act, Vice President Al Gore directed the U.S. Department of Agriculture and the Environmental Protection Agency (EPA) to work with other federal agencies to prepare a Clean Water Action Plan. When the plan was released a year later, watershed management was at its heart and touted as "a key to the future." The plan included a strategic framework for interagency partnerships to engage in new watershed management programs.[33] With the EPA now leading the way, watershed management programs blossomed across the country. By 2004, there were more than 1,000 programs in California alone.[34]

In Santa Clara County, the seeds for a multi-jurisdictional watershed program were planted prior to Gore's directive. The Santa Clara Valley Urban Runoff Pollution Prevention Program, formed in 1990, laid a working foundation for interagency effort on watershed issues.

A Collaborative
to Control Polluted Runoff

During the early years of the Clean Water Act, which became law in 1972, regulators focused on pollution that came from an identifiable point of origin, called *point source pollution*. At the time, only 30 to 40 percent of the nation's rivers, lakes and coastal waters were estimated to be safe for swimming and fishing, primarily because plumes of sewage, algae and toxic waste were choking these waterways.[35] Pipes discharging raw sewage were the most visible and abundant point source pollution problem and were quickly targeted. To control the volume and content of sewage effluent, all wastewater dischargers were required to obtain a National Pollutant Discharge Elimination System (NPDES) permit, renewable every five years.[36]

In Santa Clara County, four municipal wastewater treatment plants have been subject to NPDES permits. The three northern county plants (San Jose/Santa Clara Water Pollution Control Plant, Sunnyvale Water Pollution Control Plant and Palo Alto Regional Water Quality Control Plant) discharge their wastewater to the southern San Francisco Bay. To clean up their effluent so as to improve aquatic habitat in the Bay, these plants upgraded to tertiary (advanced) treatment in the late 1970s. The newer South County Regional Wastewater Authority, a plant in Gilroy, discharges into the Monterey Bay via the Pajaro River; it was constructed in 1995 with some tertiary treatment capacity.

With sewage effluent largely regulated by the mid-1980s, attention turned to *nonpoint source pollution*. These are pollutants that are impossible to trace back to a single discharge point because they wash into storm drains and waterways from roads, parking lots, construction sites, etc. However, because this "urban runoff" collects in storm drains, federal law made stormwater systems subject to the NPDES permit requirements in 1987.[37]

The new stormwater NPDES requirements would affect the responsibilities of the Water District. The agency has limited jurisdiction in waterways that drain areas greater than 320 acres, and regulatory agencies argued that with such jurisdiction, the Water District was responsible for preventing pollution of runoff into those waterways.[38] "This presented a new focus in the Water District's work," recalled former Director Patrick Ferraro. "It was the first time our agency had to consider the health of the southern San Francisco Bay as part of its scope of work."[39]

While regulatory agencies were developing the rules for controlling stormwater, Roger James, then head of the district's water quality program, recommended that the Water District take steps in advance of the regulatory requirements. He suggested that the district, county and 13 cities of the South Bay apply for a joint NPDES permit. With a joint permit, all 15 agencies could efficiently work toward a common goal of reducing pollutants flowing into the southern San Francisco Bay. Thus was born the Santa Clara Valley Urban Runoff Pollution Prevention Program. The program received its first joint permit in 1990, with reauthorizations in 1995 and 2001. Commented Tom Mumley, a supervising engineer at the San Francisco Bay Regional Water Quality Control Board, "The plan that the folks in Santa Clara County put together for tackling the stormwater issue resulted in one of the first municipal stormwater permits issued in the nation, and it became a model program."[40]

The success of this program is based on local governments working together to change behaviors that cause pollution. "The program focuses on educating cities, businesses and citizens on how to enact urban runoff BMPs," explained Beau Goldie, an assistant operating officer at the Water District who also chaired the program in the early 2000s.[41] The BMPs (best management practices) to which Goldie referred take aim at reducing the quantity of heavy metals, oils, pesticides, herbicides, solvents and sediment that reach the Bay through runoff.[42] Some examples of urban runoff BMPs include keeping streets clean through street sweeping; using building materials that leach fewer pollutants into stormwater; and constructing wet vaults to briefly pool stormwater and allow pollutants to settle out.

Educating the public on a key BMP—controlling what goes down a storm drain—began with a simple message stamped over the storm drains found at most corners. "No Dumping — Flows to Bay" punctuated by a clapper rail (a local shore bird listed as a threatened species because of pollutants in the Bay) was stenciled on all of the storm drains in the county by 1993. Multi-lingual brochures were distributed to homeowners to let them know that "The

"No dumping—flows to Bay."

Storm drains around the county were stamped with the message, "No dumping—flows to Bay." An endangered bird, the California clapper rail (upper left photo), punctuates the message. Multi-lingual brochures on controlling runoff pollution were also distributed countywide.

The WMI would

prove beneficial to

the Water District

on many counts.

Bay Begins at Your Front Door." The urban runoff program also offered training for city building department staff, developers and consultants regarding inspections of construction and industrial sites.[43] In October 1993, the EPA recognized the Santa Clara Valley Urban Runoff Pollution Prevention Program as one of the most advanced stormwater programs in the country with a first-place award as "Outstanding Stormwater Management Program" for its "innovative and cost-effective achievements."[44]

Citizens adopt and clean the creeks. A particularly noteworthy component of the urban runoff pollution prevention program was the Adopt-A-Creek program, which resulted in numerous community groups participating in the protection of local surface water. Though the Water District maintains the waterways by stabilizing banks, clearing fallen logs and removing debris, it cannot attend to every piece of litter along each waterway. In 1994, the Water District launched the Adopt-A-Creek program to enlist the help of those who live, work or attend school near creeks in preserving the health of those creeks.

Director Rosemary Kamei stated the goal is to have every stretch of creek adopted. She commented, "With this program, people are involved in the environment; it's not just another brochure to read."[45] The Water District supports the cleanup efforts by providing supplies and disposing of the collected debris. As of early 2004, about 100 groups have adopted creeks, and through these groups, more than 10,000 volunteers have rolled up their sleeves and pitched in.[46]

A Collaborative to Improve Water Quality in the Southern San Francisco Bay

As mentioned earlier, interagency watershed management programs were proliferating across the nation in the late 1990s. Here in the Bay Area, the EPA and San Francisco Bay Regional Water Quality Control Board (Regional Board) had long been concerned about water quality issues specifically in the southern San Francisco Bay, a waterbody affected by the many small watersheds within the greater Santa Clara Basin (see map). In 1996, the Regional Board launched the Santa Clara Basin Watershed Management Initiative, more simply called the WMI, and invited participation from business and trade associations, environmental and civic groups, and local governments—including the Santa Clara Valley Water District. The WMI would use a collaborative process "to find ways to improve Basin conditions, coordinate existing regulatory activities basinwide, and ensure that environmental protection activities are efficient and cost-effective."[47]

Clearly the WMI would be addressing many issues that were not only of concern to the Water District, but within its purview. "The WMI is a golden opportunity to build on the efforts of the Santa Clara Valley Urban Runoff Pollution Prevention Program, to support the public values expressed in the Clean, Safe Creeks measure and to provide a practical application for our new environmental stewardship mission," noted Director Greg Zlotnick.[48]

Because of its potential to affect district objectives, the Water District board gave careful consideration to the agency's participation in the initiative. In September 1997, the board clarified a number of principles that it would propose for incorporation in the WMI process. These included, in summary, that the WMI should: recognize and support the Water District's missions of water supply, flood management and environmental stewardship; address permit "certainty" and streamlining; maximize benefits and minimize adverse impacts on wildlife habitats within the basin in a practical manner; and result in an affordable, long-term watershed management plan that would be equitably funded by stakeholders.[49]

As it turned out, the WMI would prove beneficial to the Water District on many counts. It supported district efforts

Map D. Target Area of the Watershed Management Initiative

The **WMI** *aims to* improve water quality *across*

14 *watersheds, three counties,* **20** *cities and* **840** *square*

miles, all which drain into *the impaired*

southern **San Francisco Bay**.

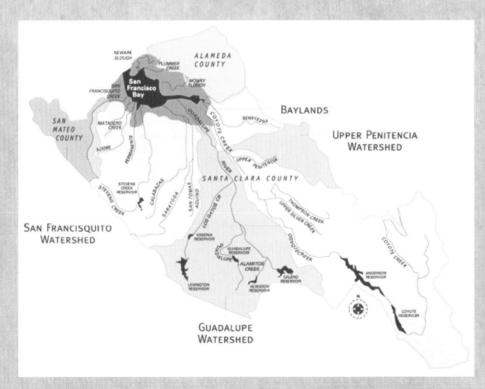

The Santa Clara Basin drains into the shallow southern end of the San Francisco Bay, a water-body that is considered "impaired" by the EPA, from both point source pollution and urban runoff. The Watershed Management Initiative aims to coordinate measures within the region to improve water quality in the southern Bay.

Participants in the Santa Clara Basin Watershed Management Initiative

Public Agencies
• California Department of Fish & Game
• City of Cupertino
• City of Palo Alto
• City of San José
• City of Santa Clara
• City of Sunnyvale
• Guadalupe-Coyote Resource Conservation District
• San Francisco Bay Regional Water Quality Control Board
• San Francisquito Creek Joint Powers Authority
• Santa Clara County
• Santa Clara County Open Space Authority
• Santa Clara Valley Transportation Authority
• Santa Clara Valley Urban Runoff Pollution Prevention Program
• Santa Clara Valley Water District
• U.S. Army Corps of Engineers
• U.S. Environmental Protection Agency
• Natural Resources Conservation Service

Business Associations
• California Restaurant Association
• Home Builders Association of Northern California
• San Jose Silicon Valley Chamber of Commerce
• Santa Clara Cattlemen's Association
• Santa Clara County Farm Bureau
• Silicon Valley Manufacturing Group

Environmental & Civic Groups
• Audubon Society, Santa Clara Valley Chapter
• CLEAN South Bay
• Greenbelt Alliance
• League of Women Voters of Santa Clara County
• Silichip Chinook Salmon and Steelhead Restoration Group
• San Francisco Bay Bird Observatory
• San Francisquito Watershed Council
• Sierra Club, Loma Prieta Chapter
• Silicon Valley Pollution Prevention Center
• Silicon Valley Toxics Coalition
• Western Waters Canoe Club

in negotiating the 10-year Stream Maintenance Program, discussed in Chapter 12. It helped promote the objectives of the Santa Clara Valley Urban Runoff Pollution Prevention Program by using its stakeholder process to adopt achievable and protective numeric standards for copper and nickel in the lower South San Francisco Bay. The WMI further helped the urban runoff program by launching a basin-wide educational program called *Watershed Watch*.

On Earth Day, April 22, 1999, WMI participants gathered at the Don Edwards National Wildlife Refuge (along the southern shoreline of the Bay) to sign an agreement that outlined the function of the WMI and principles of participation.[50] The signatories agreed that their agencies would work together to control and prevent pollution of the Bay. Director Larry Wilson, then-chair of the Water District board, said, "I have high expectations of what we're going to accomplish through the WMI. It promises to change the way we do business in the arena of watershed management."[51]

The Water District's many efforts to improve watershed conditions did not go unnoticed. In April 2003, the federal EPA recognized the Water District as a "Clean Water Partner for the Twenty-First Century," and commended the district for its "extraordinary achievement in watershed protection" beyond federal requirements. Specifically cited was the Water District's leadership on the WMI and Santa Clara Valley Urban Pollution Prevention Program, as well as its quality public outreach campaigns, including the Clean, Safe Creeks program, Adopt-A-Creek program and the regional summits on regulatory and land-use issues (the summits are discussed in Chapter 16).[52]

A Collaborative to Address Land Use Along Streams

One of the Water District's most useful tools to ameliorate impacts to watercourses is Ordinance 83-2. This ordinance—amended several times since it was first passed in 1959—requires a review and permitting process that aims to minimize impacts to watercourses resulting from development or community activities. Anyone planning a project within 50 feet of a creek or waterway, or within 50 feet of district property or a district easement, must first obtain a permit from the Water District's Community Projects Review Unit.[53]

In the early 2000s, the Water District initiated a proposal to extend the 50-foot permit requirement to a 150-foot requirement, primarily because of concerns over sensitive groundwater areas and the agency's goal to enhance riparian habitat. Cities in the South Bay erupted at the concept. "They considered the proposal to be a power grab at cities' authority over land use policies," explained Director Rosemary Kamei.[54]

To resolve the conflict, a collaborative approach similar to that of the Guadalupe River Collaborative (see p. 157) was suggested. At a December 2002 meeting hosted

---

Signatories to the
Santa Clara Valley Water Resources Protection Collaborative

• Santa Clara Valley Water District	• City of Santa Clara
• City of Campbell	• City of Saratoga
• City of Cupertino	• City of Sunnyvale
• City of Gilroy	• County of Santa Clara
• City of Los Altos	• Guadalupe-Coyote Resource Conservation District
• Town of Los Altos Hills	• Santa Clara County Farm Bureau
• Town of Los Gatos	• Silicon Valley Manufacturing Group
• City of Milpitas	• Home Builders Association of Northern California
• City of Monte Sereno	• San José Silicon Valley Chamber of Commerce
• City of Morgan Hill	• CLEAN South Bay
• City of Mountain View	• League of Women Voters of Santa Clara County
• City of Palo Alto	• Santa Clara Valley Audubon Society
• City of San José	• Families for Fair Government

by the City of Cupertino, with various city/county officials and industry and environmental representatives in attendance, Cupertino's Public Works Director Ralph Qualls got up and suggested the collaborative model as appropriate to the 83-2 controversy. "In my earlier days at the city of San José, I had seen the effectiveness of this approach; I thought it would help all sides focus on how to accomplish mutual interests in a cooperative manner," recalled Qualls.[55]

At the same meeting, Chief Executive Officer Stan Williams provided the historical background to the "shared ownership and responsibility for the waterways of Santa Clara County."[56] A collaborative approach, pointed out Williams, would allow for a balanced consideration of water and development issues, and lead to effective multi-agency coordination.

With the county and all 15 South Bay cities and towns showing interest, in early 2003, the Water District board approved moving forward with what would come to be called the Water Resources Protection Collaborative. Stakeholders engaged in a process to address concerns related to land use along waterways. The result was that by July 2003, all participating groups readily signed a "Memorandum of Consensus for Mutual Cooperation to Jointly Develop and Implement Water and Watershed Resources Protection Measures, Guidelines and Standards in Santa Clara County."

The memorandum makes clear that cities and county maintain their jurisdiction over land use planning and land use permit regulation, but underlines that all jurisdictions of the South Bay have a role in watershed protection goals, including flood management; the protection of surface water quality and groundwater quality; and habitat protection and enhancement.[57] To that end, Jim Fiedler, the Water District's chief operating officer over watersheds, explained "participants in the collaborative are developing design guidelines to address land use near streams in Santa Clara County."[58] At the time of this writing, this process is still underway; district staff anticipate that these guidelines will eventually be incorporated by municipalities into their existing practices.

Director Tony Estremera described an added benefit of this collaborative. "We've set a course for strengthened communication between the cities and the Water District," he said. "Through the early consultation that is promised in this memorandum, we should be able to work out issues of concern that involve the impact of future developments on waterways."[59]

A Collaborative to Restore Salt Marsh Habitat

Yet one more highly significant collaborative of the early 2000s is the South Bay Salt Pond Restoration Project. This project specifically addresses the loss of 85 to 90 percent of the San Francisco Bay's salt marsh habitat during the nineteenth and twentieth centuries. This loss was caused by bay infill, urbanization and salt pond development. Commercial salt production in the Bay began in 1854, and continued until salt ponds had been constructed around nearly the entire southern shoreline, covering an area of approximately 26,000 acres.

Many environmental organizations and resource agencies have longed for efforts to restore salt marsh habitat in the southern Bay. The opportunity to do so arose in October 2000, when Cargill Inc., a major salt pond owner, proposed to consolidate its operations and sell lands and salt production rights on 61 percent of its South Bay operation, equal to about 15,100 acres.[60] U.S. Senator Dianne Feinstein headed the negotiations that led to a multi-agency Framework Agreement, signed in May 2002, to acquire the properties and implement a restoration project. Participating agencies included the California Resources Agency, Wildlife Conservation Board, California Department of

At a water summit sponsored by the Silicon Valley Manufacturing Group in March 2002, Water District board directors Greg Zlotnick, Richard Santos and Larry Wilson (left to right) secured a commitment from U.S. Senator Dianne Feinstein to support the inclusion of flood management goals in the South Bay Salt Pond Restoration Project.

Fish and Game, California State Coastal Conservancy and U.S. Fish and Wildlife Service. Many local governments, including the Santa Clara Valley Water District, and non-governmental organizations signed the framework agreement as interested partners. The state of California approved purchase of the property on February 11, 2003; public acquisition was completed one month later for $100 million. The state paid $71 million; the Hewlett Foundation, Packard Foundation, Moore Foundation and Goldman Fund provided $21 million; and the U.S. Fish and Wildlife Service paid $8 million.[61]

The restored tidal marshes will provide critical habitat for endangered species such as the California clapper rail and the salt marsh harvest mouse, as well as help to filter pollutants. Restoration efforts will also improve the channels of the marshes, expanding habitat for fish, harbor seals and other aquatic life. Many of the ponds will remain as managed ponds and be enhanced as habitat for migratory shorebirds and waterfowl traveling on the Pacific Flyway.

Of particular interest to the Water District is the project's goal of improving flood management. As pointed out in the discussion of Alviso in Chapter 10, the salt ponds had caused hydrological changes that resulted in greater flood hazards by reducing the ability of storm runoff to flow easily into the Bay. Where feasible, flood capacities of local creeks will be increased by widening the mouths of the waterways and reestablishing connections to historical floodplains. As ponds are opened to the bay's tidal action, levees between the newly created tidal marsh and local communities will need to be built or enhanced to provide flood protection. This has particular implications for Alviso

and its need for tidal flood protection. "It is my hope that the Water District can influence this project to meet the flood protection needs of Alviso in a manner that preserves the views of the Bay and aesthetics of our community," said Director Richard Santos, who began representing the Alviso community on the Water District board in 2001.[62]

Leading the project is the California State Coastal Conservancy in partnership with state Department of Fish and Game and the U.S. Fish and Wildlife Service. These agencies will work closely with local governments and stakeholder interests to produce a scientifically-sound, widely-supported plan for implementation. A Flood Management Team, made up of southern Bay Area flood control districts, including the Santa Clara Valley Water District and the U.S. Army Corps of Engineers, will work to plan and design the flood management aspects of the project.

~

In response to the water management challenges of the late twentieth century, leaders of the Santa Clara Valley Water District recognized that effective solutions lay in a broader scope. They broadened the district's mission statement to include environmental stewardship, acknowledging a responsibility for the habitat that is dependent on the valley's streams. They adopted a broader management approach to flood and water quality problems, recognizing that solutions must include not just immediate waterways but entire watersheds and large basin areas. And they also sought to work in a broader manner, by pursuing collaborations with jurisdictions, stakeholders and elected representatives who had shared concerns and authority.

Yet these larger and more complex efforts still aim at basic goals for the residents of the Santa Clara Valley (and greater Bay Area): a quality of life that includes healthful water at the tap, property safe from flooding, and creeks and marshlands to be enjoyed in their natural state.■

These larger, more complex efforts still aim at basic goals for the residents of the Santa Clara Valley (and greater Bay Area): a quality of life that includes healthful water at the tap, property safe from flooding, and creeks and marshlands to be enjoyed in their natural state.

Marshland along the bay shoreline of the city of Milpitas, circa 2002.

239

SOURCES, CHAPTER 15:

[1] Staff level information from McCann, Jim (SCVWD staff). E-mail to Cheryl Wessling, May 3, 2005.

[2] The uniqueness of SCVWD and its chartered missions was expressed in interviews with industry authorities including: Robert Vining, chief of programs division, U.S. Army Corps of Engineers; SCVWD Chief Executive Officer Stan Williams; former Flood Control Manager Kay Whitlock; and former Special Programs Administrator Bill Hoeft.

[3] *Annual Report 1980*, SCVWD, p. 1; also, *Annual Performance Report, 1994-1995*, SCVWD, p. 1; also, staff level as of 2004, email to Cheryl Wessling, March 13, 2004.

[4] Esau, Ronald. Phone conversation with Cheryl Wessling, March 15, 2004.

[5] Smith, Sandra (SCVWD staff). E-mail to Cheryl Wessling, April 19, 2004.

[6] Williams, Stan, Interviewed by Cheryl Wessling, April 27, 2004.

[7] *Annual Performance Report, 1994-1995*, SCVWD, p. 2.

[8] Judge, Joe. Interviewed by Cheryl Wessling, March 13, 2004.

[9] Explanation of the SCVWD Equal Opportunity Office, available at the SCVWD Web site: www.valleywater.org

[10] *Annual Performance Report, 1997-1998*, SCVWD, p. 18.

[11] Inset taken from: *Governance Policies of the Board of Directors*, SCVWD, updated Nov. 1, 2002.

[12] Wilson, Larry. Interviewed by Cheryl Wessling, Sept. 25, 2003.

[13] Interviews by Cheryl Wessling with board directors Tony Estremera, Joe Judge, Rosemary Kamei, Sig Sanchez, Richard Santos, Larry Wilson and Greg Zlotnick, November 2003 to March 2004.

[14] Estremera, Tony. Interviewed by Cheryl Wessling, Feb. 6, 2004.

[15] *Fisheries and Aquatic Habitat Collaborative Effort Summary Report*, SCVWD, Feb. 26, 2003, introduction.

[16] Ibid, p. 6.

[17] Littlefield, Mark, as quoted in ibid, p. 6.

[18] *Fisheries and Aquatic Habitat Collaborative Effort Summary Report*, SCVWD, Feb. 26, 2003, p. 19.

[19] Wadlow, Walt. Phone interview with Cheryl Wessling, Jan. 12, 2005.

[20] *Fisheries and Aquatic Habitat Collaborative Effort Summary Report*, SCVWD, Feb. 26, 2003, p. 19.

[21] Figures from Pacific Coast Federation of Fishermen's Associations as quoted in *Fisheries and Aquatic Habitat Collaborative Effort Summary Report*, SCVWD, Feb. 26, 2003, p. 30; also, *Pacific Salmon at the Crossroads: An Assessment of Wild Salmon Populations from California to Washington* found at: http://www.environmentalreview.org/vol01/nehlsen.html; also, *Salmonids—Status of Populations* found at: http://www.nwfsc.noaa.gov/publications/techmemos/tm28/salmon.htm

[22] Whitlock, Kay. Interviewed by Cheryl Wessling, April 21, 2005.

[23] Zlotnick, Greg. Interviewed by Cheryl Wessling, Dec. 22, 2003.

[24] SCVWD News Release, "Governor signs bill ratifying Water District's environmental approach toward flood protection and water management," Aug. 21, 2001.

[25] SCVWD Agenda Memorandum, Update/Revision of District Mission, Goals and Objectives, Feb. 19, 1985.

[26] *Annual Report 1993-1994*, SCVWD, p. 1.

[27] Mission statement and district chartering act available at SCVWD Web site: www.valleywater.org

[28] Zlotnick, Greg. Interviewed by Cheryl Wessling, Dec. 22, 2003.

[29] Goldner, Bernie. Phone interview with Cheryl Wessling, Sept. 27, 2004.

[30] Ibid; also, Neudorf, Terry (SCVWD staff). Comments to draft book, Jan. 13, 2004; also, Squires, Louisa (SCVWD staff). Comments to draft book, Jan. 12, 2005.

[31] *Santa Clara Basin Watershed Action Plan*, Santa Clara Basin Watershed Management Initiative, August 2003, pp. 8-11.

[32] Natural Resources Conservation Service Web site: www.nrcs.usda.gov

[33] USEPA and USDA Clean Water Action Plan: Restoring and Protecting America's Waters, 1998, pp. ii-iv.

[34] *State Watershed Strategy Guide*, Western States Water Council, 1999, p. 31.

[35] Pitzer, Gary. "Thirty Years of the Clean Water Act: The Nation's Waters Improved, But Challenges Remain," *Western Water*, November/December 2002, p. 4.

[36] *Wastewater Primer*, U.S. Environmental Protection Agency, May 1998, pp. 7-12.

[37] *Overview of the Storm Water Program*, Environmental Protection Agency, June 1996, p. 1.

[38] Goldie, Beau (SCVWD staff). E-mail to Cheryl Wessling, April 20, 2005.

[39] Ferraro, Patrick. Comments to draft book, March 26, 2004.

[40] Mumley, Thomas. E-mail to Elizabeth Emmett, Jan. 21, 2004.

[41] Goldie, Beau. Interviewed by Elizabeth Emmett, Jan. 20, 2004.

[42] *Stormwater Best Management Practices Handbook*, California Stormwater Quality Association, n.d.

[43] *Review/Outlook, 1992-93*, SCVWD, p. 10.

[44] *Review/Outlook, 1993-94*, SCVWD, p. 15.

[45] Kamei, Rosemary. Interviewed by Cheryl Wessling, Nov. 5, 2003.

[46] Morales, Ed (SCVWD staff). Interviewed by Kathleen McNamara, April 22, 2003.

[47] *A Vision for Our Watershed*, brochure, Santa Clara Basin Watershed Management Initiative, circa 2000.

[48] Zlotnick, Greg. Interviewed by Cheryl Wessling, Dec. 22, 2003.

[49] SCVWD Agenda Memorandum regarding "District Participation in the Regional Water Quality Control Board Watershed Management Initiative," Sept. 2, 1997.

[50] *Watershed Characteristics Report*, Santa Clara Basin Watershed Management Initiative, Watershed Management Report, Vol. 1, May 2000, p. 9.

[51] Wilson, Larry as quoted in "Protecting the Environment Pact to Clean up South Bay Sealed New Rules: Officials Agree to Work Together to Tackle Pollution," *San Jose Mercury News*, April 23, 1999, p. 1B.

[52] SCVWD News Release, "Santa Clara Valley Water District earns U.S. EPA recognition for 'extraordinary' watershed protection." April 2, 2003.

[53] Engineering Policies & Procedures, Ordinance No. 83-2 As Amended 10/22/85, SCVWD; also, Jaimes, Luis (SCVWD staff). Phone interview by Cheryl Wessling, Nov. 3, 2004; also, SCVWD Web site: www.valleywater.org

[54] Kamei, Rosemary. Interviewed by Cheryl Wessling, Nov. 5, 2003.

[55] Qualls, Ralph. Interviewed by Cheryl Wessling, July 25, 2005.

[56] Williams, Stan. Interviewed by Cheryl Wessling, July 25, 2005.

[57] *Santa Clara Valley Water Resources Protection Collaborative Memorandum of Consensus*, SCVWD, July 24, 2003, p. 4.

[58] Fiedler, Jim. Interviewed by Cheryl Wessling, GET DATE.

[59] Estremera, Tony. Interviewed by Cheryl Wessling, Feb. 6, 2004.

[60] South Bay Salt Pond Restoration Project Web site: www. southbayrestoration.org

[61] *Status Report: Federal Projects for Santa Clara County, California, Fiscal Year 2005*, SCVWD, 2004.

[62] Santos, Richard. Interviewed by Cheryl Wessling, Oct. 6, 2003.

A small tributary of Los Gatos Creek , 2003.

Cait Hutnik

EPILOGUE (SECOND EDITION)

A Cleaner, Greener, Leaner Dream

By Stanley M. Williams, Chief Executive Officer, SCVWD

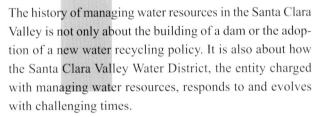The history of managing water resources in the Santa Clara Valley is not only about the building of a dam or the adoption of a new water recycling policy. It is also about how the Santa Clara Valley Water District, the entity charged with managing water resources, responds to and evolves with challenging times.

When the valley's welfare was threatened by groundwater depletion and land subsidence, the early water district solved the problem by building reservoirs and percolation ponds. When local water resources were not enough, the Water District financed and built imported water systems. When Silicon Valley became the nation's epicenter of toxic Superfund sites, the Water District quickly responded by marshalling resources for effective cleanup, and by creating new regulations for underground tank storage. When critically needed flood protection projects were delayed by regulatory issues, the Water District learned to address those issues, so that our projects succeeded in both the interests of flood protection and natural resource protection. When chlorination proved to be a problematic treatment method, we researched alternative processes and put ourselves on course to ozonation.

In all of these predicaments, the Santa Clara Valley Water District did not wait to be handed a solution, but figured out responses that often became model programs for the rest of the state and nation to follow. From its beginning, an innovative spirit has pervaded the Santa Clara Valley Water District. That spirit will keep the agency ready and able to respond successfully to the new challenges that will surely come.

A cleaner, greener, leaner dream. Without question, the most critical challenge—now and looking forward—is keeping our water sources clean and ample, for the health of human society and the environment alike. While the dream of early water planners focused solely on developing a stable water supply for the valley, today's water planners must respond to significantly expanded missions and complex mandates. Beyond supplying water, we work to ensure that the valley's drinking water is safe, not just by improving treatment technologies, but by promoting watershed practices that keep water clean at its source. We work to provide the valley with flood protection while preserving, even expanding the remnants of riparian and wetland habitat in the valley. And we work to accomplish all of these

. . . the Santa Clara Valley Water District did not wait to be handed a solution, but figured out responses that often became model programs for the rest of the state and nation to follow.

243

objectives in a financially responsible manner—often in the face of budgetary constraints. It is a cleaner, greener, leaner dream that we pursue. And it's a dream that must be shared with other governments that, by their own decisions, influence the availability and quality of water, the progress of flood protection and the financial resources to accomplish the work.

Sharing the dream. To foster more intergovernmental discussion of Water District concerns, the Water District has twice hosted a Land Use and Water Summit, in 2001 and 2002. More than 200 city council members, planning commissioners, public agency staff members, representatives from the business community and environmentalists were invited to the summits, which focused on land use and water issues in the face of certain population growth. In 2002, almost 1.7 million residents lived in Santa Clara County; Water District projections point to a population of about 2 million by 2020.[1]

Information from the state Department of Conservation also underscores the growth trend. The department reported in 2001 that between 1998 and 2000, Santa Clara County saw another 4,701 acres of land, mostly agricultural, converted to urban uses. This rate of conversion more than doubled from the previous 1996-98 period, when 2,180 acres of farmland were reclassified as urbanized.[2]

No regional authority exists to decide how the Santa Clara Valley will accommodate this new growth while protecting open space, shortening commutes and creating affordable housing. Instead, the county and cities are responsible for deciding how land is used within their respective jurisdictions. But two coalitions, the Association of Bay Area Governments and the Bay Area Alliance for Sustainable Development, began promoting land-use planning methods that foster "smart growth." Smart growth methods aim for sustainable development; development that fosters the three "e's": a prosperous economy, a high-quality environment and social equity.[3]

The summits allowed for airing of important concepts such as smart growth, but also served to air the Water District's perspective. While discussions of growth typically center on traffic congestion and housing, water is an equally important issue—arguably the most important as

At an all-employee meeting in November 2004, Chief Executive Officer Stan Williams (far right photo) discusses the forces that are reshaping the Water District's work approach.

it sustains growth and life itself. As pointed out by Director Tony Estremera, "Land-use decisions are being made every day that result in new developments that increase runoff into—and contamination of—our creeks and bays. Unless we all work together to better manage what's happening in our watersheds, our quality of life will suffer."[4] The Water Resources Protection Collaborative and other collaboratives discussed in Chapter 15 are exactly the type of interagency work needed to achieve the critical goal of protecting our water sources.

To ensure an adequate water supply for the Santa Clara Valley through 2020, the Water District's Integrated Water Resources Plan sets forth creative strategies, also formed through a collaborative process. More water recycling, more groundwater recharge, more water conservation—these are all key strategies to maintaining an adequate supply. The Water District is not looking to smart growth leaders to develop supply strategies, but to acknowledge their importance and to promote them in plan development.

Smart growth also needs to address the cost to the community of maintaining and expanding the water supply infrastructure—the many dams, aqueducts, pipelines, pumping stations and treatment plants that keep Silicon Valley alive. While there is room to maximize existing water facilities, there is also no avoiding the investment needed to maintain our aging network of pipes and reservoirs. This applies to infrastructure that is local and distant. In 2004, we are hearing from California's scientific community that one of the state's most pressing infrastructure problems is the weak levee system in the Sacramento-San Joaquin Delta, the hub of our state's water supply system.[5] A substantial failure of these levees, which could easily result from an earthquake or rising seawater levels, would be catastrophic to the water supply of 22 million Californians—including residents of Silicon Valley, who depend on the Delta for about 60 percent of their annual water supply.

Getting lean. In late 2004, the state of California threw the Water District "a curve ball." The state's decade-old pattern of shifting funds from local governments to its own programs had continued, and we expected a $22 million loss of property tax revenue in 2005-06 (see also Chapter 12). But in December 2004, the state announced its plan to siphon $51 million from district revenue—a much larger amount that will surely challenge our work plans. Already we have cut all vacant positions, about 10 percent of our planned workforce.

But even before this surprise event, the Water District was already adopting ways to provide its services more efficiently. Given its expanded and complex missions, for several years the agency has been working to aim its limited resources for maximum possible results. Since fiscal year 1995-96, the Water District has won the Distinguished Budget Presentation Award from the Government Finance Officers Association every year, speaking to the already-proven quality of our budget development practices.[6] Now, having achieved ISO 9001 and 14001 certification in March 2004 (specifically in the Watershed and Capital Improvement programs), we are on our way to providing our customers—the residents of Santa Clara County—with the most efficient and best possible service and performance.[7]

ISO standards, developed by the International Organization for Standardization, are most obviously needed in product development and trade. But ISO standards are equally important for government. ISO 9001 is a "family" of standards concerned with quality management—what the Water District will do to fulfill customer needs and regulatory requirements, while aiming for customer satisfaction and continual improvement of performance. The ISO 14001 standards are concerned with environmental management—what the Water District will do to minimize harmful effects on the environment caused by its activities, and to achieve continual improvement of its environmental

We are on our way to providing our customers—the residents of Santa Clara County—with the most efficient and best possible service and performance.

Malcolm Baldridge National Quality Award Criteria

The criteria of this prestigious national award program examine the following seven aspects of an organization:

1) Leadership—how senior executives guide the organization and how the organization addresses its responsibilities to the public and practices good citizenship;

2) Strategic planning—how the organization sets strategic directions;

3) Customer and market focus—how the organization builds relationships with customers and satisfies their needs;

4) Knowledge management—how data and information are used to support key organization processes;

5) Human resources—how the workforce is allowed to develop its full potential and how it is aligned with organizational objectives;

6) Process management—how aspects of key production/delivery and support processes are designed, managed and improved; and

7) Business results—customer satisfaction, operational performance, and governance and social responsibility.

performance.[8] A noteworthy effort aimed at reducing negative environmental impacts is the Solar Carport Project.

Green business, going solar. In April 2005, the Water District was certified as a "green business" through the Green Business Program of Santa Clara County. In addition to noting the district's compliance with a variety of environmental regulations, the county commended the district for its Solar Carport Project. In response to the 2001 energy crisis and rolling blackouts that summer, the Water District turned to the sun for help. By 2003, the district had installed a large solar array over the carport structures in the headquarter's parking lot, powerful enough to meet about 20 percent of the campus' energy needs. This switch to solar power would help reduce carbon dioxide emissions by an estimated 412,699 pounds per year, the equivalent of that produced by 53 cars. Scheduled for completion in mid-2005 was a second phase of the project—the installation of a natural gas generator and heat-recovery unit. The co-generation system will generate electricity and capture heat waste for heating and cooling the two-story headquarters building. The entire project will produce roughly 2,800 megawatt hours per year—the equivalent of the annual energy needs of 690 typical families. The cost-savings to taxpayers is about $240,000 per year; also financially significant, the Water District will receive $1.7 million in rebates from the California Public Utilities Commission once the system is fully operating.[8]

Adhering to Malcolm Baldridge model. While ISO certification sets forth high performance and operational standards, subscribing to the Malcolm Baldridge model will take us even further in our effort to best serve Santa Clara County. The criteria of this model are used by the U.S. Department of Commerce in awarding exemplary organizations, and are named for former Secretary of Commerce Malcolm Baldridge, a highly effective proponent of quality management.

Conducting our work within the ISO/Baldridge context gives us a proven framework to comprehensively and continuously improve our entire operation, enabling the innovative spirit of our agency to thrive. As in the past, the Santa Clara Valley Water District will be ready and able to respond to the challenges of the twenty-first century. ∎

SOURCES, EPILOGUE:

[1] *Integrated Water Resource Plan*, SCVWD, 1997, p. ES-1.

[2] California Department of Conservation News Release, "Pace of urbanization picks up in Santa Clara County, slows slightly in Alameda County, new doc maps show," June 27, 2001, available at: http://www.consrv.ca.gov/index/ news/2001

[3] Bay Area Alliance for Sustainable Growth Web site at: www.bayareaalliance.org

[4] Estremera, Tony as quoted in SCVWD News Release, "Santa Clara County leaders gathering to discuss rapid growth's effects on water and environmental quality," March 28, 2001.

[5] Leavenworth, Stuart. "Dire warning for Delta's future," *Sacramento Bee*, Oct. 5, 2004.

[6] *Annual Performance Report 1995-96*, SCVWD, p. 13; also, *Annual Performance Report 1996-1997*, SCVWD, p. 14.

[7] SCVWD News Release, March 9, 2004; also, International Standards Organization Web site: www.iso.org

[8] SCVWD Web site: www.valleywater. org/New_and_events/_HQ_campus_ energy_project/index.shtm

The history of managing water resources in the Santa Clara Valley

is not only about the building of a dam or the adoption of a new water recycling policy.

It is also about how the Santa Clara Valley Water District,

the entity charged with managing water resources,

responds to and evolves with challenging times.

APPENDIX A

Valley Water Entities & Their Leaders

Directors	
Leroy Anderson	1929-1933
C. D. Cavallaro	1929-1935
John A. Fair	1929-1933
R. P. Van Orden	1929-1938
Sidney D. Farrington	1929-1950
J. Fred Holthouse	1929-1936
Edgar A. Jackson	1929-1931
Ralph F. Simons	1931-1935
William F. Noethig	1933-1937
Reginald L. Parry	1933-1955
Harry G. Mitchell	1935-1954
S. W. Pfeifle	1935-1962
True T. Tourtillot	1936-1938
James Wiesendanger	1937-1956
C. G. Spargur	1938-1953
Lloyd O. Wilcox	1938-1956
Frank L. Steindorf	1950-1954
Martin Spangler, Sr.	1953-1955
Herman J. Gerdts	1954-1966
Edmund A. Mirassou	1955-1968
Otto J. Pearson	1955-1956
Frank Polak	1955-1960
E. Vernon Holthouse	1956-1960
Joseph J. Mariani, Jr.	1956-1960
Frank A. Wilcox	1956-1968
Joseph Chiri	1960-1968
James J. Lenihan	1960-1968
Dominic J. Ribisi	1962-1968
Roy Butcher	1966-1967
Richard A. Hardy	1967-1968
Robert T. Sapp	1961-1968

1919-1924: Santa Clara Valley Water Conservation Committee

On December 20, 1919, valley farmers formed a committee to address the problem of diminishing groundwater; members of the County Chamber of Commerce and the County Board of Supervisors joined in early 1920. This committee raised funds for the Tibbetts and Kieffer survey, the report that would become the foundation of the valley's water system. In 1921, the committee's measure to form a Water District narrowly failed with voters. The committee tried again in 1924, but a wet winter dampened voters' concern for water conservation. The committee then disbanded.

1926-1929: Santa Clara Valley Water Conservation Association

Incorporated on December 1, 1926, this association of farmers and businessmen tackled the need to conserve water. Under the guidance of an elected board of 12 directors, the association raised money to buy equipment and lands, and built sack dams and small concrete dams. When voters finally approved a public governing body to handle water issues in 1929, the association disbanded on November 19th and gladly turned over its properties to the new Water District.

Directors

Leroy Anderson - San José	Lloyd Gardner - Campbell	W. K. Roberts - Sunnyvale
Nelson Barton - San José	S. N. Hedegard - Campbell	R. P. Van Orden - Mountain View
Karl E. Bracher - Santa Clara	Edwin Howes - Los Gatos	Max Watson - Agnew
John A. Fair - San José	Warren E. Hyde - Cupertino	James E. Wiesendanger - Cupertino

1929-1968: Santa Clara Valley Water Conservation District

On November 5, 1929, voters approved the formation of a Water District in the more populated north-central area of the county. The district's mission was to build reservoirs to conserve the flow of runoff into the bay, and use that runoff to recharge the groundwater basin. This district would eventually annex or merge with other Water Districts that formed in the county at later dates.

Secretary of District

R. P. Van Orden	1929-1933
Leroy Anderson	1933-1937
Fay Logan Griffiths	1937-1942
Beth Townsend	1942-1946
Jean Worcester	1946-1949
Thelma M. Wright	1950-1962
Violet V. Enander	1962-1968

Chief Engineer

Fred H. Tibbetts	1931-1938
G. Walter Hunt	1938-1954
J. Robert Roll	1954-1967

Chief Administration Officer

J. Robert Roll	1948-1961
Glenn F. Dodson	1961-1968

Attorney

Herbert C. Jones	1929-1954
Albert T. Henley	1954-1968

The Santa Clara Valley Water District is a Consolidation of Four Agencies

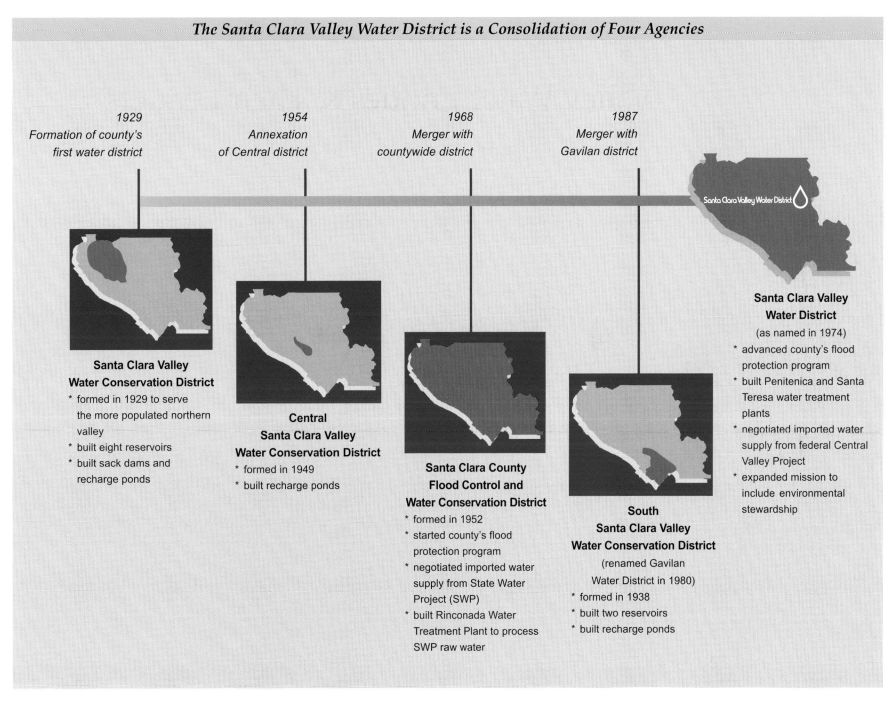

1929
Formation of county's
first water district

1954
Annexation
of Central district

1968
Merger with
countywide district

1987
Merger with
Gavilan district

Santa Clara Valley
Water Conservation District
* formed in 1929 to serve
  the more populated northern
  valley
* built eight reservoirs
* built sack dams and
  recharge ponds

Central
Santa Clara Valley
Water Conservation District
* formed in 1949
* built recharge ponds

Santa Clara County
Flood Control and
Water Conservation District
* formed in 1952
* started county's flood
  protection program
* negotiated imported water
  supply from State Water
  Project (SWP)
* built Rinconada Water
  Treatment Plant to process
  SWP raw water

South
Santa Clara Valley
Water Conservation District
(renamed Gavilan
Water District in 1980)
* formed in 1938
* built two reservoirs
* built recharge ponds

Santa Clara Valley
Water District
(as named in 1974)
* advanced county's flood
  protection program
* built Penitenica and Santa
  Teresa water treatment
  plants
* negotiated imported water
  supply from federal Central
  Valley Project
* expanded mission to
  include environmental
  stewardship

Santa Clara Valley Water District

Directors	
Elmer Chesbro	1938-1969
(founding president, serving as such until his decease in 1969)	
Thomas Hunter	1938-1953
Odilla Knepper	1938-1953
Mark Smith	1938-1956
George C. Wolfe	1938-1953
Ray Gwinn	1950-1979
Joseph Gubser	1954-1963
John Stelling	1954-1963
Leland Dauberg	1960-1979
Jack Sturla	1966-1979
Jack Martin	1967-1979
Alfred Angelino	1968-1979
Courtland Rush	1969-1974
George Azevedo	1975-1977
Mike Kennedy	1978-1984
Robert Chappell	1980-1985
John Jones	1980-1983
Louie Mammini	1980-1983
Susan Voss	1980-1982
Ben Gilroy, Jr.	1983-1987
Robert Blaine	1984-1987
Gene Gewin	1984-1987
Stephen Kover	1985-1987
William Reimal	1985-1987

1938-1987: South Santa Clara Valley Water Conservation District
(renamed to Gavilan Water District in 1980)

On August 1, 1938, voters in South County approved the formation of a small Water District that would build two reservoirs, Uvas and Chesbro, to recharge the groundwater basin in South County. The agency changed its name to Gavilan Water District in 1980. For decades, voters resisted combining with the larger Water District to its north, but to avoid paying double pumping fees, voters finally conceded to a merger with the Santa Clara Valley Water District in November of 1987.

Secretary/General Manager

P. A. Cox	1938-1957
Elmer Weymouth	1957-1965
Sidney Johnson	1965-1974
Douglas Martin	1975-1978
Jack Sturla	1979-1984, 1987-1987
Faith Stoddard	1985-1986

1949-1954: Central Santa Clara Valley Water Conservation District

On December 19, 1949, voters in the Coyote Creek narrows north of Morgan Hill approved the formation of a small Water District that sought to obtain water rights on Coyote Creek and to build additional groundwater recharge facilities. The agency was unsuccessful in securing water rights, but did secure bonds for purchasing lands for the Main Avenue Percolation Ponds near Morgan Hill. On August 19, 1954 voters here supported annexation by the Santa Clara Valley Water Conservation District.

Directors	*Secretary of the Board*
Ed Acton	Superior Court Judge Harold Holden
Joseph Chiri	
Andrew Costa	
John Reynolds	
Harold Thomas	

1959-1966: Tri-County Water Authority

By the 1950s, the booming central coastal counties were anxious to plan for water importation. In 1955, the State Legislature established the Santa Clara-Alameda-San Benito Water Authority with the power to levy a tax for conducting importation studies, if approved by voters. In 1959, the Water Districts in Santa Clara, Alameda and San Benito counties succeeded with voters in forming the authority, which came to be called the Tri-County Water Authority. During the first year, the Alameda district—content with its water supply—dropped out. The Water Districts in Santa Cruz and Monterey counties then joined, involving four counties in the Tri-County Water Authority. Monterey would eventually drop out, but then rejoin in 1964. The Tri-County studies pointed overwhelmingly to the San Felipe Division of the Central Valley Project (CVP) as the best means to supplementing water for the central coastal counties. Having concluded its work, in 1966 the Authority was dissolved.

1954-1968: Santa Clara County Flood Control and Water Conservation District
(renamed to Santa Clara County Flood Control and Water District in 1964)

Under state legislation, this countywide agency formed on November 1, 1954 under the Santa Clara County Board of Supervisors with authority to build flood protection projects and import water. This agency contracted with the State Water Project to import water through the South Bay Aqueduct, beginning in July 1965, and built the Rinconada Water Treatment Plant in Los Gatos. County supervisors eventually agreed that flood management and water supply required a board devoted solely to such issues, and supported the merger of their agency with the Santa Clara Valley Water Conservation District on March 7, 1968.

County Supervisors (who served during the life of this agency)

A. W. Brown	1954-1958	
Sam P. Della Maggiore	1954-1968	
Walter S. Gaspar	1954-1956	
Ed R. Levin	1954-1965	
J. M. McKinnon	1954-1956	
Oran L. Slaght	1956-1960	
Wesley L. Hubbard	1957-1961	
Howard R. Weichert	1959-1962	
Ralph H. Mehrkens	1960-1968	
Martin Spangler	1962-1968	
Sig Sanchez	1963-1968	
Charles A. Quinn	1965-1968	

Engineer

Lloyd C. Fowler	1962-1968

Chief Administration Officer

Donald K. Currlin	1954-1968

Clerk of the Board of Supervisors

Richard Olsen	1954-1960
Jean Pullan	1960-1968

circa 1962-*: Santa Clara County Water Commission

Established in the early 1960s under the county's Unified County Water Plan, the commission was eventually comprised of one elected representative from each of the county's 13 cities; one county supervisor; and one elected director from the Santa Clara Valley Water Conservation District. In the 1960s, this commission made the final determination of which agency in the county would import water and serve as the contracting agency for the entire county. In later years, the commission continued to meet monthly and review water issues of countywide concern.

1966-1987: San Felipe Committee

After the Tri-County Water Authority was dissolved in 1966, the "baton" was handed to a newly formed San Felipe Committee to oversee the multi-jurisdictional San Felipe Water Project. Former members of the Tri-County Water Authority joined the committee, thus including representatives from the Santa Clara Valley Water District, San Benito County Water Conservation and Flood Control District, Monterey County Flood Control and Water Conservation District, and Santa Cruz County Flood Control and Water Conservation District. Unlike the Tri-County entity, this committee had no taxing authority. It served only to negotiate the contracts concerning the San Felipe Water Project with the U.S. Bureau of Reclamation.

Directors

Joseph Chiri	1968-1979
Victor F. Corsiglia, Sr.	1968-1972
Maurice E. Dullea	1968-1982
James J. Lenihan	1968-1997
Robert T. Sapp	1968-1981
R. Jack Sturla	1968-1973
Frank A. Wilcox	1968-1972
Edmund A. Mirassou	1972-1976
Patrick T. Ferraro	1973-1995
Courtland M. Rush	1973-1981
Linda Peralta	1976-1982
Arthur T. Pfeiffer	1979-1982
Sig Sanchez	1980-*
Robert Gross	1981-2000
Audrey Fisher	1982-1986
Joe Donohue	1983-1993
Joe Pandit	1983-1993
Joe Judge	1986-*
Rosemary Kamei	1993-*
William Gissler	1994-1995
Larry Wilson	1995-*
Tony Estremera	1996-*
Gregory Zlotnick	1997-*
Richard Santos	2001-*

1968-*: Santa Clara Valley Water District

On March 7, 1968, the Santa Clara County Flood Control and Water District merged with the Santa Clara Valley Water Conservation District. The merged agency used the name "Santa Clara County Flood Control and Water District" until January 1, 1974, when the name was officially changed to Santa Clara Valley Water District (SCVWD). The agency focused on its missions to provide flood protection and a safe, adequate water supply to Santa Clara County. In 1987, the Gavilan Water District finally merged with SCVWD. In 2001, the agency expanded its charter through a state legislative act to include environmental stewardship as a third official mission.

General Manager (renamed to Chief Executive Officer in 2001)

Donald K. Currlin	1968-1972
John T. O'Halloran	1973-1989
Ronald R. Esau	1989-1994
Stanley M. Williams	1994-*

Clerk of the Board of Directors

Violet Enander	1968-1979
Susan Ekstrand-Pino	1979-1995
Lauren Keller	1995-*

General Counsel

Albert T. Henley	1968-1990
Anthony Bennetti	1990-2004
Debra Cauble	2004-*

Chief Engineer (this position ended in 1980)

Lloyd C. Fowler	1968-1980

1968-*: Agricultural Water Advisory Committee

In the negotiated terms of the 1968 merger which resulted in the Santa Clara Valley Water District, this committee was formed and mandated to advise the new Board of Directors regarding agricultural uses of water and water quality.

1968-*: Flood Control and Watershed Advisory Committees

At the time of the 1968 merger, an advisory committee was formed for each of the five flood control zones (see Map A in Chapter 10). Each city with territory in a particular flood control zone would have representation on that zone's advisory committee, and the County of Santa Clara would have one representative on all zone committees. In the early 1970s, representation was expanded to include private citizens. A major focus of the committees has been to help determine the priority of projects within the zones.

1989-*: Landscape Advisory Committee

During the 1987-1992 drought, the landscaping industry stood to be strongly affected by policy decisions of water management agencies (see Chapter 11). The board of the Santa Clara Valley Water District invited local landscape representatives to form a committee to advise the board on water conservation practices in the landscaping industry and related issues.

2004-*: Environmental Advisory Committee

In 2004, the board of the Santa Clara Valley Water District directed that an Environmental Advisory Committee be established to advise the board on issues concerning environmental restoration and enhancement. The formation of this commitee is underway at the time of this writing.

Entrance to the Water District headquarters in 2005.

APPENDIX B

Water Retailers & Wholesale Water Rates

Water Retailers. As of 2005, fifteen entities (see inset) purchase either wholesale treated water or groundwater from the Santa Clara Valley Water District and, in turn, sell the water to residents and businesses in their respective service areas. Some of these retailers may also have their own surface water or groundwater supplies. The price of water paid by consumers has depended on the retail rate set by the water retailers, and may vary from one area to another.

Wholesale Water Rates (1964-2004). The zone system for water rates bears relationship to Santa Clara County's five zones associated with the Water District's receipt of the 1 percent ad valorem property tax revenue. Treated water charges apply only in the North County (Zone W-2); groundwater charges apply in both North County (Zone W-2) and South County (Zone W-5). The rates table shows how the cost of wholesale water has increased over the decades (only the years in which price increases took place are shown). Factors and policies driving these increases included:

* Pricing of agricultural water was originally based on what valley farmers could afford. Today, pricing of agricultural water is subsidized to help maintain open space. Over the years, the South County rate climbed, although slowly relative to the North County rate and to other areas in the state. For example, in 2002, the South County agriculture rate for groundwater was only $14 per acre-foot; comparatively, the neighboring Pajaro Valley Water Management Agency charged its agricultural customers $80 per acre-foot.

* As explained in Chapter 11, dramatic rate increases occurred between 1988 and 1992 because of the prolonged drought. Rates then remained stable until 1998. That year, rates again climbed as three main cost drivers came into play: 1) the capital-intensive Treated Water Improvement Project; 2) efforts related to the Integrated Water Resource Plan, including new investments in water banking, water recycling and water conservation; and 3) costs associated with the Fisheries and Aquatic Habitat Collaborative Effort. (See Index for locating pages where these projects are discussed.)

▶ **Note:** Only the years in which rate increases took place are shown.

| Year | North County | | | South County | |
| | Treated Water (Zone W-2) | Groundwater (Zone W-2) | | Groundwater (Zone W-5) | |
		M&I	Ag	M&I	Ag
1964-65	*Treated water charges began in 1967.*	20.00	5.00		
1965-66		16.00	5.00		
1967-68	$ 62.00	16.00	5.00		
1968-69	62.00	26.40	8.00		
1969-70	64.60	29.00	8.00	*Until annexed by the*	
1971-72	65.00	30.00	8.00	*Santa Clara Valley Water District*	
1976-77	75.00	34.00	8.50	*in 1987,*	
1978-79	80.00	39.00	9.75	*South County water users*	
1979-80	85.00	44.00	11.00	*paid a pumping tax to the*	
1980-81	95.00	54.00	13.50	*Gavilan Water Conservation*	
1981-82	130.00	70.00	17.50	*District.*	
1982-83	140.00	75.00	18.75		
1983-84	150.00	80.00	20.00		
1984-85	160.00	85.00	21.25		
1985-86	170.00	90.00	22.50		
1986-87	180.00	95.00	23.75		
1987-88	190.00	100.00	25.00	22.00	5.50
1988-89	195.00	100.00	25.00	26.00	6.50
1989-90	210.00	135.00	31.25	39.00	9.75
1990-91	245.00	175.00	43.75	46.00	11.50
1991-92	332.00	262.00	43.75	117.00	11.50
1993-94	310.00	240.00	43.75	108.00	11.50
1998-99	330.00	260.00	26.00	108.00	10.80
1999-00	355.00	285.00	28.50	115.00	11.50
2000-01	380.00	310.00	31.00	115.00	11.50
2001-02	410.00	330.00	33.00	130.00	13.00
2002-03	420.00	340.00	34.00	140.00	14.00
2003-04	460.00	375.00	37.50	160.00	16.00

*Source: * Santa Clara Valley Water District History and Statistics (revised May 1998), updated by SCVWD staff, December 2004.*

APPENDIX C

Compendium of Flood Protection Projects, 1980-2004

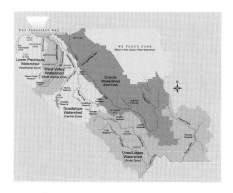

See page 104 for enlarged map.

Flood protection projects have been constructed in the Santa Clara Valley since the mid-1950s, but as pointed out in this history, work on the major projects really began in the 1980s. With the launching of the Benefit Assessment Program in 1981, the Water District gained a local revenue source to help fund these capital intensive projects. The assessments funded projects that were paid for entirely by the Water District, as well as funded the local share on projects approved by Congress for state and federal funding.

Program snapshot. The list of flood protection projects provided in this appendix reflects the work conducted under the Benefit Assessment Program (1981 to its sunset in 2000; see Chapter 9 for additional information) and the Clean, Safe Creeks Program (approved by valley voters in 2002; see Chapter 12 for more information). Note that dollar figures are historical and have not been adjusted for current values. The estimated costs are also subject to change.

Zone by zone approach. Early flood planning officials divided Santa Clara County into zones for organizing flood protection activities (see Chapter 10). The zones reflect the natural boundaries of the county's watersheds. As discussed in Chapter 12, in the early 2000s, the zones were renamed to reflect the watershed names.

	Year Completed or Estimated Completion	Construction Cost or Estimated Cost

Lower Peninsula Watershed
(Northwest Zone)

1. Adobe Creek		
Reaches 1 to 4 (Hwy 101 to Miller Ave.)	*1987-1992	10,490,000
Bridges (at El Camino Real, Foothill Expwy)	2005	4,160,000
Reaches 1 to 4, erosion repair	2005	410,000
2. Barron Creek (Adobe Creek to Louis Rd.)	1988	930,000
3. Matadero Creek		
Reaches 1 to 5 (Palo Alto Flood Basin to Barron Creek)	*1989-2000	21,900,000
Revegetation (Park Blvd. to Stanford Channel	1999	200,000
Remediation Project (Palo Alto Flood Basin to Alma St.)	2005	11,380,000
Revegetation (Matadero/Barron creeks)	2008	780,000
4. Permanente Diversion Channel (Reaches 1 to 3)	*1981-1986	1,540,000
5. San Francisquito Creek		
Marlowe to Chaucer St.	1981	70,000
Crescent Dr. to Maple St.	1983	270,000
Upstream of Fulton Ave.	1984	110,000
Cowper to Waverly	1987	210,000
Emerson Ave. to Alma St.	1990	470,000
Levee project	2003	1,600,000
6. Stevens Creek		
Homestead Rd. to Evelyn Ave.	1982	950,000
Hwy 101 to Shoreline Park	1983	1,410,000
Dana St. to Hwy 101	1985	1,760,000
Revegetation at Evelyn Ave.	1985	10,000
Drop Structure	2003	540,000
7. Palo Alto Flood Basin	1987	560,000
TOTAL:		**59,750,000**

A range of years indicates the span of completion dates for more than one project element.

	Year Completed or Estimated Completion	Construction Cost or Estimated Cost
West Valley Watershed (North Central Zone)		
1. Calabazas Creek		
Erosion protection at Mt. Eden Rd.	1981	30,000
Benton to Pomeroy (culverts/channel)	1983	1,340,000
Erosion protection at three stretches	1984	410,000
Reaches 1 to 3 (Lawrence Expwy to Central Expwy)	1996	12,820,000
Reach 4 (Homestead Rd. to Miller Ave.)	2000	6,750,000
Revegetation (reaches 1 and 4)	2003	1,110,000
2. Regnart Creek (erosion protection downstream of SPRR)	1986	60,000
3. San Tomas Aquino Creek		
Upstream of confluence with Saratoga Creek to Hwy 101	1981	2,740,000
Maintenance downstream of Hwy 101	1981	260,000
4. Saratoga Creek		
Cabrillo Ave. to San Tomas Aquino Creek confluence	1980	160,000
Minor work on Bollinger to I-280	1984	70,000
Cabrillo Ave. to Benton St.	1986	1,530,000
Benton St. to Homestead Rd.	1986	1,810,000
Drop structures (Homestead to Pruneridge)	1988	820,000
Homestead Rd. to Prunridge	terminated	1,380,000
Revegetation	*1988-1995	570,000
5. Guadalupe Slough (Calabazas retarding basin to SF Bay)	1986	N/A
TOTAL:		**31,860,000**

	Year Completed or Estimated Completion	Construction Cost or Estimated Cost

Guadalupe Watershed (Central Zone)

1. Alamitos Creek

Camden Ave. to Almaden Lake	1981	1,530,000
Graystone Lane Bridge	1983	620,000
Revegetation (Camden Ave. to Almaden Lake)	1987	310,000

2. Guadalupe River

Revegetation (Blossom Hill Rd. to Alamitos Creek)	1982	40,000
Erosion control at six locations	*1982-1984	1,300,000
SPRR to Hwy 101	1984	2,350,000
Marina to SPRR	1985	1,060,000
Gold St. bridge raising	1987	770,000
Home and building demolitions	*1989-1998	570,000
Relocate Hetch Hetchy pipeline	1994	2,560,000
● Contract 1 (I-880 to Hedding St.)	1994	4,180,000
Relocate Central Pipeline	1995	1,960,000
● Contract 2 (Hedding St. to Coleman)	1998	8,020,000
Mitigation plantings at Children's Discovery Museum	2000	130,000
● Contract 3C, Phase 1 (upstream of Woz Way, east bank)	2000	2,600,000
● Contract 3C, Phase 2 (Woz Way to Grant St.)	2004	11,060,000
Guadalupe Creek Restoration Project	2005	3,880,000
● Contract 3A, Phase 2 (Coleman Ave. to UPRR)	2005	17,510,000
● Contract 3B, (Santa Clara St. to Park Ave.)	2005	20,380,000
● Contract 3C, Phase 3 (flood training walls at I-280)	2005	3,140,000
● Contract 3A, Phase 1 (UPRR to Santa Clara St.)	2005	31,260,000
Hwy 237 Bridge	2007	15,150,000
Alviso Marina to I-880	2009	32,690,000

3. Los Gatos Creek

Retaining wall upstream of Hamilton Ave.	1984	220,000
Erosion control (Leigh Ave. to Meridian Ave.)	1984	120,000
Erosion control and maintenance (two locations)	1987	940,000
Erosion repair	2002	310,000

4. Ross Creek (Cherry Ave. bridge) — 1983 — 120,000

TOTAL: **164,780,000**

A range of years indicates the span of completion dates for more than one project element.

	Year Completed or Estimated Completion	Construction Cost or Estimated Cost
Coyote Watershed (East Zone)		
1. Wrigley Ford Creek (pump station, Berryessa Creek to Railroad Ct.)	1993	1,980,000
2. Berryessa Creek (I-680 to Cropley Ave.)	1980	360,000
3. Calera Creek floodwall and access bridge at UPRR	2002	600,000
4. Coyote Creek		
Test levee, Leslie Salt Ponds	1985	890,000
Demolition of Milpitas Sewerage Treatment Plant	1987	110,000
Reach 1A, across Leslie Salt Ponds	1988	1,970,000
Reach 1B, Leslie Salt Ponds to MSTP	1989	3,270,000
Reach 2A, MSTP to 3500' downstream of Hwy 237	1990	1,590,000
Revegetation (at salt ponds and Reaches 1 and 2)	*1989-1993	600,000
Reach 2B, downstream of Hwy 237	1993	1,530,000
Reach 3A, demolition (including buildings at Agnews)	1994	90,000
Hwy 237 to Tasman Dr.	1997	460,000
● Reach 3B, Tasman Dr. to Montague Expwy	1997	5,310,000
Other minor projects (outdoor classroom, floodwalls)	2002	960,000
5. Los Coches Creek (erosion protection upstream of Carnegie Dr.)	1984	10,000
6. ● Lower Silver Creek		
Reach 2A, McKee/King intersection	1993	190,000
Reach 1 and 2, Coyote Creek to McKee Rd.	2004	14,670,000
Reach 3, Phase 1, McKee Rd. to Lausett Ave.	2004	10,410,000
Reach 3, Phase 2, Lausett Ave. to I-680 (including demolitions)	2005	6,370,000
Reach 3, Alum Rock Ave. to Lausett Ave.	2006	9,810,000
Sediment removal at Thompson Creek	*2003-2004	2,650,000
7. Lower Penitencia Creek		
Berryessa Creek to Marylynn Ave.	1984	1,670,000
Marylynn Ave. to Montague Expwy	1985	2,390,000
Floodwall at Dixon Landing Rd.	1997	380,000
8. Upper Silver Creek (repair Silver Creek Diversion)	1984	250,000
9. Thompson Creek		
Quimby Rd. to Aborn	1980	680,000
Landscaping	1984	10,000
Quimby Rd. to Westgrove Ave.	1991	240,000
TOTAL:		**69,450,000**

KEY

NA - *Not Available*

● *U.S. Army Corps of Engineers project involving federal funding.*

● *PL-566 project involving federal funding.*

	Year Completed or Estimated Completion	Construction Cost or Estimated Cost

Uvas/Llagas Watershed (South Zone)

1. Uvas Creek

Miller Ave. and Uvas Park Dr.	1988	150,000
Thomas Rd. bridge	1989	2,190,000

2. West Little Llagas Creek

La Crosse Dr. box culvert	1990	520,000
Middle Ave. bridge	1990	370,000
Watsonville Rd. bridge	1991	950,000
Cosmos/Edes box culverts	1991	570,000

3. ● Lower Llagas Creek

Reach 2, WW ponds along Little Llagas	1983	280,000
Luchessa bridge	1986	680,000
Murray Ave. bridge along West Branch	1987	720,000
Leavesley Rd. - RCB	1988	1,310,000
Monterey - SPRR box	1988	1,260,000
Santa Teresa box culverts at Morey Channel	N/A	N/A
North Morey Channel and Lions Circle	1988	580,000
Leavesley Rd. bridge	1989	950,000
Mitigation along Reach 3A	1989	300,000
Lions Circle interceptor	1994	650,000
Reaches 10 and 12A, Lions Circle	1997	150,000
3204' upstream of Leavesley Ave. to Buena Vista Ave.	1998	580,000

TOTAL: **12,210,000**

* A range of years indicates the span of completion dates for more than one project element.

APPENDIX D

Groundwater Levels Chart

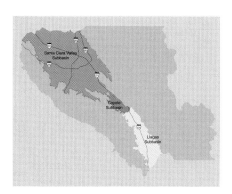

See page 206 for enlarged map.

The aquifer system underlying the Santa Clara Valley consists of three subbasins. District staff estimate the total subbasin capacity to be about three times greater than all of the district's ten surface reservoirs combined: As of 2004, total surface reservoir capacity was 170,137 acre-feet, and total subbasin operational storage capacity is estimated at 530,000 acre-feet. The subbasin system can be viewed as the county's largest "subterranean reservoir."

Recharging to counterbalance pumping. Groundwater plays a vital role in meeting water demand in Santa Clara County. In 1997, for example, 179,954 acre-feet of groundwater was pumped, supplying almost half of the water used in the county that year. To counterbalance pumping, the Water District recharges the basin with water released from local surface reservoirs and also with imported water supplies. The water is conveyed to a network of percolation ponds, built in locations where the gravelly soils allow for optimal percolation. Recharge also occurs naturally with rain, and with seepage in creeks and streams.

Preventing land subsidence. Recharging the subbasin is also necessary for the prevention of land subsidence. Subsidence is the broad sinking of the land surface as a result of decreased water pressure in the basin. Subsidence occurred in several areas of Santa Clara County between the 1920s and late 1960s—with a number of serious consequences, as discussed in Chapter 7.

Chart Explanations

1 The chart pertains only to data collected in downtown San José. The index well for measuring depth to groundwater is located at Santa Clara Street and Delmas Avenue. Within walking distance of the index well is the benchmark disk used by Water District surveyors to assess land subsidence.

2 Notice how years of above average rainfall generally correlate with higher groundwater levels. The index well level reflects both the natural seepage of rainfall into the subbasin as well as the effects of the district's recharge operations.

3 Groundwater is shown to rise above the land's surface in 1915 because groundwater pressure was so high that year that the water actually bubbled up at the index well (see also discussion of artesian wells in Chapter 1).

4 The survey benchmark, P7, was set in the original Hall of Records building in downtown San José. That benchmark was removed when the building was demolished. It was replaced in 1965 with a new benchmark disk, set in the wall of a new Superior Court building erected at the same site.

5 It is water pressure, rather than the water table itself, that affects land subsidence. The aquifer can withstand varying rises and drops in water levels, but when there is a significant and steady drop in water pressure, the clay layers of the soil compress and the land surface sinks. It is the Water District's policy to maintain groundwater levels above the level where subsidence was last noted.

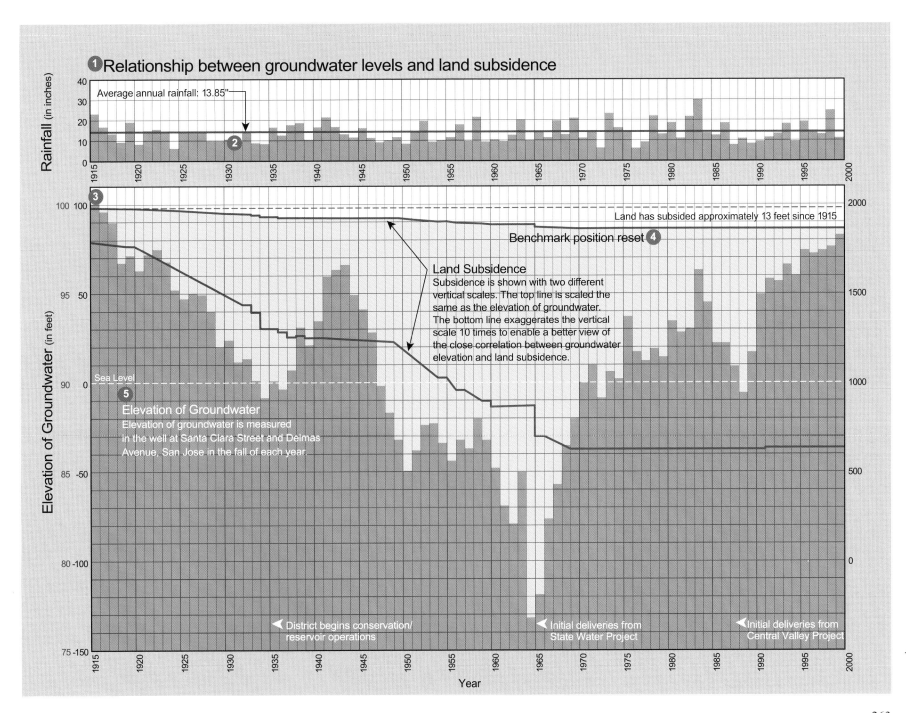

1 Relationship between groundwater levels and land subsidence

Rainfall (in inches)

Average annual rainfall: 13.85"

2

3

Land has subsided approximately 13 feet since 1915

Benchmark position reset **4**

Land Subsidence
Subsidence is shown with two different
vertical scales. The top line is scaled the
same as the elevation of groundwater.
The bottom line exaggerates the vertical
scale 10 times to enable a better view of
the close correlation between groundwater
elevation and land subsidence.

Sea Level

5

Elevation of Groundwater
Elevation of groundwater is measured
in the well at Santa Clara Street and Delmas
Avenue, San Jose in the fall of each year.

Elevation of Groundwater (in feet)

◄ District begins conservation/
reservoir operations

◄ Initial deliveries from
State Water Project

◄ Initial deliveries from
Central Valley Project

Year

APPENDIX E

Endangered & Threatened Species in Santa Clara County

(as of October 2004)

Key:

● Endangered - Listed in the Federal Register as being in danger of extinction.

● Threatened - Listed as likely to become endangered within the foreseeable future.

● Proposed - Officially proposed for listing as endangered or threatened.

● Candidate - Candidate to become a proposed species.

● Species of Concern - Other species of concern to the Sacramento Fish & Wildlife Office.

● Listed by the State of California but not by the U.S. Fish & Wildlife Service.

● Critical Habitat designated or proposed.

Invertebrates

● *Branchinecta lynchi* - vernal pool fairy shrimp
●● *Euphydryas editha bayensis* - bay checkerspot butterfly
● *Adela oplerella* - Opler's longhorn moth
● *Calicina minor* - Edgewood blind harvestman
● *Hydrochara rickseckeri* - Ricksecker's water scavenger beetle
● *Linderiella occidentalis* - California linderiella fairy shrimp
● *Microcina homi* - Hom's microblind harvestman
● *Microcina juni* - Jung's microblind harvestman
● *Speyeria adiaste adiaste* - unsilvered fritillary butterfly

Fish

● *Eucyclogobius newberryi* - tidewater goby
● *Oncorhynchus tshawytscha* - winter-run chinook salmon
● *Hypomesus transpacificus* - delta smelt
● *Oncorhynchus kisutch* - coho salmon, central CA coast
● *Oncorhynchus mykiss* - Central California Coastal steelhead
● *Oncorhynchus tshawytscha* - Central Valley spring-run chinook salmon
● *Acipenser medirostris* - green sturgeon
●● *Oncorhynchus tshawytscha* - Central Valley fall/late fall-run chinook salmon
● *Pogonichthys macrolepidotus* - Sacramento splittail
● *Spirinchus thaleichthys* - longfin smelt

Amphibians

●● *Ambystoma californiense* - California tiger salamander
●● *Rana aurora draytonii* - California red-legged frog
● *Rana boylii* - foothill yellow-legged frog
● *Spea hammondii* - western spadefoot toad

California clapper rail

California red-legged frog

Reptiles
- *Thamnophis sirtalis tetrataenia* - San Francisco garter snake
- *Masticophis lateralis euryxanthus* - Alameda whipsnake
- *Anniella pulchra pulchra* - silvery legless lizard
- *Clemmys marmorata marmorata* - northwestern pond turtle
- *Clemmys marmorata pallida* - southwestern pond turtle
- *Masticophis flagellum ruddocki* - San Joaquin coachwhip (whipsnake)
- *Phrynosoma coronatum frontale* - California horned lizard

Birds (resident or migratory)
- *Pelecanus occidentalis californicus* - California brown pelican
- *Rallus longirostris obsoletus* - California clapper rail
- *Sterna antillarum (albifrons) browni* - California least tern
- *Vireo bellii pusillus* - Least Bell's vireo
- *Brachyramphus marmoratus* - marbled murrelet
- *Charadrius alexandrinus nivosus* - western snowy plover
- *Haliaeetus leucocephalus* - bald eagle
- *Agelaius tricolor* - tricolored blackbird
- *Amphispiza belli belli* - Bell's sage sparrow
- *Athene cunicularia hypugaea* - western burrowing owl
- *Botaurus lentiginosus* - American bittern
- *Buteo regalis* - ferruginous hawk
- *Calidris canutus* - red knot
- *Calypte costae* - Costa's hummingbird
- *Carduelis lawrencei* - Lawrence's goldfinch
- *Chaetura vauxi* - Vaux's swift
- *Charadrius montanus* - mountain plover
- *Contopus cooperi* - olive-sided flycatcher
- *Cypseloides niger* - black swift
- *Elanus leucurus* - white-tailed (black shouldered) kite
- *Empidonax traillii brewsteri* - little willow flycatcher
- *Geothlypis trichas sinuosa* - saltmarsh common yellowthroat
- *Lanius ludovicianus* - loggerhead shrike
- *Laterallus jamaicensis coturniculus* - black rail
- *Limosa fedoa* - marbled godwit
- *Melanerpes lewis* - Lewis' woodpecker
- *Meloszpiza melodia pusillula* - Alameda (South Bay) song sparrow
- *Numenius americanus* - long-billed curlew
- *Numenius phaeopus* - whimbrel
- *Rynchops niger* - black skimmer

- *Selasphorus rufus* - rufous hummingbird
- *Selasphorus sasin* - Allen's hummingbird
- *Sphyrapicus ruber* - red-breasted sapsucker
- *Toxostoma redivivum* - California thrasher

Mammals
- *Reithrodontomys raviventris* - salt marsh harvest mouse
- *Sylvilagus bachmani riparius* - riparian brush rabbit
- *Vulpes macrotis mutica* - San Joaquin kit fox
- *Corynorhinus (Plecotus) townsendii townsendii* - Pacific western big-eared bat
- *Eumops perotis californicus* - greater western mastiff-bat
- *Myotis* – Five bats in the Myotis family are species of concern
- *Neotoma fuscipes annectens* - San Francisco dusky-footed woodrat
- *Sorex vagrans halicoetes* - salt marsh vagrant shrew

Plants
- *Castilleja affinis ssp. neglecta* - Tiburon paintbrush
- *Ceanothus ferrisae* - Coyote ceanothus
- *Chorizanthe robusta var. robusta* - robust spineflower
- *Dudleya setchellii* - Santa Clara Valley dudleya
- *Lasthenia conjugens* - Contra Costa goldfields
- *Streptanthus albidus ssp. albidus* - Metcalf Canyon jewelflower
- *Suaeda californica* - California sea blite
- *Trifolium amoenum* - showy Indian clover
- In addition, there are 49 more plants that qualify as species of concern.

Chinook salmon

Source: U.S. Fish & Wildlife Service, Sacramento Fish and Wildlife Office. List downloaded on Oct. 5, 2004 from http://sacramento.fws.gov/es/spp_lists/auto_list_form.cfm

Index

Page entries in boldface refer to illustrations or captions of photographs.

About the Authors

First Edition contributing writers:

Under the supervision of Seonaid McArthur, then-director of the California History Center, the following students in the De Anza College history program researched and wrote several chapters in the 1981 edition of this history, including:

David W. Rickman
Kevin Fish
Kenneth E. Dickey, Sr.
Charles K. Hart
Lynn Longa

Contributing writers from the Santa Clara Valley Water District personnel included:

James R. Melton, Public Information Officer
Albert T. Henley, General Counsel

Second Edition contributing writers:

Cheryl Wessling — Ms. Wessling is a freelance writer and editor, but was employed in the public information office of the Santa Clara Valley Water District during the 1990s. In this latter capacity, she closely followed many of the stories told within this history, enabling her to provide editorial direction to the overall book and to author several chapters.

Donna Krey — At the height of the 1987-1992 drought, Ms. Krey was the public information officer for the City of Cupertino, closely following the critical water issues of that time. She is now a magazine editor and freelance writer.

Elizabeth Emmett — Ms. Emmett worked as a writer in the public information office of the Santa Clara Valley Water District for more than 10 years, and has since undertaken various freelance writing assignments.

Kathleen McNamara — Ms. McNamara is a Bay Area freelance writer and has often written on infrastructure. Her clients include both private and public entities.

The following officials at the Santa Clara Valley Water District also contributed to the writing and/or editorial direction of the book:

Walt Wadlow, Chief Operating Officer
Stanley M. Williams, Chief Executive Officer
Gregory Zlotnick, Board Director

"This history is a solid account of how our residents and leaders alike have worked with fore-sight and fortitude in managing water resources, and how this management has played a key role in the transformation of the Valley of Hearts Delight into Silicon Valley—one of the most successful regions in the world."
~ Congresswoman Zoe Lofgren, 16th District of California

"This book is a wonderful addition to Santa Clara County history sources. It will be used by researchers, students, historians, environmentalists and many others, well into the future, and it is a valuable public service by the Santa Clara Valley Water District."
~ Mary Jo Ignoffo, historian

"The Santa Clara Valley Water District has become a recognized leader in California water policy and integrated water resources management. This history tells the important story of how the District grew into the role, confronting challenges unique to its diverse mission but with lessons that are applicable throughout California as we seek to secure our state's water future."
~ Lester Snow, Director, California Department of Water Resources

"Water has played a crucial role in the Santa Clara Valley's 150-year evolution from one of the richest agricultural regions of California to a high-tech mecca of the world. The writers of this book have made an important contribution to our understanding of this evolution, and have succeeded in richly illuminating the history of water management in this influential region."
~ James C. Williams, professor of history, De Anza College, and author, *Energy and the Making of Modern California*

"In an area that gets the same meager rainfall as Los Angeles or parts of North Africa, the visionaries who created our water system realized that unchecked groundwater pumping could not long sustain the vast orchards of the Santa Clara Valley, let alone the population boom that would soon come. With Herculean effort, they built a network of reservoirs, tunnels and pipelines that today helps protect one of Californa's largest metropolitan areas from nature's caprices of drought and floods. This is their story."
~ Frank Sweeney, retired *San Jose Mercury News* reporter